100 LOCAL HEROES

ADAM HART-DAVIS presents *Local Heroes*. A freelance writer and television presenter since 1994, he previously worked for YTV as a researcher and producer, devising both *Scientific Eye*, the most successful school science series on television, and *Mathematical Eye* (1989–92), as well as five programmes on Loch Ness for the Discovery Channel (1993). He is also a science photographer, and his photographs have appeared in a wide selection of publications. He has written eleven books, including *Thunder, Flush and Thomas Crapper* (1997), *The Local Heroes Book of British Ingenuity* (1997) and *Amazing Math Puzzles* (1998). He lives in Bristol, and travels by bicycle. . . .

PAUL BADER is the owner and managing director of Screenhouse Productions Limited, a television company which specialises in popular science programmes, and is producer and director of *Local Heroes*. He previously worked for YTV, producing medical, health and science programmes for the ITV network and for Channel 4. Among other programmes, he has worked on *Discovery*, *The Buckman Treatment*, *The Halley's Comet Show* and *On the Edge*. He lives in Leeds, and travels by car.

100 LOCAL HEROES

from
ADAM HART-DAVIS
and **PAUL BADER**

SUTTON PUBLISHING

First published as *The Local Heroes Book of British Ingenuity* and *More Local Heroes* in 1997 and 1998 by
Sutton Publishing Limited · Phoenix Mill
Thrupp · Stroud · Gloucestershire · GL5 2BU

This combined, revised edition first published in 1999 by
Sutton Publishing Limited

Reprinted 2000, 2001 (twice), 2002 (twice)

British Library Cataloguing in Publication Data
A catalogue record for this book is available from the British Library.

ISBN 0-7509- 2373-3

Typeset in 11/15 pt Melior.
Typesetting and origination by
Sutton Publishing Limited.
Printed in Great Britain by
J.H. Haynes & Co. Ltd, Sparkford.

Preface

The television series *Local Heroes* started on 7 August 1990, when Adam Hart-Davis, then working as a producer of science programmes at Yorkshire Television, decided he was getting too old and fat to play squash. In an effort to get fit and thin he bought himself a mountain bike, deliberately choosing pink and yellow for both bike and clothes in order to be bright and so stay alive on the roads. He still wears pink and yellow, and he is still alive!

Riding to work one day, he noticed, as he toiled up the long hill from Birstall to Drighlington, that on the old farmhouse now poised above the M62 there was a blue plaque, which he decided to read, because any excuse was good enough to take a rest. It said that Joseph Priestley had been born there at Fieldhead Farm. Ten minutes' research revealed that Joseph had spent his teenage years living in the Old Hall in Heckmondwike (Adam's local pub) and had discovered oxygen in Leeds as a result of watching the beer being made in the Yorkshire Squares at the Meadow Lane Brewery. Here were a farm, a pub, and a brewery, all linked by a bike ride and the discovery of oxygen – there must be a story to tell. Adam has been telling these stories ever since, and this book contains a hundred of his favourites. Perhaps the most dramatic story of all is that of Henry Winstanley, joker, engraver and builder of the world's first offshore lighthouse. The most surprising? Perhaps Alexander Bain and the fax machine, invented in 1843 – 30 years before the telephone. The most scientific? Try Isaac Newton and the incredible ideas he dreamed up in 1666. The most down-to-earth? Probably the lawnmower, invented in 1830 by Edwin Budding, and made in the same building as this book!

The stories are arranged alphabetically by hero; so finding the heroes is easy. In the index you can easily look up any invention that takes your fancy. But why not simply open the book at random and see what you find?

Adam Hart-Davis and Paul Bader
June 1999

1 Alcuin, Puzzler to Charlemagne

Puzzle 1: You have to cross a river, taking with you a wolf, a goat and a cabbage. You have a boat, but in it you can carry only one of these at a time. The problem is that if you take the wolf, then while you are away the goat will eat the cabbage. However, if you take the cabbage, then the wolf will eat the goat! The puzzle is, how can you get them all across the river safely?

This puzzle was written down as one of a collection of 'problems to sharpen the young' by an English scholar called Flaccus Albinus Alcuinus, or Alcuin, as he is generally remembered.

Alcuin was born in York about AD 735, went to Rome in 780, became Abbot of Tours, and settled in Aachen as what would now be Minister of Education for the European Community, but was then a close adviser to Charlemagne, who became Holy Roman Emperor on Christmas Day in the year 800.

Some of Alcuin's *Propositiones ad acuendos juvenes* are fairly trivial, but among the river-crossing puzzles are some really tricky ones. Try this on your friends:

Puzzle 2: Mum and dad and two children have to cross a river. The boat will hold only one adult or two children; not even one adult and one child. How do they get across?

And if they manage that, here's a really tough one:

Puzzle 3: Three married couples have to cross a river, and for religious reasons no woman must be left with a man unless her husband is there. The boat will carry only two. How do they all cross?

What is fascinating about these puzzles is not just that they are good puzzles – they challenge the mind, they seem impossible, and then when you work one out you get a sense of achievement – but that they are 1,200 years old, and still as good as new.

The solution to Puzzle 1, in case you are still suffering, is to take the goat across, leave it, return for either the wolf or the cabbage, take it across, *bring the goat back*, take the cabbage or the wolf, and finally return for the goat.

St Peter's School, Clifton, York, claims to have been founded by Alcuin, and a college at York University, 4 miles to the south-east, is named after him.

2 Tempest Anderson and the Power of Volcanoes

Modern science does not seem to have much room for the amateur, a trend already established in the late nineteenth century. Dr Tempest Anderson (1846–1913), an eye surgeon from York who described himself as an 'amateur of limited leisure', was looking for a suitable scientific pastime. Curiously, he hit upon vulcanology – the study of volcanoes – because it offered 'exercise in the open air, often in districts remote and picturesque'. He intended to combine his new hobby with his other great love, photography. The result was a stunning record of dramatic eruptions from all over the world, and a new understanding of the destructive force of volcanoes.

Stonegate, one of the main streets of ancient York, is now filled with shops and tourists, but the elegant black and gold plaque outside no. 23 has survived: 'T. Anderson, Surgeon'. This is where Anderson practised as an ophthalmic surgeon, and is only yards from the house where he was born, at no. 17. But with a name like Tempest, he was never going to settle quietly. He used to keep two travel bags permanently packed, one for hot climates and one for cold. When word came of an eruption, he was off on the first available ship. There is no record of what happened to the patients in his waiting-room.

The idea of going to an erupting volcano by ship seems a bit daft: surely by the time news reached York, and Anderson had reached the volcano, it would all be over? In fact Anderson captured many eruptions on film, but his pictures of the aftermath of eruptions are just as powerful. The pictures are especially impressive when you consider the extraordinary lengths photographers routinely went to in those days. Wet plates, where you had to sensitise the glass photographic plate immediately before exposure by dipping it into silver-nitrate solution, had begun to disappear in 1874, the year after Anderson qualified as an MD, so he would have used dry plates for most of his work. But he would have taken hundreds of these glass plates with him on an expedition, together with several wooden cameras, many of which he made himself. Not only would he have to haul the cameras, lenses and plates up mountains in dangerous and inhospitable circumstances, but once on location the plates would have to be loaded, inside a light-proof bag, into 'dark slides' to hold them in the camera. It is a tribute to the pioneers of photography that early pictures progressed beyond posed studio shots. Anderson was clearly a genial chap, who made friends wherever he went. His new friends are recorded on his glass negatives and lantern slides, which feature many pictures of young women. As well as recording them playing cricket on board ship and so on, Anderson photographed many of these women up the mountain, posed in ridiculously unsuitable gear with an erupting volcano in the background.

Having fun was clearly part of the point, and Anderson brought back many rather non-PC stories from his travels. One picture records the famous 'Fainting Dog of Vulcano'. Several times a day this unfortunate beast was led into a cavern with a layer of heavy volcanic gases near the floor. To the apparent amusement of the tourists, it would faint, only to revive again when carried outside. Anderson also visited Yellowstone in the USA to photograph the geysers, and was amused by a tale of an unfortunate Chinaman. The enterprising chap had set up a laundry in a hut on a hot spring. When he tipped in his soap powder, it set off the dormant geyser, which exploded into life, taking the hut with it.

However, Anderson's purpose was serious, and he became a respected authority. He made a thorough and systematic study of volcanoes, calling it a 'clinical or bedside study'. He was especially impressed by the destructive power of volcanoes, and by a paradox that reminded him of the Alps. A keen alpinist and member of the Alpine Club, Anderson had examined trees felled by avalanches. He found that those furthest from the origin of the avalanche had only a light sprinkling of snow. He concluded that they had been knocked over not by the rush of snow, but by the powerful wind the avalanche creates. He arrived at the same conclusion when considering the devastating eruptions on Martinique. The eruption of Mont Pelée had destroyed the town of Saint-Pierre in 1902. When Anderson arrived, the scene was one of complete destruction. The only building left standing was part of the bank, the only survivor a man incarcerated in the underground cells of the jail. Yet, as his photographs show, there was not much ash or lava in the town itself.

The 'ground surge', as he called it, seems to precede the main eruption, and as its name implies it hugs the slopes of the volcano, destroying buildings and trees in its path with more than hurricane force. Sometimes the ground surge contains small rock particles as well as hot gas, and is also known as a 'pyroclastic flow'.

Anderson's pictures are all preserved at the Yorkshire Museum in York. There are over five thousand negatives and slides, some of which were published in Anderson's book *Volcanic Studies in Many Lands*. Sadly the museum is not able to display them at present, which is a pity, because the photography is superb and the collection includes many self portraits of the bearded Anderson clearly enjoying himself. Although Anderson found much of science closed to amateurs, he was part of a long tradition of amateur science in York, where the Literary and Philosophical Society, of which Anderson became president, was perhaps the greatest scientific society in Britain; in 1831 its members had founded the British Association for the Advancement of Science.

Because he was a scientific photographer, Tempest Anderson was keen to use only standard lenses, which have an angle of view the same as that of the human eye, rather than telephoto lenses that would produce an odd perspective. This meant, of course, that he had to get closer to the eruption he was photographing – which increased the risk. A friend said, 'you know, Anderson, you are sure to be killed, but it will be such a very great satisfaction to you afterwards to think that it was in the cause of science'. Tempest Anderson died of fever in 1913, crossing the Red Sea on the way back from the Philippines, and is buried at Suez.

Tempest Anderson's home was at 17 Stonegate, York, with his surgery just up the road at no. 23; there is still a plaque on a pillar.

3 Mary Anning, the Fossil-finder

In the centre of Lyme Bay lies the attractive town of Lyme Regis, its tiny harbour protected by the great curving rock wall known as the Cobb, made famous in Jane Austen's *Persuasion* and John Fowles's *The French Lieutenant's Woman*. For hundreds of years Lyme Regis has been famous for what used to be called 'curiosities'.

We know them as fossils, and they are found in the Blue Lias in the cliffs on either side of the town. Walk along the beach and you can see how the cliffs are gradually eroding and tumbling into the sea. Each time a slab falls off it brings with it nodules of grey rock containing fossils – the remnants of the rich life in the warm muddy sea that swirled there two hundred million years ago. Fossil-hunters are out in force each time the tide goes out, especially when the cliffs are washed down with heavy rain. They seek out new nodules and crack them open with hammers, looking for the fossils that may lie within.

Mary Anning was born in Lyme Regis in 1799. At the age of fifteen months she survived a lightning strike which killed the three women she was with. Family legend has it that she had been a dull child before, but after this accident she became lively and intelligent, and grew up so. Mary's father Richard was a carpenter, but he used to supplement his income by selling curiosities, and following his death when she was twelve, Mary did the same. But if fossils had been a sideline for Richard, they became Mary's life, and she became the greatest fossil-hunter of the age. She was poor, and had little formal education; yet she helped to bring about one of the truly great scientific revolutions, which overturned our view of the history of the world and the origins of life.

Her astonishing success began one day in 1811, the year after her father's death, when Mary and her brother Joseph were looking for curiosities somewhere under Black Ven, the hill half a mile east of the town. Scraping around in the muddy rock, they found the skull of what looked like a crocodile. The following year Mary returned and extracted the body – an amazing feat, because the creature was 30 feet long and entirely encased in rock! In fact she had to hire a gang of men to help her. The skeleton turned out to be not a crocodile, but one of the finest specimens of the recently discovered icthyosaurus.

The icthyosaurus was sold for £23, a tidy sum for a very poor family, and Mary's mother encouraged the girl to look for other specimens. In 1823 she found the first ever plesiosaur fossil, and in 1828 the first pterodactyl. In the intervening years, she found several examples of each, in addition to coprolites, a cephalopod and a fossil fish called *Squaloraja*. All of these she extracted, prepared and reassembled with incredible skill – so much so that Lady Silvester wrote on 17 September 1824: 'The extraordinary thing in this young woman is that she has made herself so thoroughly acquainted with the science that the moment she finds any bones she knows to what tribe they belong.'

The Philpot Museum stands above the sea at the very centre of Lyme Regis, where the road, after plunging down the hill, turns sharply back up the other side. It was named after a family Mary knew; the three Philpot daughters were well-known fossil-collectors, and may have inspired her in her work.

However, they were young ladies; Mary lived a very different life. The house where she lived and worked was on the same site – it was pulled down to make room for the museum. Outside was a table where she showed off and sold her latest specimens, and down below was the basement workshop where Mary brought the raw specimens from the cliff to be 'developed'.

Developing a specimen means separating it from the surrounding rock – fantastically delicate work, especially with an unknown species where you don't know what it is supposed to look like. Mary was a brilliant developer. She also understood anatomy enough to get her specimens assembled correctly, and of course she had the amazing ability to find them in the first place. A poem was written about her in 1884:

> Miss Anning, as a child, ne'er passed
> A pin upon the ground
> But picked it up; and so at last
> An icthyosaurus found.

Mary Anning was born in the right place at the right time. Philosophers were just beginning to think about what fossils meant. Until that time they were regarded simply as curiosities, because they didn't fit into the history of the world as portrayed in the Bible. The Earth was supposed to be only a few thousand years old, and the fossils were reckoned by many to have been in the rocks from the start – perhaps put there by God as a test of faith.

Mary Anning's skill meant that fossils of real scientific value were available to scientists like William Buckland (*see* page 97), who were formulating a new history of the earth that led eventually to the idea of evolution. Mary was well known to scientists and fossil-collectors. Some said she became a little arrogant, and she seems to have been a tough, slightly difficult character. Anna Maria Pinney wrote in her journal on 25 October 1831: 'Went out at 11 o'clock fossilising with Mary Anning . . . She has been noticed by all the cleverest men in England, who have her to stay at their houses, correspond with her on geology etc. This has completely turned her head, and she has the proudest and most unyielding spirit I have ever met with . . . She glories in being afraid of no one and in saying everything she pleases.'

But if she was temporarily famous, she certainly wasn't rich; the family still teetered on the brink of poverty. On one occasion they hadn't had a really good fossil find for over a year, and were selling their furniture to pay the rent; a kind collector sold his collection to save them. Mary's specimens were all sold to collectors, but when they ended up in museums they bore the names of the men who had bought them, rather than the woman who had discovered them.

If Mary Anning had been an educated man, and so able to publish her own scientific papers, she might now be seriously famous. How unfair that most people have never heard of the carpenter's teenage daughter who helped to unravel the history of life on earth.

The Philpot Museum in Lyme Regis, on the site of Mary Anning's house, has a collection of memorabilia.

4 Richard Arkwright's Water-frame and Mill

There are plenty of candidates for the invention that powered the industrial revolution. But what would all these engines drive? Sir Richard Arkwright (1732–92) built the first machine that could accurately reproduce the actions of a skilled manual worker – but he went much further. One of his 'water-frames' could replace not one but nearly one hundred workers; and Arkwright was a businessman with the vision to see that these new machines would allow him to organise labour in more efficient ways, opening up what was probably the world's first single-purpose factory. Arkwright was compared by Sir Robert Peel to Nelson and Wellington, and yet this industrial hero had a very modest start in life.

Richard's father was a peruke or wig-maker in Preston, Lancashire, and as the youngest of thirteen children Richard was last in line for the education his brothers received. Instead he, too, was apprenticed as a hairdresser and earned a living as a wigmaker, basing himself in Bolton from about 1750. Not much is known about Arkwright's early life, but a letter about the great man's time in Bolton written in 1799 concludes: 'He was always thought to be clever in his peruke making business and very capital in Bleeding and toothdrawing and allowed by all in his acquaintance to be [a] very ingenious man.' The account may benefit from hindsight, because we know of no Arkwright inventions from this time. As well as a barber, Arkwright became publican of the Black Boy Inn.

In Bolton, as in much of Lancashire, the textile trade was growing fast, fuelled in part by new technology. The fly shuttle had been patented by John Kay in 1733, and greatly speeded up the operation of the hand-loom while making it possible for one person to operate it. This increased the demand for thread and in about 1738 Lewis Paul, son of a French refugee, invented a mechanical process which he failed to make work, but which formed the basis for Arkwright's invention. Spinning thread on a spinning wheel is a skilled manual job. The cotton (or wool) has already been combed or carded to untangle and roughly align the fibres, but to the untutored eye it looks like cotton wool. The spinster, as the female spinners were known, holds a handful of the raw cotton and lets it tease out through her fingers as it is wound on to a bobbin. So the first part of the process is teasing, which reduces the handful to the number of fibres needed in the thread. As the teased fibres are wound on to the bobbin, they are given a twist which locks the fibres together and tightens or hardens the thread. It was the finger-tip control of the spinsters that Paul and Arkwright would try to mimic, and to multiply.

The spinning wheel already inserted twist as it wound the thread. The challenge was to tease the cotton mechanically. Arkwright hit upon the same idea as Lewis Paul – roller spinning. The carded cotton is fed through two or more sets of rollers which pinch it tightly. But the second set of rollers goes faster than the first, and thus stretches or teases out the thread. Further sets of rollers can be used to tease the cotton further. But making this work in practice was another matter, and while Paul's business gradually failed, Arkwright used roller-spinning to found an empire. Arkwright teamed up with a watchmaker called John Kay (though not the man of the same name who had invented the flying shuttle). Kay was to help him build his machine, which was completed in about 1767. They had moved to Preston where Arkwright maintained the deceit that the machine was for calculating longitude. Preston is also the location for the story about 'strange noises' in the night as the men worked on the machine, forcing the neighbours to conclude that this was 'the devil tuning his bagpipes'. This seems so unlikely that it must have been made up – there are similar stories accompanying other inventions. Despite the strange noises, the men had made the machine work. In particular, Arkwright had worked out how the distances between rollers and the force with which they were squeezed together could be used to mimic the control of the skilled spinsters.

The following year Arkwright and Kay took the invention to Nottingham, then the centre of the cotton stocking trade. At about this time another invention, the famous 'Spinning Jenny', was put into operation in Nottingham by James Hargreaves. This too could produce cotton thread, but only for the 'weft', the threads that run along the length of a cloth. Arkwright's invention could produce thread for the warp as well.

The first 'spinning-frame' was driven by horses, but this proved both inconvenient and uneconomical. He had patented his invention in 1769, the year James Watt took out his master patent for improving steam engines, and no doubt the idea of motive power for industry was in the air. Arkwright settled on water power, and teamed up with Mr Need of Nottingham and Mr Strutt of Derby, who had the patents for the manufacture of ribbed stockings, and set up his spinning-frame at Cromford in Derbyshire. The area is famed for its spring water, and it was the same water that drew Arkwright there. Cromford was served by a warm spring that never froze even in the coldest winter. It was the ideal place for the world's first factory.

A single spinster could spin a single thread. A Spinning Jenny could produce perhaps twenty threads at a time. But in its final form Arkwright's machine, now called the 'water-frame' thanks to its new motive power, could spin ninety-six threads at the same time using just one unskilled operator. Arkwright had made cotton spinning into child's play. So, of course, he needed children to operate it.

He advertised for workers with large families, all of whom could be employed. Arkwright seems to have supported the idea of child labour because it took such a long time to learn the trade that if 'they were not to go until they were twelve or thirteen they would be leaving when they became useful'. He favoured a minimum age no higher then ten. But for the time, conditions at Cromford were extremely good. Decent houses were built for the mill workers, and also for the weavers and the others who supported or were fed by the water-frame. Although he used children, they were not admitted until they could read, and he made sure that there was schooling for all. Indeed it was pressure from the parents that made sure plenty of children were available. Profits from the mill were so great that it was kept working twenty-three hours a day, with an hour for oiling and cleaning the machines.

Arkwright's thread was better than any cotton thread then available in Britain. The only full cotton fabric had come from India, the locally produced cloth being a mixture of cotton and flax because the

British cotton thread was not hard enough. This caused an anomaly because cotton cloth was subject to duty, supposedly because it was imported. An Act of Parliament put the matter right and allowed Arkwright to reap the rewards of his invention. His empire expanded into mills all over the country.

He also sold and licensed the machines to others, raking in a vast income for himself but stoking up resentment at his stranglehold on the industry. There were many attempts to use the technology – both the water-frame and later a very successful carding machine – without paying the inventor. The matter came to a head in a series of trials in which Arkwright attempted to prosecute those who had tried to 'steal' his patented machines – but the result was not as he had hoped. In 1781 before the King's Bench, Arkwright's case against Charles Lewis Mordaunt was heard before Lord Mansfield. Surprisingly, Mordaunt did not deny that he had infringed the patent. Rather, he argued, the patent itself was not valid. The court found in Mordaunt's favour, agreeing that Arkwright had not fully revealed the specification as a patentee is required to do, but 'did all he could to hide and secrete it'. In the subsequent trial of 1785, it was suggested that the invention was not new, having been secretly stolen and passed to Arkwright by John Kay, the man who helped him build the prototype spinning machine. James Watt himself had been called as a witness and wrote, 'Though I do not love Arkwright,

I don't like the precedent of setting aside patents . . . I fear for our own.'

Despite the loss of his patents, it is difficult to feel sorry for Sir Richard Arkwright. The invention was merely the starting point for the real revolution – the organisation of mills along factory lines. Arkwright was so brilliant a businessman that by the time he died in 1792 he had amassed £500,000, worth perhaps £200 million today. There is a wonderful description of the great man by Carlyle: 'A plain, almost gross, bag-cheeked, potbellied Lancashire man, with the air of painful reflection, yet also of copious free digestion.' Not a conventional hero, then, but he changed the face of British industry.

The mill at Cromford in Derbyshire is being restored, and is open to the public. There is an original water-frame in the Helmshore Textile Museum in Rossendale (01706 226459).

5 Joseph Aspdin and his Portland Cement

Portland cement is one of the most important raw materials in the building trade. Hardly a building goes up in the industrialised countries of the world without its share of Portland cement, and sometimes vast structures are made entirely of cement, with merely some sand and gravel aggregate to turn it into concrete, and some reinforcing rods to add tensile strength. By one of those delightful quirks of fate, Portland cement was invented as the result of a careless mistake by a bricklayer in Leeds.

Concrete has a long history: it was used for the floors of huts on the banks of the Danube in about 5600 BC; in the construction of the Great Pyramid of Giza in 2500 BC; and spectacularly by the Romans. They found they could make strong cements by using volcanic ash from Vesuvius. The dome of the Pantheon in Rome is almost 50 yards across, and is made of a lightweight concrete using pumice stone as aggregate; this dome inspired Christopher Wren when he came to design St Paul's Cathedral. Similarly, the Pont du Gard aqueduct and Hadrian's Wall were held together with concrete.

John Smeaton, commissioned in 1756 to build the third Eddystone Lighthouse, experimented with types of concrete that would set under water, and eventually produced a complex mixture of burnt Aberthaw blue lias (Welsh limestone) and Italian pozzolana, which was the best cement produced since the Romans left – and Smeaton's Stump still stands on the Eddystone rocks to prove it! Because Portland stone had an excellent reputation as a building material, Smeaton set out to make a cement that would not only look as good but also be as strong as Portland stone, and he called it Portland cement. But the most important advance in technology came seventy years later, in a grubby back yard in Yorkshire.

On Christmas Day 1778, Thomas Aspdin, a bricklayer of Hunslet near Leeds, celebrated when his wife produced a son, whom they called Joseph. He followed in his father's footsteps and became a bricklayer, too. In 1817 he decided to cut out one of the middlemen and make his own cement, so he moved into Leeds and bought an old glassworks in Slip-in Yard, Back of Shambles, off Briggate. This was where his chemistry went wrong.

Simple lime mortars are made from chalk, limestone or shells, which are all forms of calcium carbonate ($CaCO_3$). Heating this in an oven at about 1000°C drives off carbon dioxide to produce quicklime (CaO). Adding water to quicklime makes slaked lime ($Ca(OH)_2$), which will mix with more water to make a smooth paste of lime mortar. This mortar is easy to work with, and it sticks bricks together slowly but effectively, because although it does not set on its own, it reacts very slowly with the carbon dioxide in the atmosphere to make calcium carbonate, which is hard. Adding a little clay to the lime makes the cement harder, and it sets more strongly, although too much clay makes the mortar difficult to use.

Apparently Joseph Aspdin used a mixture of one part of clay to three parts of limestone, and he melted them together. Had he been using a lime kiln at around 1000°C that would have been fine, and he would have made conventional lime mortar. But his glass furnace was designed to reach higher temperatures, and probably by mistake he heated his mixture to about 1300°C. When he cooled it down again he found the furnace was full of lumps of clinker, so hard they were difficult to get out of the furnace. When he did get them out he had tremendous trouble grinding them into powder and his investment in the furnace must have seemed rather dubious. And when he found that the powder would not even slake properly, as lime should when mixed with water, he must have come close to abandoning the whole enterprise.

But then he discovered that this new powder behaved strangely with water. Instead of just getting wet it reacted slowly to make a solid and insoluble mass: an incredibly strong artificial stone. Here at last was the product that everyone wanted – a cement that would set hard throughout its bulk, not merely on the surface. It would even set like a rock under water; John Smeaton would have been delighted. And when Aspdin applied for his patent in 1824, he followed Smeaton's example and called his new product Portland cement. He outgrew his little factory in Leeds, moved to larger premises in Wakefield, and made both cement and money.

The high temperature in the furnace was critical, for it causes the chalk and the clay to react together to produce a new compound: calcium silicate. This is the rock-like mass on which most of the world's buildings now stand. In fact, Joe Aspdin never really understood the potential of his creation. He thought of it merely as a material for facing brick buildings, to make them look like stone. He died on 20 March 1855, and was buried at St John's Chapel in Wakefield. He would have been amazed at a typical modern cement works, using huge rotating kilns to melt together a 3:1 mixture of chalk and clay at 1450°C, and producing 3,000 tonnes of Portland cement every day. And all because the brickie from Hunslet had bought a second-hand glassworks. . . .

There remains one building still faced with Aspdin's original artificial stone – the Wakefield Arms pub, beside Kirkgate station in Wakefield. The smooth facing of the pub is a testimony to the quality of his product, and the lunch in the pub isn't bad either! A curious memorial is the Ship-on-Shore pub at Sheerness, which is made entirely from solidified barrels of cement. These were being transported down the Thames when the ship ran aground; local people thought the barrels contained whisky and quickly hauled them ashore, only to find they were full of rapidly hardening cement, so they turned the barrels into a pub!

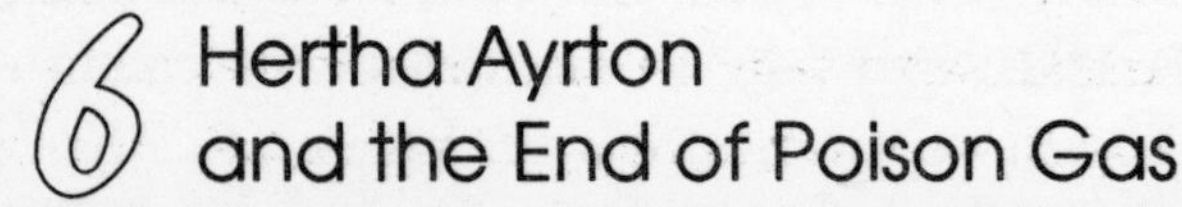

6 Hertha Ayrton and the End of Poison Gas

In the early stages of the First World War, hundreds of thousands of soldiers were pinned in trenches by the machine-gun bullets whizzing overhead. To begin with, the commanders thought they could silence the machine-guns by bombardment with heavy artillery. They were wrong. On the first day of the battle of the Somme, when the troops went 'over the top' in the 'great push', struggling with the mud and the barbed wire, twenty thousand men died, probably within a couple of hours.

In the first six months of the battle, neither side advanced more than half a mile. The way forward eventually was found, in the shape of the tank, but meanwhile both sides looked for ways to kill the enemy where they were. They were dug down out of the reach of bullets, but they could still be reached by poison gas.

Thousands of artillery shells were filled with liquid gas; these exploded on impact and spread the gas. But probably more lethal were the cylinders stored in the front line. On suitable days, when the wind was blowing gently towards the enemy lines, the stopcocks were opened, and poison gas was allowed to roll silently across no-man's-land and into the enemy trenches, ravaging the unsuspecting troops. There was no warning – just a sudden curious smell, a choking sensation, and sometimes streaming eyes.

Many types of gas were tried. Chlorine, now used in very dilute form for disinfecting swimming pools, caused choking and lung damage. Mustard gas caused terrible irritation of the eyes; the soldiers could not see, and the skin often blistered. One of the most deadly was phosgene, with a sweet smell of new-mown hay, but lethal after-effects.

Troops were issued with gas-masks, but wearing them all the time was impossible; what was needed was a way to get the gas out of the trenches when it had drifted in. The solution was the Ayrton Fan.

Phoebe Sarah Marks was born on 28 April 1854, one of eight children of Alice and Levi Marks, a clockmaker. Later, in her teens, she changed her name to Hertha. Fascinated by science, she went to Cambridge and on to Finsbury Technical College, where she assisted Professor William Ayrton in his research with arc lamps. She did well; not only did she work out what made arc lamps so noisy; she also married the Professor in 1885, becoming Hertha Ayrton. In 1899 she became the first woman member of the Institute of Electrical Engineers, as a result of her arc-lamp work. In 1902 she was proposed for election to the Royal Society, but was rejected because they had no legal charter to elect a married woman as a Fellow. Her breakthrough came in 1901, when she spent the autumn in Margate. The wide curving beach below the town is a lovely place to walk, and at low tide presents a fascinating array of ripples in the sand. To her sharp scientific mind they presented a challenging question – how and why were ripples formed?

One afternoon Hertha shocked her landlady when she returned from her walk and declared, 'I will have my bath in the sitting room after tea, please.' Hertha used the galvanised tub to perform the first of many experiments on sand ripples. She had already realised, from her observations on the shore, that ripples are not formed by waves crashing on the beach. So presumably they can be formed in deep water by the back and forth movement of the water above. If you look closely at the sand near a small bump, you can see that the water swirls over it and eddies back toward the bump. This swirl, or vortex, carries sand with it, makes the bump a bit bigger, and starts to make a trough where it took the sand from. When the water flows back the other way, the same thing happens on the other side of the bump. As the water ebbs and flows, each vortex takes more sand from the trough and dumps it on the bump. So the bump becomes a ripple. Back in London Hertha started serious research on ripples, which was to last for many years. In 1904 she became the first woman to read a paper to the Royal Society; needless to say it was about the origin and growth of ripples.

In 1915 the troops in the trenches in northern France were dying in huge numbers from the effects of poison gas. Like everyone else in Britain, Hertha Ayrton was worrying about them when she went to the Royal Society on 6 May. On her way home in a taxi – she lived at 41 Norfolk Square, near Paddington, London – she had a brainwave. If a flow of water can create vortices, then the opposite should also be true: the right type of vortex should be able to create a flow of air, which could drive back the gas.

She walked into her house and told her maid she was not to be disturbed for the rest of the day. Then she set about testing her idea by means of a table-top experiment. She built a small-scale parapet with little sand bags, and flapped a postcard on her 'sandbags' to create a local vortex, hoping it would generate a flow of air along the table. Then she made some smoke to monitor the flow of air. If a postcard could drive away the oncoming smoke, then perhaps a full-size fan would be able to drive poison gas out of a trench. Her results were so astonishing that she 'laughed aloud at the simplicity of the solution'. It turned out to be so effective that a close friend of Hertha's, Mr Greenslade, used to demonstrate its use in training trenches in 1916 using cyanide gas – without a gas-mask! As a direct result of her scientific curiosity and intuition, the Ayrton Fan was developed, and 104,000 were sent to the trenches to save the soldiers from the lethal drifting gas.

There is an original Ayrton Fan at the Imperial War Museum. Hertha lived at 41 Norfolk Square, near Paddington station.

7 Francis Bacon, who Died Inventing the Frozen Chicken

Francis Bacon was the sixth child of Sir Nicholas Bacon, Keeper of the Great Seal at the court of Elizabeth I. He was born into a position of great privilege, but no money – he was too far down the line to inherit anything. So he turned to the law, and was a professional lawyer all his life. He lived in St Albans, once the Roman town of Verulamium, and celebrated both those names because he became Viscount St Albans and Baron Verulam. He reached the highest office in the land, but seriously fell out with two monarchs; in his spare time, he laid the foundations for modern science – and died inventing the frozen chicken.

Despite his family connections, he had difficulty getting into court. He insisted on offering advice to Queen Elizabeth, and supported laws she didn't like, so it's not surprising he was less than popular. He found himself in the tricky position of having to support the execution for treason of a good friend of his, the Earl of Essex. When James I took over things looked up, and Bacon's brilliant legal mind was rewarded with a succession of posts, culminating in his becoming Keeper of the Great Seal, as his father had been, and Lord Chancellor of England, the most powerful minister in the land. In 1621 he was created Viscount St Albans. But just five days later it all went horribly wrong when he was charged with bribery. The House of Lords fined him £40,000 and banished him from the 'verge of court' – which meant he had to stay 12 miles away from the King at all times, which is a tricky navigational problem. Although the King later did away with the fine and the sentence, this was the end of Bacon's public life and he retired to Gorhambury, his fine Tudor house, to concentrate on his writing.

What really interested him was truth, and in particular scientific truth. He was worried that a lot of supposedly scientific ideas were simply made up.

In particular, he was disturbed to find that Tudor science was based largely on the ideas of Aristotle, who had died in 322 BC. Aristotle, tutor to Alexander the Great, had tried to show how knowledge could be obtained. Many of his conclusions – the earth at the centre of the universe, species of animals never changing – have been overturned. But what Bacon objected to was his method – the idea that scientific truth could be found by authority and argument. If you had clever enough men and they discussed something for long enough, the truth would result. Bacon went out of favour in the late nineteenth century because people said he hadn't fully developed the scientific method, but he it was who suggested that evidence, rather than imagination, should be the basis for scientific truth.

Bacon parodied these 'authorities' as spiders – spinning webs from their own substance. What you needed, he said, was evidence from the real world. He set out ways in which you could accumulate evidence, and one of these was by experiment. Suppose you wanted to investigate gravity, and whether something falls because it is pulled by the earth, or has its own tendency to move downward – which was the old Aristotelian idea. He suggested using two clocks, one regulated by springs, the other by weights. Take them to the top of the highest church, and down the deepest mine. If gravity is a property of the weight itself, the clocks won't be affected, but if it comes somehow from the earth, then the weight-driven clock will speed up or slow down as you go closer to or further from the centre of the earth. This is a neat example of the 'Scientific Method', where you test a theory by a controlled experiment. In this case the 'control' is the spring-driven clock, which should always run at the same speed.

He summed up his idea neatly: 'Whether or no anything can be known, can be settled not by arguing, but by trying.' In his spare time he began publishing his new ideas. The frontispiece of his book *Novum Organum* shows the Pillars of Hercules, symbolising in the ancient world the limit of man's knowledge, and a ship sailing through into the modern world of knowledge Bacon dreamed of. The Latin inscription means: 'Many shall sail through and knowledge shall be increased.'

Francis Bacon recorded a curious phenomenon; he said that hot water freezes more quickly than cold water. He did not claim this was his discovery; indeed he said it had been known for a long time. However, it's a claim that you can easily test with your own experiments; fill one glass or ice-cube tray with water from the cold tap and an identical one with water from the hot tap, put both in the freezer, and see which is frozen solid first. Why hot water might freeze first is a bit of a mystery. One possibility is that if your freezer is frosted up, the warm glass melts through the frost and gets better contact; another is that a thin 'lid' of ice forms quickly on the cold water, which actually helps to keep some of the heat in by stopping convection currents in the water. But does it depend on the container? It's certainly a fascinating phenomenon, and an example of something you probably wouldn't have discovered simply by argument. Bacon suggested that as well as doing experiments, scientists should rigorously collect and organise data from the natural world, to make sure their ideas match what really goes on.

There are quite a few odd theories surrounding Bacon. Some people think he is the author of Shakespeare's plays – because a mere actor like William Shakespeare couldn't possibly have done it. Others believe that he was in fact a son of Queen Elizabeth herself. I doubt if either theory would stand up to scientific investigation by Bacon himself.

One snowy day in early April 1626, Bacon was travelling through Highgate, then outside London, when he was seized by a sudden scientific impulse. At the foot of Highgate Hill he obtained a chicken from a peasant. He had a life-long interest in heat and cold, and wanted to find out whether cold could be used to preserve meat. So he stuffed the chicken with snow, which was conveniently lying about on the ground. But while he was doing this, he was suddenly taken ill. He was taken to his friend Lord Arundel's place, which was just round the corner. In the carriage he suffered a fit of 'casting' or vomiting, and had to go to bed as soon as he reached the house. And having invented the frozen chicken, he died a few days later on 9 April.

Gorhambury House was demolished in the eighteenth century to make a picturesque ruin for the new mansion that was being built, but the remains are still visible on the Gorhambury Estate in St Albans. Bacon died in the Old Hall on the corner of The Grove and Bacon Lane, at the top of Highgate Hill.

8 Donald Bailey and his Bridge to Victory

Sir Donald Coleman Bailey's invention was hardly glamorous. Indeed it was so simple and unassuming that at first it was ignored in favour of more complicated designs. But in the end, his revolutionary bridge proved to be a vital link in the road to victory in Europe in 1944 and 1945.

Bailey came from Rotherham, went to Sheffield University and got his first job with Rowntree in York, before joining the Military Engineering Experimental Establishment in 1928 as a civil engineering designer. The problem he was to solve so spectacularly well was familiar from many military campaigns. In retreat, as the Allies had been, you cut communications and blow bridges to hold up the progress of the enemy. But what happens when the tables are turned and you need to invade? The tactics that had been so sensible in retreat make an attack almost impossible. In the Second World War the problem was worse than in any preceding conflict because aerial bombing had been able to destroy an amazingly high proportion of bridges. Bailey had in fact dreamed up the design for a bridge as early as 1936, but the War Office wasn't interested. Bailey must have been sure his design was right, because he kept working at it in his own time.

By 1941 the government had realised that a portable military bridge would indeed be necessary in Europe, and settled on a design by Charles Inglis. Bailey had seen the design and predicted that it wasn't strong enough – a prediction fulfilled when the Inglis Bridge failed under test. This could have set the war back – but luckily Colonel Fowle had seen Bailey's design sketched on the back of an envelope (which seems too good to be true) and asked him to work it up. Bailey was ordered to go ahead in February 1941, but because he had been working on the design in private the first prototype was ready by 5 May. The idea was simple: the bridge was made up from a kit of components, the key one being the panel, 10 feet by 5 feet, made of steel girders, and reinforced in a diamond pattern. The panel was small enough to fit into a standard 3-ton army truck, strong enough to make a bridge that could carry a tank, but light enough to be carried by six soldiers. The panels were joined by beams that could also be carried by a few men, and the whole lot bolted together in a wonderfully low-tech way so that on the front line you didn't need specialists to do the work.

Naturally the bridge had to be tested. The 70-foot span was completed in just thirty-six minutes, then loaded up with a 1917 Mark V tank filled with pig iron. It must have been a tense moment, remembering the fate of the Inglis Bridge, but the Bailey Bridge passed with flying colours and was soon in production. The first bridges went into service in December 1941, just ten months after Bailey was given the order to proceed, and entirely due to the faith its inventor had had in his own idea and the unpaid work he had done to develop it.

The bridges were a tremendous success. Between 1944 and 1945 two thousand Bailey Bridges were erected in north-west Europe alone, and one general reckoned the Bailey Bridge doubled the value of Allied armoured and mechanised units. The Bailey Bridge solved one of the trickiest problems in bridge-building. It was in the nature of the situations in which they were used that the bridges would often have to be built from one side of a river or chasm, with no hope of getting men on to the far bank. Bailey simply rolled the bridge from one bank to the other, the first part to cross being a lightweight 'nose' that would later be discarded, and always making sure that enough bridge had been built on land to counter-balance the part suspended in mid-air.

The system was so versatile that huge engineering projects could be undertaken with the panel and beam kit, and Bailey's name became legendary among Allied troops. He was rewarded with an OBE before the war ended, and a knighthood in 1946.

The bridges lived on after the war, one being bought for £300 as surplus and erected over the River Don by Rotherham Corporation and the neighbouring Rawmarsh Urban Development Council as a tribute to Donald Bailey.

Alexander Bain and the Fax Machine

The telephone was invented in 1875 by a Scotsman in America, and the instrument has utterly changed our lives. The fax machine brought about another substantial change when it came into general use in about the 1970s. I was astonished to discover that the fax machine was actually patented thirty years before the telephone was invented, by an ingenious shepherd from the north of Scotland called Alexander Bain.

Alexander Bain and his twin sister Margaret were born in October 1810. Their dad was a crofter, and he had six sisters and six brothers. They grew up in a remote stone cottage at Leanmore, a few miles north of Wick. The vast expanse of peaty countryside has only occasional scattered cottages, and the Bain house, close to a small wood, became a sheep byre, and is now little more than an outline of low stone walls. In the winter Sandy walked a mile or two to school in Backlass; in the summer he worked as a shepherd.

He was bottom of his class in school, and was a poor shepherd too, because he was always dreaming. But he was fascinated by clocks, and actually made himself a model clock using heather for the spring and the cogwheels, so his sympathetic father got him apprenticed to a clockmaker in Wick.

In January 1830 he walked 21 miles through the snow from Wick to Thurso to hear a lecture on 'Light, heat, and the electric fluid'. The lecture changed his life, for he decided then and there that electricity was the stuff to work with. He began inventing electrical devices, including various types of automatic telegraph, an electric clock, an earth battery, insulation for electric cables and an electric fire alarm. He took out patents on all these, and also on inkstands, inkholders and a ship's log. The most amazing idea he had was for what he called the electro-chemical telegraph, which we would call a fax machine. However, before he had a chance to develop it, he ran into an unpleasant spot of trouble in London.

In 1840 Bain was desperate for money to develop his clocks and his fax machine; he talked about his financial problems to the editor of the *Mechanics Magazine*, who introduced him to the well-known and highly respected Professor Sir Charles Wheatstone. Bain took his models to demonstrate at Wheatstone's house.

Wheatstone watched Bain's gadgets with fascination, and then, when asked for his opinion, said 'Oh,

I shouldn't bother to develop these things any further! There's no future in them.' Bain went away disconsolate, but three months later Wheatstone went to the Royal Society and before the leaders of the scientific establishment demonstrated an electric clock, claiming it was his own invention. Luckily, Bain had already applied for his patent.

Professor Sir Charles Wheatstone had all the advantages of rank and social position, and did his level best to block Bain's patents. He failed, and rumours of his skulduggery began to circulate. So when Wheatstone organised an Act of Parliament to set up the Electric Telegraph Company, the House of Lords summoned Bain to give evidence, and eventually compelled the company to pay Bain £10,000 and give him a job as manager. Wheatstone resigned in a huff.

In 1841 Sandy Bain made a new kind of electric telegraph, the first of three devices he dreamed up to send pictures or printed words along telegraph wires. This was an idea decades ahead of its time: in those days messages were sent by Morse code – people had to wait thirty years for the telephone – so even a skilled operator could send only a few words a minute. Bain's machine was to change all that.

Bain had already worked out how to set up a system of clocks that would remain exactly synchronised. He put a master clock in the railway station in Edinburgh, and another clock in the railway station in Glasgow. Then he arranged that every time the

Edinburgh pendulum swung it sent a pulse of electricity along the telegraph wires, which drove a solenoid in Glasgow and pushed the Glasgow pendulum at exactly the same time. Bain's electrical mechanism didn't just make the clocks run at the same rate, it forced the pendulums to stay precisely in step.

When he wanted to send a picture along the wires, he made a copy of it in copper, and etched away everything but the lines he wanted. Then he arranged for a metal needle or stylus to swing across the picture. Each time it touched copper it made contact and sent a pulse along the telegraph wire.

The needle was attached to the pendulum of the clock at each end, so the positions of the contacts were faithfully reproduced at the receiving end by a matching stylus running across electro-sensitive paper; whenever there was a blip of current the stylus left a black mark on the paper, corresponding to the position of the line in the original picture.

Finally he arranged for both pictures – the one being sent and the one being received – to drop down by a millimetre at every swing of the pendulum. Thus the outgoing picture was gradually scanned by the stylus swinging across it and moving down line by line, and at the receiving end the new copy picture was gradually built up.

The whole concept was an outstanding example of pushing the available technology to its limits. Unfortunately, Bain, despite his ingenuity, was hopeless with money. He wasted lots in litigation in America, and lots more on trying to achieve perpetual motion. He eventually died in Glasgow, poor and sad, in 1877.

Wheatstone is famous, Bain is forgotten. But the man who invented the fax machine, a vital feature of every office today, was that unknown shepherd from Caithness, Alexander Bain.

The main Telecom building in Thurso is called the Alexander Bain Building, and there is an original Bain electric clock in the hall at Watten, between Wick and Thurso.

10 John Logie Baird, Inventor of Undersocks and Television

Quite a lot of these heroes have been loners, working away on their own with inadequate resources and no recognition from the authorities until it was too late. But in the twentieth century, most science is done by professionals, often in universities or proper laboratories. So it is rather surprising to find that one of the greatest inventions of this century was made by a man literally starving in a garret. Using his own pathetic finances he beat huge organisations in many countries to one of the holy grails of engineering – the ability to send moving pictures from one place to another.

The inventor of television was the son of a

Scottish minister in Helensburgh, north-west of Glasgow, and his name was John Logie Baird. Baird was a sickly boy, and was dogged by ill-health all his life. He was declared unfit for army service, and recurring bronchitis cut short many of his business ventures. Unable to pursue more conventional careers, he devoted his energies to the passion he developed at the age of thirteen – for television. As a boy he was already inventive. He rigged up a telephone exchange between his parents' house and those of his friends Whimster, Bruce, Norwell, and Wadsworth. It all came to a disastrous end one stormy night when one of the wires dangled too low and lifted a passing cab-man clean out of his seat.

The idea of television was not new. Even the word television had been coined in 1900 when JLB was only twelve years old, and he must have dreamed about the possibilities. The key discovery had been that the element Selenium is photoelectric – its electrical resistance changes as the light falling on it goes from bright to dim, an effect which is used in the light meter. Around the world people wondered whether this phenomenon could somehow do for vision what the telephone had done for speech. So the race to develop television was on.

Not surprisingly, although John's dad was a minister in the church and wanted his son to follow in his footsteps, John had other ideas and enrolled instead in the Royal Glasgow College of Technology to study electrical engineering. By an amazing coincidence, a fellow student was John Reith who was to become the first director-general of the BBC. The two did not get on. Unfit for service when the war broke out in 1914, Baird spent his time instead maintaining the Glasgow electricity supply, plunging large parts of the city into darkness on one occasion when he connected an experiment in artificial diamond production across the terminals of a power station.

After the war, Baird began to show an entrepreneurial streak. With no career, he turned to commerce and invented the 'Baird Patent Undersock'. These wonderful things were supposed to be worn under your socks, to keep the feet warm and dry, and so prevent rising damp! They were treated with borax, although Baird apparently once revealed that the secret lining was old newspapers. Baird made the socks himself, writing testimonials from fictitious satisfied customers, and then sold them round the stores of Glasgow. His marketing stunts included 'the first sandwich women in Glasgow'. It sounds like a bit of a joke – but at one time he was making £200 a week. He also sold soap and boot-polish, until his bronchitis forced him to give up. Hoping for a healthier climate, he headed for Trinidad where his first commercial ventures failed, so instead he set up a jam factory. He carried on in the same vein on his return to Britain until his health was so bad that he virtually retired to Hastings, aged thirty-four.

This was 1922, and Baird may have been experimenting with television all along. He now decided to devote himself to it. Television was much more difficult than radio. A single microphone can pick up all the sound in a room and convert it into an electrical signal, which can be fed down a wire. A single photocell can do the same thing for light – but all you would get is a reading of the average brightness of the scene – not very interesting. You could have thousands of these cells, one in each part of the picture, connected by wires to thousands of light-bulbs or whatever in your receiver, but that is completely impractical and could never work over radio. In all his experiments Baird was constantly thinking about how his pictures might be delivered, and was careful not to generate more information than the medium (literally the medium wave in his day) could handle.

Baird was by no means the only television experimenter, and he made use of whatever existing technology seemed to work. A German engineer called Paul Nipkow worked out in 1884 how to transmit pictures using a single photocell. He realised that you could scan points in the picture one after the other and then somehow reassemble them at the other end. If you could do this quickly enough you might fool the eye into seeing moving pictures. The 'Nipkow Disc' remained a central part of all Baird's mechanical television experiments and consisted simply of a spinning disc with a spiral of holes punched in it. Placed in front of a picture, the effect was of a hole scanning gradually over the picture, first down one line, then the next and so on.

Baird realised that this scanning system was key – at any time there is only one hole scanning the picture, so you only need one photocell behind the disc to measure the light coming through.

This is the sort of system he used in Hastings, in his room over an artificial flower shop, from 1922. At the other end, the receiver, you had an almost identical machine – called by Baird the 'Televisor'. But instead of a photocell, there was a lamp whose brightness varied in proportion to the signal from the transmitter. Crucially he worked out how to get the transmitter and the Televisor synchronised. He first televised a Maltese cross, and although the picture quality was poor – just a black and white silhouette – what impressed people was the fact that these were moving pictures. He had found a system that could scan a picture and transmit enough information to fool the eye.

In 1924 Baird moved to London, and in March 1925 Mr Gordon Selfridge Jnr, of the Selfridges department store, heard about the experiments and suggested a public demonstration in the shop; he would pay Baird £25 a week for three weeks. It was the world's first public demonstration of television. People flocked to see his crude pictures, made up of just 30 lines – today we use 625. Nevertheless, it was hailed as a great success, and some visitors worried that since this thing could send pictures through walls, this could mark the end of privacy. Despite his amazing achievement, Baird soon ran out of money. People who visited him were shocked to see him working in carpet slippers and no socks. He persuaded some Scottish relations to invest, which let him continue work on the photocell.

He couldn't improve on the black and white image – he wanted shades of grey. At one point he had been so desperate for a new device that he persuaded an eye surgeon to give him a fresh human eye so that he could try an extract from the retina, but it didn't help. Finally, on 2 October 1925, Baird sat 'Bill', a ventriloquist's dummy, in front of the transmitter so that he could watch the Televisor. What he saw was amazing – a face, in reasonable detail. Baird rushed downstairs and grabbed William Taynton, an office boy working on the floor below, and sat him in front of the transmitter. But Baird saw nothing from the next room. Puzzled, he returned to the transmitter to find that William had moved his chair back from the transmitter as he couldn't stand the ultra-bright light Baird had to use. Half a crown solved the problem. Baird told him to open his mouth and move his head – so William was the first person to be televised – though several other people claim the honour.

Baird went public the following summer, inviting fifty scientists and others to his Soho attic; they queued in the street and on the stairs as only five at a time could fit in. In the USA Radio News confirmed that 'Mr Baird has definitely and indisputably given a demonstration of real television. It is the first time in history that this has been done in any part of the world.' He soon managed to send pictures via the telephone, and in 1928 across the Atlantic by radio. It is claimed that although he already had the ability to produce far superior pictures, he revealed only the 30-line transmissions because nothing with more information could have been squeezed through a telephone line.

Baird had done it. Although most of the technology – like the Nipkow Disc – had been invented by other people, only Baird had made television work, despite the attempts of huge corporations in America and elsewhere. He became a bit of a celebrity, especially when he finally got the BBC to agree to a broadcast trial. Amazingly, they didn't seem to be interested at first: they had a system of sending still pictures by wireless – rather like having a fax attached to your radio. Eventually the postmaster-general, who supported Baird, insisted that the BBC test Baird's system. Regular transmissions started less than thrillingly on Monday 30 September 1929 with a message from the President of the Board of Trade, who said that 'This new industry will provide employment for large numbers of our people and will prove the prestige of British creative energy.'

For the first six months, sound and vision were sent alternately, as only one transmitter was available. From 31 March 1930 sound and vision broadcasts were possible, and a Televisor was installed in 10 Downing Street for Prime Minister Ramsay MacDonald and his family. MacDonald immediately realised what television was all about. On 5 April 1930 he wrote a wonderful letter:

Dear Mr Baird,

I must thank you very warmly for the television instrument you have put into Downing Street. What a marvellous discovery you have made! When I look at the transmissions I feel that the most wonderful miracle is being done under my eye . . . You have put something in my room which will never let me forget how strange is the world – and how unknown. Again and again I thank you.

With kindest regards,
J. Ramsay MacDonald

On 3 June 1931 Baird triumphantly televised the Derby from Epsom. It seemed that television had arrived, and Baird was the man who had done it. But of course that isn't the end of the story. We don't watch television through spinning discs, even though Baird quickly produced much better pictures including colour and 3D television.

At the same time Baird was making mechanical television, another system was being developed. The cathode ray tube had been invented in 1897. We now call cathode rays electrons, and they are fired from the back of the tube. You can make them light up the front of the tube and you can steer them electrically to scan in lines – like the holes in the disc, but with far more lines than Baird's mechanical television could achieve. The cathode ray tube was adapted for the television camera as well. The BBC ran twin trials of a Baird mechanical 240-line system, and the Marconi-EMI electronic system at 405 lines. In 1937 the Baird system was switched off: electronics had won.

All television shut down during the war, and although Baird kept working at new ideas, he died in 1946 – the year television really took off in Britain. There are conflicting views of Baird. Some regard him as a brilliant but misguided pioneer, who backed the wrong system and rightly lost out to electronic television. Others point out many experiments that Baird himself made which could have led to – some say did result in – a Baird electronic system far better than the one we ended up with. That he lost out is thanks to the terms of the 1937 trial and the government backing a system under American pressure. This is still controversial, and new information is still being uncovered. Whatever the final conclusion, no one can take away the fact that John Logie Baird was the first person in the world to demonstrate the transmission of moving images from one place to another – television.

There is a bust of John Logie Baird at his birthplace, Helensburgh. It looks wistfully out to sea. There is also a plaque on the house in which he was born in West Argyle Street in Glasgow. There is a memorial at Central Hotel, Glasgow, the site of an early transmission, and a blue plaque at 22 Frith Street, where his first demonstration took place.

11 Joseph Banks's Chowder 'Recipe'

Sir Joseph Banks was a fat, arrogant, amusing and talented botanist who, as president of the Royal Society, ruled British science for more than forty years. He brought back exotic specimens from all around the world, but the strangest – and most useful – was a recipe from Newfoundland for fish chowder.

Joseph Banks had a house in London and a large estate at Revesby near Lincoln, which he inherited, along with a substantial fortune, when his father died in 1761. His interest in botany started when he was still at school, and continued at Oxford, and he was elected a Fellow of the Royal Society in 1766. He then delighted his mother by announcing that he was going to travel. She assumed he was thinking of the Grand Tour around the cultural capitals of Europe, and was horrified when he explained that was not quite what he had in mind; instead he planned to go to Newfoundland on a fisheries protection vessel, in order to look for plants.

He was horribly seasick, and didn't enjoy the trip much, but he brought home a number of specimens, and a rather jolly account in his journal of some mysterious stuff called chowder that the natives used to eat.

> It is a soup made with a small quantity of salt Pork cut into Small Slices a good deal of fish and Biscuit Boyled for about an hour unlikely as this mixture appears to be Palatable I have scarce met with any Body in this Country Who is not fond of it.

Unfortunately, not being used to doing his own cooking, he failed to write down a proper recipe, but we tried a genuine experiment, starting with a piece of gammon (in place of the salt pork), boiling that in a saucepan half full of water, and then adding in succession pieces of halibut, cod and prawns, all from Newfoundland, which seemed appropriate. We seasoned the mixture and let it simmer for five minutes, and then crumbled into it a packet of dry biscuits. The whole concoction thickened to the consistency of wallpaper paste, and looked rather grey and unappetising, but it tasted wonderful. Do try it yourself!

The trip of Banks's life came in 1768, when he persuaded the First Lord of the Admiralty that he was the right man to go as botanist with Captain James Cook on his scientific voyage around the world. He insisted on taking along another botanist, Dr Solander, two draughtsmen, two servants, and two greyhounds – but he did pay for all their expenses. For this important voyage Cook had been offered a ship of the line, but he chose instead the *Endeavour*, a second-hand coal barge from Whitby, and Banks's quarters were therefore fairly cramped.

The primary objective of the trip was to observe the

Transit of Venus from Tahiti on 3 June 1769. They did this successfully, but on the way they had a host of amazing experiences, which Banks described in his extensive journals. They almost died from cold on what was supposed to be a simple exploratory trip in South America. In Tahiti the natives were extremely friendly, especially the women, and Banks enjoyed himself enormously. However, he was embarrassed when a lovely lady suggested the floor would be comfortable to lie on – but the house had no walls. . . .

One lady invited him to spend the night with her in a canoe. When he woke up he found that all his clothes had been stolen – as had the pair of pistols he had placed in his pockets to protect himself against thieves. He did not say whether he walked back to the *Endeavour* 'wearing' the canoe.

After Tahiti they sailed round much of Australia, collecting and surveying, and then returned to England. Later Banks went to Iceland, but he then settled to a life of luxury at home, becoming a grand patron of science, rather than an active practitioner. He was invited to go round the world with Cook again in 1772, but this time insisted on taking a retinue of fourteen assistants and servants, not to mention two horn-players. In order to accommodate them, a new cabin and a new deck were built on the ship, the *Resolution*, but when she put to sea this extra superstructure made her completely uncontrollable. Cook ordered it all to be removed, and Banks huffily refused to go.

Whenever you see a plant labelled xxx Banksii you know it is descended from one of the plants he brought back from his foreign trips. Many of them grow in the Sir Joseph Banks conservatory in Lincoln. And curiously his names were given to an American who went on to set up the world's first department of parapsychology at Duke University, North Carolina, and coined the phrase extra-sensory perception – Joseph Banks Rhine.

12 William Banting's Diet for Corpulence

William Banting, born in 1797, was a short, fat undertaker and furnisher of funerals in St James's Street, London. As he grew older he became more corpulent; he was only 5 feet 5 inches tall, but by the time he was sixty-five he weighed 14 stone 6 pounds (92 kg), and could no longer tie his own shoelaces. He had to go downstairs backwards, and slowly, to avoid excessive strain on the ankle joints, and with every exertion he 'puffed and blowed' in a most unseemly way. This was most distressing for him, since his job as a smart undertaker required the utmost in decorous behaviour and respectful quietness.

He consulted several doctors, and asked how he could reduce his size. They told him to take plenty of exercise, so he walked long distances, and then tried rowing. He actually rowed a boat for two hours before breakfast every day. But the result was that he grew hungrier and hungrier – and heavier and heavier.

He visited fifty Turkish baths in a vain attempt to sweat off his pounds, and he drank gallons of patent slimming medicines. He visited spas to take the waters. He even – as a desperate resort – tried the new-fangled practice of sea-bathing. None of these things did any good at all. Then, because he was going deaf, he went to Soho Square and consulted Mr William Harvey. Mr Harvey said his deafness was caused by corpulence, and that the remedy was to go on a diet. He told Banting not to eat bread, butter, milk, sugar, beer, soup, potatoes or beans, but to eat mainly lean meat, fish and dry toast.

This is basically a high-protein, low-carbohydrate diet, although it seems to have been pretty generous with alcohol. Indeed the quantities of everything seem

BANTING'S DIET

Breakfast	4–6 oz beef, mutton, kidneys, broiled fish, bacon, or any cold meat except pork 1–2 oz dry toast	1 large cup black tea
Dinner	10–12 oz of any fish except salmon, any meat except pork, any vegetable except potato 2 oz dry toast fruit out of a pudding any kind of poultry or game	2 or 3 glasses of good claret, sherry, or Madeira but NO champagne, port, or beer
Tea	4–6 oz fruit a rusk or two	1 large cup black tea
Supper	6–8 oz meat or fish, as dinner	1 or 2 glasses claret
Nightcap		1 tumbler gin, whisky, or brandy

substantial, with three square meals a day, topped off by a nightcap of a tumbler of gin, whisky or brandy – although without any added sugar! In spite of the enormous intake of alcohol, the diet was successful. Within a year, Mr Banting lost more than 3 stone, and he felt better than he had for twenty years. He was so delighted at having lost so much weight by such simple means that in 1863 he wrote a pamphlet called 'A Letter on Corpulence, addressed to the Public'.

This, too, was an immense success. Tens of thousands of copies were bought by others who wished to be slimmer. The word 'Banting' became synonymous with dieting; and 'to bant' became a household phrase – 'I say, you do look well! Are you banting, my dear?' As a result of this, William Banting became quite rich and enormously famous, and thousands of people followed his advice – which seems rather unfair, really, since the advice came in the first place from Mr William Harvey of Soho Square.

So many copies of his pamphlet were sold that many must still exist, but they are hard to find.

13 Alexander Graham Bell and the Telephone

Alexander Graham Bell was born at 16 South Charlotte Street, on the corner of Charlotte Square, in Edinburgh, on 3 March 1847. His father and his grandfather were both authorities on elocution, and it wasn't long before the young Alexander was teaching people how to speak. He was enormously inventive, and not only made the first iron lung, but also bred special sheep with multiple nipples because he thought they would have more lambs. However, what makes him a legendary inventor is the telephone.

In 1863, at the age of sixteen, Alexander and his brother Melville began some serious research into how speech worked. They started with the anatomy of the mouth and throat and even examined the family cat (after it had died) so they could study the vocal cords in more detail. Studying the pitch of the vowel sounds, they imagined the throat and the mouth like two different-sized bottles. Each makes a different pitch, and they realised that the vowel sounds were a combination of two pitches. Their father, Melville senior, had spent years classifying vocal sounds and came up with a shorthand system called *Visible Speech*, where every sound was represented by a symbol. The idea was to teach the deaf to speak by putting all these sounds together.

They eventually made an elaborate speaking machine to test their theories. Later in 1863, Alexander went to Elgin near the Moray Firth in the north of Scotland to teach elocution at the Weston House Academy, and there, in what is now a Comet store, he first conceived the idea of transmitting speech with electricity.

When Alexander's two brothers died in 1870, the

family moved to North America. Alexander settled in Boston, the scientific and academic centre of America, and was soon using *Visible Speech* to teach the deaf. The idea of transmitting speech along a wire never left him, and though he knew little about electricity he knew a good deal about speech and sound. His years of research led him up a few blind alleys, but by 1875 he had come up with a simple receiver that could turn electricity into sound: in other words, a speaker. It was essentially a magnet glued to a diaphragm, and able to move within a coil of wire, so that a change of electric current in the coil would cause the magnet, and therefore also the diaphragm, to move in or out. Thus a varying electrical signal produced a varying sound wave from the speaker.

But he still needed a transmitter. He had no effective way of converting the sounds of the voice into an electric signal. What he needed, as his assistant Tom Watson put it, was to 'generate voice-shaped electric undulations'. He tried a few weird contraptions, including a diaphragm connected to a needle. As he spoke into it, the needle dipped in and out of a bowl of acid. The varying resistance produced a varying electric current from a battery. The great breakthrough came quite by accident on 2 June 1875. Bell and Watson were testing a circuit with one transmitter and two receivers in separate rooms, when Bell switched off the transmitter. Then he heard a note coming from the receiver in his room. Puzzled by this, he went through, and found Watson adjusting the other receiver. Bell realised that, with the transmitter turned off, the note must be coming from the other receiver acting as a transmitter – in other words, as a microphone. At that moment, the telephone was born.

By a fluke, Bell had discovered that the receiver could also work in reverse – instead of making sound when he sent electricity through it, it made electricity when he supplied sound, because the sound moved the diaphragm, the diaphragm moved the magnet in the coil and this generated electricity. Six months went by before he was able to send intelligible speech down the wire, and according to popular legend, and Bell's diary, the first words ever spoken on the telephone were, 'Mr Watson, come here; I want to see you.' Rather peremptory, but no doubt the great man was excited, and no doubt Mr Watson jumped to it with alacrity.

Bell developed his system – he certainly needed a much better microphone – and submitted his patent on St Valentine's Day, 1876, just two hours before Elisha Gray, his main rival. The patent was granted on 7 March, and was one of the most valuable patents ever issued. Over 600 lawsuits followed before a Supreme Court decision ruled in Bell's favour in 1893. Meanwhile, Bell had made the telephone available to the public in 1877, when the Bell Telephone Company was created. Developments were swift; within a year the first telephone exchange was built in Connecticut and within ten years more than 150,000 people had telephones in the United States alone. Bell married Mabel, the deaf daughter of his financial partner, and signed nearly all of his stock over to her, keeping just ten shares for 'sentimental reasons'. Within three years the price of Bell Telephone Company shares soared from fifty dollars to over a thousand dollars. Alexander was finally a man of independent means.

Bell eventually built a large house in remote Nova Scotia, where the landscape and weather reminded him of Scotland. Here he continued his work with the deaf, including the young Helen Keller. He invented weird aircraft with wings based on triangles; he built a resuscitation device, the forerunner to the iron lung; and experimented with sheep. He had a peculiar notion that sheep with extra nipples would give birth to two or more lambs, and be more productive for farmers. He built Sheepville, a huge village of sheep pens, and spent years counting sheep nipples. The work continued for decades before the US state department announced that there was no link between extra nipples and extra lambs.

Alexander Graham Bell was kind and generous and gave much of his money and time to improving the lives of those around him. He died in 1922 and will be revered for his work with the deaf and celebrated for his invention of the telephone.

There's a plaque on the wall of the house where he was born, 16 South Charlotte Street, Edinburgh, and a little sign on a pillar in the Comet store in Elgin – and many telephone companies still carry the name of Bell.

14 Edward Lyon Berthon and his Folding Lilfeboats

In April 1912, on her maiden voyage, the 'unsinkable' SS *Titanic* hit an iceberg and sank. Because there were not enough lifeboats, 1,490 people drowned in the icy waters of the north Atlantic. Had she been equipped with Berthon folding lifeboats, most of those people might well have survived.

Edward Lyon Berthon was born in 1813. He did rather badly in school, and often had to write out lines as punishment; so he tied three quills together to speed things up a little. This triple quill was one of the earliest examples of his inventive genius.

After training as a doctor he entered the clergy, and eventually went to Romsey in Hampshire, where he was rector of the abbey for thirty years. Like most men of the cloth, he spent a lot of time repairing the church. Unlike most vicars, Berthon used boat-building techniques because he was obsessed with everything nautical.

A friend of his nearly drowned when his ship sank, and there weren't enough lifeboats for all the passengers. Berthon decided this was intolerable, and devised an amazing folding lifeboat. It was made of lengthways timbers, joined by waterproof fabric and pivoted at the ends; so the boat folded like two Japanese fans, joined at the tips. Three or four of these boats fitted in the space of one ordinary lifeboat; they occupied little space on the deck of a ship. They came in various sizes, from little ones designed for six to huge beasts that could carry over a hundred people. The design was simple and clever. There was one layer of canvas outside the wooden ribs, and another layer inside. When the boat was hung in davits over the side of the ship, it unfolded automatically, under its own weight. Then the bottom boards and thwarts were pushed in, and held the ribs and sides of the boat apart; so it was locked into its final shape. The two layers of canvas then formed a series of air-filled buoyancy tanks between the ribs, so that the boats would not sink even if they capsized.

Berthon had great difficulty getting his lifeboat accepted. He tried every dodge he could think of to bring it to the attention of the authorities. One day he took the prototype to sail on the Serpentine in London, hoping to get it noticed there. As luck would have it, Queen Victoria had finally got to hear of his fabulous folding lifeboat, and demanded a demonstration. Unfortunately she wanted to see it at eleven the next morning – at her house on the Isle of Wight. By the time he received the royal command it was already four o'clock in the afternoon. Berthon immediately hired three Hansom cabs and used the horses to tow the boat to the railway station, put it on the train and eventually made his royal date with fifteen minutes to spare. The Queen was impressed and instructed the Admiralty to test the boat.

Perversely, the Admiralty tested the lifeboat not by 'rescuing' sailors, but by firing a 21 lb mortar from it; the lifeboat sank, killing a midshipman. The Admiralty reported that it was 'useless'. However, all was not lost, since twenty years later Berthon lifeboats became standard equipment on troop-carrying ships. The Berthon Boat Company built hundreds of folding lifeboats, one of which is shown on a stained glass window in Romsey Abbey. The chap in the middle is Edward Berthon, and on the other side of him is another of his inventions – a type of telescope.

On 28 June 1834 Berthon was sketching on a ferry on Lake Geneva. When a splash of water from the paddle-wheel landed on his sketch-book, he pondered on the inefficiency of paddle-wheels. He reasoned that the whole thing should be under water, so it couldn't splash and would waste less energy. When he returned to Britain the following year, he set about solving the problem. His first idea was to use a spiral like the screw thread on a bolt, only bigger. He thought he would need several turns of thread to get a good grip of the water. But his experiments suggested otherwise. He dug a huge ring-shaped pond in his garden, and sailed a model boat around it using different sorts of screw, and timing each version. Every time he shortened the screw, the boat went faster, until he ended up with not ten turns, not five, not even one, but one-sixth of a turn. The rest of the screw, it turned out, was simply slowing the boat down through friction. Berthon called his invention the 'screw propeller'.

Surprise, surprise, the Admiralty mocked the idea, stating that it 'was a pretty toy which never would and never could propel a ship'. Berthon was so dispirited by the Admiralty's response that he gave up. A few years later another man, Francis Smith, had the same idea and after many years of argument he managed to get the screw propeller accepted. Eventually, the two men had the satisfaction of watching a naval review in which three hundred Admiralty ships were all powered by screw propellers. Nowadays, of course, screw propellers are standard.

Another of Berthon's inventions he called the Nautochrometer, or Perpetual Log, and this one did amuse the Queen. The old method for measuring speed was to tie a piece of rope, knotted at measured intervals, to a lump of wood – the ship's log – and throw it off the back of the ship. The log dragged the rope out, and by counting the knots in the rope as they went past you could calculate your speed – in knots.

Berthon wanted to produce a device which showed the ship's speed continuously. His invention was essentially just a piece of pipe. The closed end of it stuck down into the water, and had a hole drilled in the side. As the boat moved along, the water rushing past this hole lowered the pressure just inside, by the Bernoulli effect. At the top of the tube was a manometer – water or oil in a U-tube. When the boat was stationary, the level of the liquid would be the same in the two arms of the U, but when it was moving, the reduction of pressure would make the liquid lower in one arm than the other. The faster the boat moved, the greater the difference in level; so you could read off the ship's speed directly in knots from the level of liquid in the tube. Berthon fitted one of these indicators to Queen Victoria's yacht *Victoria and Albert*. Apparently she used to spend hours watching the liquid levels going up and down in the U-tube, and liked to think that hers was the fastest ship in the world.

A stained glass window in Romsey Abbey shows Edward Lyon Berthon with one of his folding lifeboats, and his head is carved on one of the choirstalls.

15 Henry Bessemer's Anti-seasickness Boat

Seasickness can be a nightmare; many people start to feel queasy long before the mooring ropes are cast off, and spend even the smoothest Channel crossing retching miserably over the rail. One such person was Henry Bessemer, millionaire and steel king, and he decided to do something about it. He didn't just take pills; he designed and built the SS *Bessemer* as a permanent preventer of seasickness.

Henry Bessemer was born near Hitchin, Hertfordshire, on 19 January 1813. His father was a rich engineer, and Henry always enjoyed messing about with scientific and technical things. When he was seventeen, and in love, he made his first serious invention – embossed stamps to use on title deeds. People who needed a £5 stamp would usually peel one off an old deed, and thus avoid buying a new one. The government was losing £100,000 a year in revenue. His invention made this impossible, and he convinced the Stamp Office at Somerset House. They offered him the post of Superintendent of Stamps, at a salary of £700 a year – a small fortune in 1830! He was over the moon – now he could marry his beloved.

She then had an even better idea, which was simply to print a date on the stamps. When he told the Stamp Office, they said, 'Thanks very much, brilliant; we won't need you as Superintendent of Stamps now.' And he got nothing at all for his invention.

This made him furious; two brilliant ideas, but no money. After that, he found out about patenting. In all he took out 150 patents, covering a huge variety of ideas.

His first fortune came from making brass powder to use in 'gold' paint. His sister had made a portfolio of her paintings of flowers, and asked him to do the title on the outside:

STUDIES OF FLOWERS
FROM NATURE
BY
MISS BESSEMER

He thought this deserved better than just ink; so he went to a shop and bought some 'bronze powder' in two different colours, and had to pay 7*s* an ounce for it. He realised that if he could make this stuff cheaply he could also make a fortune. So he invented machines to do it. The first one failed, but the second was a success.

Reckoning that a patent would not protect this process; he determined to keep it utterly secret. He had the full-size machines made in sections all over the country, and assembled them himself in his house in St Pancras, north London. He hired his three brothers-in-law to run the plant, and kept every room locked and the whole factory sealed against snoopers. Only five people ever went into the building, and they managed to keep the process secret for thirty-five years – much longer than a patent would have lasted.

But he really became an international jet-setter when he invented the artillery shell. The army were still using cannon balls, but Henry was sure that if they used a long thin projectile it would be not only heavier but also more accurate, because you could cut spiral grooves around it which would make it spin, and keep it on target. He built his own mortar, and made some experimental shells, which were highly successful. So he took out a patent in November 1854, and then tried to sell his idea to the War Department. They weren't interested; but a few months later he happened to have dinner with Napoleon in Paris. He sold the idea of shells to Napoleon, and had several trips to Paris on expenses. Unfortunately he found he was a terrible sailor; every time he crossed the English Channel he got horribly seasick.

The trouble with his new heavy shell was that the existing gun barrels weren't strong enough to take the extra pressure; so he decided to find a way of making better steel – which was how he came to invent the Bessemer Converter, which made him several million pounds.

Henry Bessemer was an astonishingly successful inventor and businessman; he was knighted in 1879. But I am relieved to say that even he did not always get it right. His most dramatic failure was the Bessemer Saloon Ship Company. He had suffered terribly from seasickness on his trips to France; so in December 1869 he began to spend time and a lot of money designing and making a cross-Channel boat in which no one could be seasick. He had two ideas. First, the boat was to be very long and thin, so that it would have minimal pitch – the ends of the boat would not go up and down much. Second, the entire cabin was mounted in gimbals with a great weight or even a gyroscope underneath it, so that however rough the sea was the cabin would always stay horizontal; while the hull of the boat would just roll and pitch about it.

He built a little model of his boat, but people remained unconvinced; so he constructed a full-sized mock-up of the cabin in a mobile hut mounted on a huge deck in a field near his house. He used a large steam engine to make the deck rock and roll, and then tried to keep the cabin horizontal. People still said it would never work, but he went ahead anyway, and spent more than £40,000 on floating the company and the boat.

Unfortunately, the huge heavy moving cabin made the boat so unstable that she was impossible to steer. On her maiden voyage on 8 May 1875, a beautiful calm day, the ship sailed from Dover, and in broad daylight comprehensively demolished the pier at Calais. The SS *Bessemer* never sailed again, and the company sank without trace!

Henry Bessemer ran his steel works from Bessemer House, which still stands on Carlisle Street in Sheffield. The last Bessemer Converter to run stands outside Kelham Island Industrial Museum in Sheffield.

16 William Bickford's Safety Fuse

For thousands of years Cornwall has been a mining area; all sorts of useful minerals have been dug out of those tough hills. At first the miners used picks and shovels, but as the demand increased and the stakes got higher they turned to gunpowder. Large quantities of rock can be quickly shifted with an explosive charge.

However, the problem about setting off any explosion safely is to do it without blowing yourself up. The simplest method is to lay a trail or 'train' of gunpowder along the ground from the main charge for about 30 yards; this will take between five and ten seconds to burn. Then you light the end of the train and either crouch behind a large rock, or sprint off to a safer distance, while the fire sputters and fizzes all the way along the train and ignites the main charge. At least, that's the theory. However, there are several difficulties with powder trains.

Quite often the flame stops, and doesn't set off the explosive; this is called a 'hang-fire'. Sometimes sparks jump ahead along the train, so that it goes too quickly and you blow yourself up. The most dangerous is when you think it's stopped, and you go to have a look – but in fact it was just having a rest and you get blown up.

The weather often prevents powder trains from working. Wind can blow away some powder, leaving gaps in the train, before you have a chance to light it. When the ground is wet or there are puddles or perhaps a stream to cross, you can't lay a train because the gunpowder gets wet easily, and then won't burn. The slightest rain rules out the use of powder trains completely.

And there is a more fundamental problem. Miners often want to place the main charge in a hole they have drilled in a wall of rock. There is no way of laying a trail up a cliff, or into a hole drilled into rock – especially as the hole has to be filled to contain the blast.

For many years shot-firers used goose quills to make a fuse. Fill each hollow quill with gunpowder, then push the point of one into the back of the next, and push together as many as you need. In theory the powder will burn along each quill, then burn through the point and light the powder in the next one.

The quills protect the powder from wind and damp, and in principle you can lay a goose-quill fuse up a cliff and into a hole in the rock. Goose-quill fuses were fairly convenient but not entirely predictable. The main trouble is that quills are rather delicate. When the shot-firer rammed rubble into the hole containing the fuse, he often broke a quill or two. This might cause the fuse to fail, or let some powder escape which set off the charge too soon.

Often there was simply a break in the gunpowder train, causing a hang-fire. After waiting till he thought it was safe the shot-firer came back, only to find the quill had actually been smouldering slowly, the flame had just carried to the other side of the break, and the charge exploded, causing injury or death.

William Bickford had an inspiration in a rope factory that did away with all this, saved hundreds of lives, and was in use for 150 years – though he didn't make a penny. He was born in January 1774 in Ashburton in Devon, and went to Truro as a currier (that's a chap who prepares leather), but he wasn't very successful so he moved to Tuckingmill near Camborne.

Tuckingmill was right in the middle of the most significant mining centre in the country. Bickford had no connection with the mining industry, but he was apparently 'particularly distressed' at seeing the results of blasting accidents, and he set his mind to the possibility of a safety fuse. His first idea was to put the main explosive in a cartridge made of parchment, and to attach a small parchment tube containing powder as the fuse. The principle was rather like that of the quills – but sadly the practice was just as unreliable.

One day in 1831 he visited his friend James Bray who owned a rope factory in Tolgarrick Road, and as they chatted Bickford had an inspiration. In those days rope was made in a rope-walk; the rope-maker first tied one end of each strand to the wall, and then walked backwards while twisting the separate strands together to make the rope. As he watched the rope-maker, William Bickford realised that he might be able to adapt this process to make a fuse.

Bickford watched fascinated as the strands of rope came together, and noticed that they always twisted round a narrow space in the middle. This disappears as the rope is tightened, but Bickford wondered whether he could fill the middle of the rope with gunpowder. If he could do so, he would get a convenient fuse, and a simple and continuous method of manufacture. He designed a machine to do the work, and patented it later the same year, 1831. The machine wound strands of rope around a central core of gunpowder. Then it wound another layer in the opposite direction in order to prevent the rope untwisting. Finally the rope was varnished to make it waterproof.

His invention was brilliant in its simplicity. When one end was lit, the rope safety fuse would burn steadily along its length at a rate of perhaps one foot every ten seconds. It hissed and spluttered and sparked, but it never went out. Because it burned at a steady rate, the shot-firer could simply cut off the right length to give himself time to escape – say six feet if he wanted it to take a minute to burn. The safety fuse consumed much less powder than a powder train, it burned much more slowly, and it was far more reliable. It was not affected by weather, and would even burn under water if the fuse had to be laid across a stream.

Even though the miners disliked having to buy safety fuse, they were quick to realise that its reliability made it much the best – and safest – fuse available. In its first year, the Bickford factory in Tuckingmill made 45 miles of fuse; this is a colossal amount when you consider that it was used in quantities of only a few feet for each blast. A hundred years later, in 1930, the same factory, somewhat enlarged, made 104,545 miles of fuse.

Over the years various specialised fuses were developed, suitable for use in specific conditions, such as: waterproof fuse for use under water, and extra-safe fuse which did not make sparks, for mines where explosive gases were present. Fuses had coverings of various colours to show up on different sorts of rock. However, the basic process of making safety fuse is essentially unchanged to this day; Bickford's was one of those brilliant inventions that fills a want so precisely that no one can improve it.

Sadly William Bickford knew nothing of this success. He became paralysed in the year following his great invention, and died two years later in 1834, just before the fuse factory opened for business.

The remains of Bickford's factory, beside the main crossroads in Tuckingmill, is now occupied by a number of small businesses grouped around a courtyard.

17 George Parker Bidder, the Calculating Boy

There have been a number of stories about mathematical prodigies – children and adults who could do any calculation in their heads in an instant, for whom lightning mental arithmetic seemed to be a pleasure. Among the most amazing was George Parker Bidder.

George was born on 14 June 1806 in Moretonhampstead on the edge of Dartmoor, the third son of a stonemason. He was supposed to go to the village school, but in fact played truant most of the time. His elder brother taught him to count up to ten, and then up to a hundred; that was the limit of his mathematical education. An old blacksmith used to work across the road; from about the age of six George used to sit in his workshop and help operate the bellows. People who came in found he could quickly sing out the answers to simple sums. They would say, 'Thirty-seven times sixty-nine', and without a pause he'd pipe up, 'Two thousand five hundred and fifty-three.' He could easily do two-figure multiplication sums, and just about managed three figures. Soon he was able to answer tricky problems: *If one man takes twenty days to do a job, and another takes thirty days, how long would they take working together?* The answer came instantly: 'Twelve days.'

His dad began to take him round to local fairs, exhibiting him as 'The Calculating Boy' and charging money for admission. George soon became famous, and travelled to Brighton, Cheltenham, Tewkesbury, Dudley, Worcester, Birmingham, Oxford, Cambridge, Norwich and London; the Duke of Kent asked him to multiply 7,953 by 4,648; he quickly answered 36,965,544. When he was about ten he was summoned to appear before Queen Charlotte, who asked him, *How many days would a snail be creeping, at the rate of 8 feet per day, from the Land's End in Cornwall to Farret's Head in Scotland, the distance by admeasurement being 838 miles?* He answered 553,080. The famous astronomer Sir William Herschel asked him, *Light travels from the Sun to the Earth in 8 minutes, and the Sun being 98 million miles off, if Light would take 6 years and 4 months travelling from the nearest fixed star, how far is that star from the Earth, reckoning 365 days and 6 hours to each year, and 28 days to each month?* Answer: 40,633,740 million miles.

George produced these answers with amazing speed – taking perhaps a minute for the longer sums – and with stunning accuracy. Rarely did he make a mistake. Books were published of the questions he was asked, although since they must have been produced after the events, they carry no proof of his speed or accuracy. On a show visit to the Bank of England, when he was twelve, he was asked to multiply together two nine-digit numbers: 257,689,435 × 356,875,649. He got the answer right, but it took him thirteen minutes.

He tried to explain his processes of mental arithmetic, in two lectures to the Institution of Civil Engineers in 1856. He said he did not have a remarkable memory; nor was he a great mathematician, as he found to his cost when he was struggling with a maths degree at Cambridge. Mental arithmetic was a skill, he said, that anyone of reasonable capacity could learn. The main rule, he said, is to take the steps of a calculation in such a way as to minimize the use of the registering power of the mind, because remembering intermediates is what limits calculating ability. He always began at the left, and added after each multiplication. So, if asked for 89 × 73 he would say instantly 6,497, but to spell it out in stages, his process would be 80 × 70 and remember, 80 × 3, then add this and remember the total, 9 × 70 then add and remember, 9 × 3 and add to give the answer. He was frequently asked to work out square roots or cube roots, but was greatly helped by the knowledge that the answer would be a whole number, because the asker would have squared or cubed a whole number, in order to know what the answer would be. The first square root he was asked for was of 390,625. He later said: 'It occurred to me immediately that 5 must be the last figure, and that since 600 times 600 is 360,000, the first figure must be 6.' So he needed only the middle digit, and quickly found that 1 worked; so the answer was 615. So, asked to find the cube root of 188,132,517, he knew that 500 cubed would be 125 million and 600 cubed would be 216 million; so the answer must be in between. He also happened to know that 73 was the only number between 1 and 100 whose cube ended in 17. So he guessed 573 – checked – and it was the answer.

His calculating started when he was a little boy, lying in bed at night, thinking about numbers. He loved to count to ten and then on from there. He would play with adding – six and six is the same as six and four and two, the same as ten and two, the same as twelve. He was glad he had never been taught any rules for doing sums; because he had worked them out for himself he understood them thoroughly.

In the first draft version of his lecture, all the numbers are written out in full – sixty-seven times ninety-three. When he was young, he was always given his challenges out loud, and he was being exhibited before he learned to read; later he found the process much slower if he had to read digits on paper. So seeing Arabic numerals actually hindered his calculations.

Being exhibited as a boy did not ruin his life. He surveyed for the Ordnance Survey, became an engineer and made use of his genius. He was a friend and from 1834 often a partner of Robert Stephenson; they built many railways together. He was one of the founders in 1846 of the Electric Telegraph Company. He was also involved in the building of the sewers of London around 1860. He built railways in Norway and in Denmark, where he also introduced gas lighting. Unlike his contemporary Isambard Kingdom Brunel, he completed his projects on time and within budget. Indeed the wonderful Clifton Suspension Bridge was unfinished when Brunel died because they had run out of money, and it was George Parker Bidder who raised the money and got the job finished in the early 1860s. He also invented the railway swing bridge. While building the Norwich & Brandon railway line in 1845 he had to cross the River Wensum, which was used by many boats coming into the port of Norwich. So he constructed the Trowse Swing Bridge, which lasted until 1905.

He retained his calculating ability throughout his life. In September 1878 the Revd E.M. Johnstone came to visit; they talked about light giving notions of the infinitely great and the infinitely small; that it travels at almost 190,000 miles per second through space, and that red light has 36,918 wavelengths in one inch. Johnstone wondered how many waves from a red object would strike the eye in one second, and reached for pencil and paper, but George stopped him, and said, 'You need not work it out; the number of vibrations will be 444 billion, 433,651 million, and 200,000.' And this was the day before he died.

George Parker Bidder's birthplace in Moretonhampstead was about 20 yards west of where the information office now is, on the site of the present bakery.

18 George Boole and his Vision in a Field in Doncaster

Life today is full of computers; sometimes they seem to run our lives. But they might not run at all if it had not been for a vision experienced by a seventeen-year-old assistant teacher in a field in Doncaster.

George Boole was born in Lincoln on 4 November 1815. His father was a shoemaker, but probably spent too little time making shoes and too much messing about with scientific instruments and mathematical ideas. However, he did succeed in giving his son a lust for learning. Young George was a precocious schoolboy, and astonished the readers of his local newspaper by producing an elegant translation of some Greek verse – so elegant that another pedantic reader wrote to the editor and protested that such a young lad could not possibly have produced such a translation without a good deal of help. He probably hoped to go to university, but in 1831 his father's business failed, and so fifteen-year-old George had to go out to work in order to support the family.

Unable to find a job in Lincoln, he walked 40 miles north to Doncaster, and in July secured the post of usher, or assistant teacher, in Mr Heigham's School in South Parade. He did not enjoy being so far from home; it must have been at least two days' walk. He was lonely, and wrote home often, complaining that no one in Doncaster made gooseberry pies as good as his mother's. He was also rather unhappy at the school, a strict Wesleyan establishment where religion came first, and nothing else must be allowed to interfere. Some of the parents suspected George of reading mathematics books on Sundays, and even worse, he was accused of doing sums in chapel!

One problem was that he loved to read, but had no easy access to a library or other source of free books; so he had to buy his own. Because he didn't have much money, he always bought books that took a long time to read and therefore provided good value. He found the best of all were textbooks of mathematics, which took many hours to plod through. Later in life, he claimed that this was how he became seriously interested in mathematics. When he was neither teaching nor absorbing mathematics, he liked to go walking. He was lucky, for directly across the Great North Road he found Town Fields, a great expanse of common land, ideal for walking off the pain of a teenage exile. This was where he had his vision – a revelation that changed the world.

One cold day in January 1833 George was walking along thinking, when he was suddenly struck by an astonishing idea. He often talked about the moment later in life, and compared the experience with that of Saul on the road to Damascus. It changed his life, and it changed our lives too. George had learned from his reading that mathematics was highly successful in describing the working of the physical world; ever since Newton, scientists had been applying mathematics to all sorts of moving systems – from cannon balls to planets – and had found their motions could be described and predicted using simple mathematical laws. George's idea was this: if mathematics could describe the physical world, could it also describe the mental world? If mathematical principles explained the functioning of cogwheels of machines, could they also explain the cogwheels of thought? Could he develop the maths to unravel the human mind?

At first this was only a flash of inspiration, and it took him fourteen years to work out the details, but eventually he wrote a long essay called *The mathematical analysis of logic, being an essay towards a calculus of deductive reasoning* (1847), and then a book called *An investigation into the laws of thought* (1854). These created tremendous interest. Bertrand Russell said: 'Pure mathematics was discovered by Boole, in a work which he called The Laws of Thought.' In his day he was regarded as the greatest logician since Aristotle.

According to Boole's system, logical problems could be expressed as algebraic equations, and therefore solved by mechanical manipulation of symbols according to formal rules. There were only two values – 0 and 1, or False and True – and logical ideas could be added to one another: if (day = Wednesday) and (time = afternoon) then the shops are shut. The shops remain open if either value is False.

Although Boole thought he had solved the mystery of the human mind, others were not convinced. Nevertheless, Boolean algebra was such an elegant system that it became widely known, admired and used. And in the 1930s, when Claude Shannon was trying to build the world's first computer at Massachusetts Institute of Technology, he found that it precisely described the behaviour of an array of electrical switches – each of which has just two positions, Off or On.

Shannon was working on the mathematics of

information, and had reduced every choice to Yes or No. He represented these with a binary code, and called each unit of information a 'binary digit' or bit. So the fundamental ideas for electronic computers came straight from Boolean algebra.

George Boole was fired by Mr Heigham within a few weeks of his revelation, but he went back to Lincoln and started a school of his own. He married Mary Everest, niece of the surveyor of northern India, who gave his name to the world's highest mountain, and they produced a horde of successful children. He went on to become Professor of Mathematics at the University of Cork. Maybe he did not solve the mystery of the human mind, but the logic of every computer today is based on the idea that came to him in that flash of inspiration, in a field in Doncaster.

You can still go for an inspiring walk in Town Fields, Doncaster. Boole is commemorated by a window and brass plaque in Lincoln Cathedral and a plaque on the wall of 3 Pottergate, nearby.

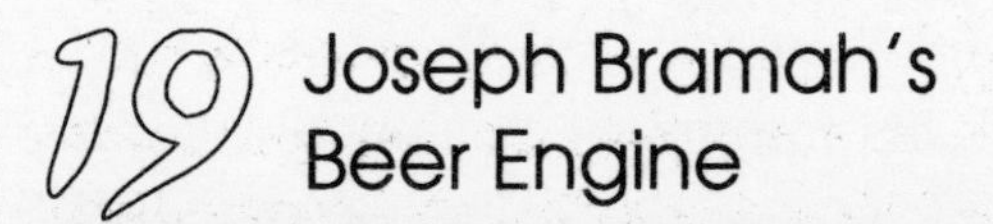

19 Joseph Bramah's Beer Engine

Silkstone in South Yorkshire is famous for two things; first, coal, which they've been digging out of the ground for a thousand years, and second, an appalling pit disaster. In the churchyard there's a monument to those who died in the Huskar Pit on

4 July 1838. The shocking thing is that the twenty-six dead were all children who worked in the mine. But the other thing that strikes you is the chilling warning on the monument: not to make mines safer, not suggesting that children shouldn't work in dangerous jobs, but pointing out that since you might be called to meet your maker at any time, you had better be in a fit state.

What Silkstone should be famous for is Joseph Bramah – the man who invented a brilliant water-closet, the first unpickable lock, the whole science of hydraulics and – some might say most important of all – the beer engine. He was born at Stainborough Lane Farm on 2 April 1749, and his father probably expected him to work on the farm, but he became friendly with the local blacksmith and carpenter. Furthermore the story goes that at the age of sixteen he injured his leg 'while jumping at the Annual Feast at Bolton-on-Dearne', and this injury may have prevented him from becoming a farmer. In any case, he became apprenticed to a carpenter. Then, after the disastrous harvest of 1772, he decided to leave Yorkshire to seek his fortune as a cabinet-maker in London.

The aristocracy in the big city were looking for ways to improve their grand homes, and do better than the neighbours, and one of the smart things to have was a water-closet. There was little piped water, and no real sewers. Most people could not afford to install such things, so the demand for water-closets was limited. Nevertheless owning one showed real class.

In 1775 Alexander Cumming took out the first English patent for a water-closet. Bramah may have come across one of Cumming's closets, for in 1778 he patented his own water-closet, which was a considerable improvement. Cumming's closet had a sliding valve across the bottom of the pan. The user arrived to find a few inches of water in the pan, on top of the valve. Having finished, the user pulled a lever to one side to slide the valve open and release the contents of the pan into the trap below and thence into the sewer. However, the valve tended to get encrusted, making it hard to slide, and since most closets were in outhouse privies, the valve often froze solid in winter, which must have been disastrous.

The Bramah water-closet had a hinged valve in place of the sliding one – so it could not freeze up – and incorporated several other refinements. Pulling the handle to open the valve also turned on the water to flush the pan. Pushing it down again closed the valve and activated a neat delay mechanism in the shape of a brass air-cylinder, which kept the water running for about fifteen seconds, so as to fill the pan ready for the next person. Bramah water-closets were rather complex and therefore liable to go wrong, but they were splendidly built in mahogany and brass. Within twenty years he sold 6,000, and they were the best water-closets in the country for about seventy-five years.

As a cabinet-maker, it was natural for Bramah to be concerned with locks. Security was clearly a problem and the Society of Arts offered a prize for the best lock. Unfortunately most of the 'unpickable' locks entered were nothing of the kind, and according to the records Bramah himself picked one in just fifteen minutes. Most locks of the time were 'warded' locks, in which an obstacle called a 'ward' prevented the key from turning. The right key had a complex-shaped cut-out which fitted over the ward, and so was able to open the lock.

The trouble was that the tricky part of the lock was accessible from the outside, and anyone could take a wax impression of such a lock and make a new key. Bramah realised that a secure lock would have nothing in the key-hole to reveal what key would open it. He came up with a most elegant secure lock whose exterior revealed nothing about the cryptic parts within. Bramah locks became highly fashionable, and people used to wear the tiny keys round their necks as status symbols. Demand soon outstripped supply, and he had to introduce mass-production for the first time in precision engineering. Before then every lock had been an individual item, with no part from one being of any use in another.

In order to make his locks in large numbers he hired a young man called Henry Maudslay, who designed and built the machines to manufacture the locks, ran Bramah's Denmark Street workshop, married Bramah's housekeeper, Sarah Tindale, and had four children. But even after eight years of service Maudslay was still paid only 30*s* a week, and he quite reasonably asked his boss for a rise. Bramah (a Yorkshireman) said no, so Maudslay left, set up his own business in Wells Street, and went on to become the father of precision engineering.

In 1790 Joseph Bramah issued a challenge. On a lock in the window of his workshop there was engraved:

> The artist who can make an instrument that will pick or open this lock shall receive 200 guineas the moment it is produced. Applications in writing only please.

At that time, 200 guineas was an enormous amount of money: a vast reward for the simple task of picking a lock. And sure enough, the Bramah lock was eventually picked by an American called Hobbs. However, it took him forty-four hours spread over sixteen days – and he did not manage it until 1851, more than sixty years after the challenge, and thirty years after Joseph Bramah's death! The Bramah locks were so good that the expression 'a real Bramah' entered the English language, meaning anything ingenious and beautifully made.

For some people, however, Bramah's most important contribution to society was the beer engine. When he went into a pub and ordered a pint of beer, the landlord had to send a boy down to the cellar to fetch it in a jug. Frequently the boy felt he had to check the beer, and would emerge twenty minutes later slightly wobbly, with only half a jug of beer, having drunk the landlord's profits. Joseph Bramah was determined to put this right. So in 1797 he patented 'Certain methods of Retaining, Clarifying, Preserving and Drawing off all kinds of Liquors commonly used for the beverage of mankind, more especially those Liquors called Malt Liquors, such as Porter, Ale, Beer etc., together with sundry improved casks and implements necessary to give the contrivance full effect'.

Joseph Bramah's beer engine was a barrel with straight sides, into which fitted a piston with a leather seal to keep it beer-tight. The piston had a great weight on top, which put the beer under pressure, and pushed it up a pipe which led from the bottom of the barrel to the bar, where beer could be delivered just by opening a tap. What was more, the landlord could keep the cellar door locked, saving his profits and avoiding the evil of what Bramah called 'private drunkenness'. With this device Bramah had invented far more than a rather complicated way to get a pint. He went on to develop the hydraulic press, and these were the first practical uses of a whole new science – we call it hydraulics.

There is an original Bramah water-closet in the Gladstone Pottery Museum near Stoke-on-Trent; you can admire the works in all their brass glory, although you cannot actually use the lavatory! The Bramah lock was so successful that it is still in production, or at least the Bramah Group now offer comprehensive security systems from 30 Oldbury Place, London W1.

20 David Brewster and the Kaleidoscope

The kaleidoscope, that perennial Christmas stocking filler, was discovered by accident in 1816. The circumstances were so trivial – you only need two mirrors at an angle – that it is surprising no one had found the effect before. But the man playing with mirrors happened to be one of the greatest optical theoreticians of the nineteenth century, Sir David Brewster (1781–1868).

Brewster was the sort of scientist who simply could not exist today. Born in the Scottish Borders, he went to university at the age of twelve (not so unusual at the time) and became a minister in the Church. However, he got so nervous about having to give sermons that sometimes he fainted, so he gave it up, became a tutor, and studied science in his spare time. He became a popular science writer, editor of a magazine and an encyclopedia, and published many papers on optics. Although he started out as an amateur, he was knighted, made a fellow of the Royal Society, and ended up as Principal of Edinburgh University.

His main research was on polarised light, and he is remembered for inventing the Brewster Angle: the angle at which light strikes a particular surface to give maximum polarisation. One day he was experimenting with an 'optical trough', a long trough with triangular ends and mirrors for sides. He was known for his fine practical work, but this time he was a bit careless and got a blob of glue on the mirrors where they joined. He was surprised to see that the ugly blob formed a rather beautiful flower-like pattern. He realised it must be something to do with the angle between the mirrors. He found that as the angle increased, he got a succession of these symmetrical images, whenever the angle would go exactly into 360°. He named his invention the 'Kaleidoscope' from the Greek for 'beautiful form', and patented it. He also wrote a long and rather tedious treatise on the use of the device, which he reckoned would be good for designing things like carpets. Sadly for Brewster, his patent was not watertight, so others hijacked the idea, and the kaleidoscope was all the rage. Interestingly, the early kaleidoscopes were made with two mirrors. The triangular version came later.

David Brewster lived in Melrose, where there is a lovely ruined abbey. His best memorial is the kaleidoscope which he invented.

21 William Brownrigg: Pouring Oil on Troubled Derwentwater

Derwentwater near Keswick was the site of one of the more bizarre experiments in the history of scientific endeavour. The man who did it wasn't one of the greatest scientists ever, but he took a very serious interest in salt, and showed that oil really does calm troubled waters.

William Brownrigg (1711–1800) was a doctor, living and working mainly in Whitehaven. Despite suggestions that he should move to London, he preferred to stay in the Lake District, tending his patients and studying science. He remains a rather obscure figure in part because he refused to publish much of his work, insisting that he would prefer to wait until it was complete. Brownrigg is rather typical of many eighteenth-century scientists. At that time, science certainly wasn't a full-time profession, so being a doctor or vicar was a useful starting point. Education was a problem, and even provincial doctors had to travel to study – Brownrigg went to the University of Leyden in the Netherlands.

Back in Whitehaven he became interested in problems caused by gases in mines, and arranged to have flammable fire-damp pumped directly into his house for experiments – which sounds rather dangerous. He became a bit of a damp guru, and was apparently able to predict when there would be explosions in mines by the speed of descent of the barometer, and he was often consulted by mine owners. But the work that first brought him to national attention was his treatise on salt. Because Britain was so often at war, supplies of the best salt were often hard to get. Salt was important as a condiment, but also for preserving fish and meat in those days before the fridge. So Brownrigg examined all the ways of producing salt, and suggested that we could make salt every bit as good as that imported at great expense from France, Spain and Portugal.

On the continent, salt was made by using sun and wind to evaporate sea water. British salt, he discovered, was generally made by heating briny water, in the belief that we don't have enough sun. The trouble is that this is very expensive. He also found all sorts of impurities in the salt, including the 'seeds, sperm and excrements of innumerable kinds of plants and animals'. Also, the salt-makers added various things to get the salt to crystallise more quickly – particularly popular was dog fat. Brownrigg said it was quite wrong that we didn't have enough sun in Britain to evaporate sea water into the finest salt, and there were some experiments in Hampshire to prove it. He showed what sort of saltern (the name for a pond where salt is made) would work best, and that the only modification for the British climate was a removable cover rather like that used on a cricket pitch to keep off the rain, which would otherwise dilute the brine. His treatise, published in the *Philosophical Transactions* of the Royal Society, got him elected a fellow of the Society.

Remember, this was in the days before modern chemistry – Joseph Priestley hadn't really got going – so such a thoroughly scientific approach was very impressive. This work alerted the scientific world to the Cumbrian doctor's existence, and many great scientists made a point of stopping off in the Lakes to see him. But undoubtedly the most amazing incident concerning Brownrigg happened on Lake Derwentwater when, accompanied by a vicar, the President of the Royal Society, and the American scientist and diplomat Benjamin Franklin, Brownrigg investigated the effect of oil on troubled waters. Benjamin Franklin was famous as the man who had proved lightning was electric by flying a kite on the end of a wire during a thunderstorm. To Americans, he is more important as one of the authors of the Declaration of Independence, though he had spent many years as a diplomat trying to avoid revolution.

Like most of us, Franklin had heard the expression 'pouring oil on troubled waters', and Pliny the Elder, the Roman writer, had given an account of it, but Franklin assumed it was all nonsense. But while travelling in a convoy of ships he noticed that the wake of one ship was particularly smooth. Asking why this might be, he was told that the cooks had probably just discharged greasy water through the scuppers. Franklin began to collect other anecdotes. Bermudans used oil to calm the water above fish they hoped to spear if the surface was ruffled. Fishermen of Lisbon supposedly used oil to suppress the breakers as they returned to harbour. Portuguese clam divers would actually dive down with their mouth full of olive oil, and release some to calm the surface above, giving them a clearer view of the sea-bed, presumably because the light illuminating the bottom normally passes through waves, resulting in confusing patterns. There were yet more stories: harbours in northern regions were supposed to be very calm when blubbery whales were brought in, and the sea over oily fish like mackerel is said to be still.

Franklin determined to try this himself, and first did so on the pond at Clapham Common in London, where he happened to be. The effect of just a little oil was so striking that from then on he kept some oil in the hollow handle of his walking cane in case the opportunity arose to try it again. In 1772 Franklin travelled north with Sir John Pringle, President of the Royal Society, and they dropped in on Brownrigg. The three men, together with the Revd Farish of Carlisle, set out to pour oil on to Derwentwater. We know about this from a letter Franklin wrote to Brownrigg the following year, summarising his investigations. Franklin noticed the dramatic spreading of even a little oil, forming a film so thin it produces what he called 'prismatic colours'. We now know that some oil films are just one molecule thick, and that the colours result when the thickness of the film is similar to the wavelength of light, so that certain colours in the reflected light from the water interfere with those in the reflection from the film of oil.

Strangely, neither in Franklin's letter to Brownrigg

nor anywhere else does he record exactly what took place that day. However, Franklin describes what generally happens. Clearly the oil does have an effect – at least on the tiniest wind ripples. Franklin then speculated that the oil prevents the wind 'getting a grip' on the water, and this not only prevents tiny ripples, but stops the wind making existing waves bigger. Actually, there are a couple of modern explanations. It may be to do with surface tension trying to keep the oil film flat, but there is also a more surprising explanation. When waves form on water, the surface of the wavy water must be larger than that of flat water. But if the oil film is just one molecule thick, it cannot stretch over the waves without breaking. The force holding the film together is enough to flatten the waves. But whatever the reason, the mythical 'pouring oil on troubled waters' really does work. It is wonderful to think of a Cumbrian doctor, the President of the Royal Society, one of the greatest Americans of all time and a vicar all taking time to pour oil on to a lake.

Brownrigg remained in the lakes, refusing to be tempted by London scientific society. As a result, no one much has heard of him. A nice tribute was paid by the president of the Royal Society, who called him 'my very learned, very penetrating, very industrious but too modest friend, Dr Brownrigg'.

Brownrigg's home is a private house, but Derwentwater is still sometimes troubled.

22 Isambard Kingdom Brunel and his Atmospheric Railway

In 1844 there was railway mania. All over the country companies were being set up and permanent way laid down. The Stephensons and Locke had started in the north-west, while the Great Western Railway had been built with speed and enthusiasm by a young, thrusting, dynamic engineer; even his name was over the top: Isambard Kingdom Brunel.

Son of French engineer Marc Isambard Brunel and Sophia Kingdom, Isambard was born on 9 April 1806. As chief engineer for the Great Western Railway, he built Paddington station and Bristol Temple Meads, and invented Swindon. He designed the Clifton Suspension Bridge, the Tamar Bridge, and many others. He also built some of the first great iron ships – the *Great Western*, the *Great Britain*, and the gigantic *Great Eastern*, which in 1866 laid the first cable across the Atlantic.

For Isambard Kingdom Brunel, only the biggest and best was good enough. His projects were usually years late and hopelessly over budget, but he was the showman of the engineers. Even his top hat was vast, and he used to carry his plans in it. Once, when he was introduced to Queen Victoria, he bowed low, swept off his hat . . . and his plans cascaded across the ground.

The railway reached Bristol in 1841 and Exeter in 1844, and Brunel became engineer to the South Devon Railway, incorporated on 4 July 1844 with a capital of £1,100,000. He chose a flamboyant route down the west bank of the Exe, and along the seashore to Dawlish and Teignmouth, where the trains still thunder along within yards of the sea. And he persuaded the directors of the SDR to approve the latest and most fashionable propulsion system. It had been tried out on a couple of test lines, but this was to be the first major railway designed from the start to be atmospheric.

The rails were normal, but on the sleepers between them was a cast-iron tube, 15 inches in diameter. A close-fitting piston ran along inside the tube, and was connected to the leading passenger car. The air was pumped out of the tube in front of the train, thus creating a vacuum; so the piston was pushed along by the pressure of the atmosphere behind it, and the piston pulled the train. It was indeed an atmospheric railway.

The piston was connected to the train by a rod which passed through a 3-inch wide slot along the top of the cast-iron tube. The slot was closed by a continuous flap of leather strengthened with iron framing and hinged along one edge, the other edge closing on the opposite side of the slot, the whole being made airtight with grease. The leather flap lifted to allow the rod to pass, and was then pressed shut again by a roller behind.

The vacuum was created by huge Boulton & Watt steam engines driving air pumps in pump-houses every three miles along the track. This created tremendous force. Suppose they pumped half the air out of the tube, and lowered the pressure inside to 8 lb/sq. in, then the force acting on the piston would have been more than half a ton – more than enough to move a lightweight train. On one epic test run outside Dublin, a young man called Frank Ebrington got into the front carriage, didn't realise the other carriages had not been coupled to it, and was hauled along a sharply curving track at a terrifying average speed of 84 mph. For the 1840s he was certainly the fastest man on Earth!

After many teething problems the South Devon atmospheric railway was opened to the public in September 1847. By January 1848 atmospheric trains were running all the way from Exeter to Newton Abbot. When the train reached a station they telegraphed ahead to the next pump-house and told them to switch on the pumps and make a vacuum ahead of the train. When all the passengers were aboard, the brakes were released and the train slid silently forward.

The passengers loved it. The trains ran quietly and smoothly, and without steam, smoke or smuts. What's more, they were often on time or even ahead. Speeds of 40 or 50 mph were normal, and one train ran from Newton Abbot to Exeter in 20 minutes, which is faster than today's Intercity trains! Because the trains didn't need locomotives they were much lighter, and so had tremendous acceleration and deceleration. Also the rails could be lighter and cheaper.

The SDR atmospheric system cost £300,000 to install, and worked more or less satisfactorily for nine months, but then it ran into all sorts of problems. Casting the pipe was difficult; eventually it was done in Bristol by Tom Guppy, brother-in-law of Sarah Guppy (*see* page 169), who managed to turn it out at the rate of a mile a week. Even more of a problem was the leather flap along the top. It had to be there to maintain the vacuum, but in the winter it sometimes froze solid and let in the air, while in the summer it dried out and cracked. In an effort to solve the problem and maintain the vacuum, greasers walked along the track smearing the leather flap with a mixture of lime soap and seal oil, or whale oil. Unfortunately the oil attracted rats, and the rats ate the leather – and that didn't do the vacuum any good either.

There were also pumping problems. When they switched on in the morning each pumping station was like the inside of a vacuum-cleaner bag; the first rush of air brought a mixture of oily water, rust, and dead rats and mice. The telegraph never worked, and the leather seal leaked; so the pumps had to run continuously to maintain the vacuum. This was very expensive. There were other technical hitches. Atmospheric trains could not reverse; if they overran the platforms by a few yards, the passengers had to jump out and push the train back in. Shunting around stations was impossible. What is more, no one solved the problem of points – one track could not meet another, because there was no way of getting the rolling stock across the cast-iron tube between the rails.

However, what finally scuppered Brunel's atmospheric railway was a piece of financial sharp practice. In 1844 railway fever had been at its height, and Brunel had persuaded the Board to go atmospheric with a flurry of magnetic personality and the promise of cheaper running. By 1848 the tide had turned. The atmospheric system was out of fashion, and by a bit of dubious accounting the anti-atmospheric lobby managed to persuade the shareholders that the railway had made a loss in the first six months of the year. This was unheard of; no railway company had ever made a loss. In fact, they were owed a great deal of money for carrying mail, and the company was moving sharply into substantial profit, but the fudged accounts were enough; the atmospheric system was voted out. The last atmospheric train went up the line in the early hours of Sunday 10 September 1848, and the system closed down for ever.

When Isambard Kingdom Brunel worked himself to death at the age of fifty-three, his long-term friend and assistant Daniel Gooch wrote in his diary that he was a 'man with the greatest originality of thought and power of execution, bold in his plans but right. The commercial world thought him extravagant, but although he was so, great things are not done by those who sit and count the cost of every thought and act.'

The only remaining pumping station is next to the Courtenay Arms at Starcross, on the A379 5 miles south of Exeter; it now houses the Starcross Fishing and Cruising Club. A section of the cast-iron tube is displayed in the GWR Museum at Swindon; 01793 493189.

23 William Buckland and Hyena Bones in Yorkshire

In 1820 workmen repairing roads in Kirkdale, North Yorkshire, were surprised to find a large number of old bones mixed up with the rocks they were taking from the quarry. At first they thought the bones must have belonged to cows that had fallen in, although there seemed to be more of these bones in the cave beside the quarry, known as Kirkdale Cavern.

When the news of the bones spread, collectors turned up in droves to add to their cabinets of curiosities. A local vicar sent some to his friend the Bishop of Oxford, and he in turn showed them to the newly appointed Professor of Geology at the University, the Revd William Buckland. Buckland was a splendid chap. He was profoundly interested in the history of the Earth, and he believed in the dramatic. He took his Oxford students for field trips on horseback. On one memorable occasion he found a huge fossil, an ammonite. It was too large and heavy to balance on his horse, but luckily the middle had disappeared, leaving a hole big enough to get his head and one shoulder through, so he rode home with the vast ammonite slung uncomfortably round his neck. The students laughed aloud at the sight, and dubbed him Sir Ammon, or Ammon Knight. In one of his lectures he greatly offended his stuffier colleagues by goose-stepping about the lecture theatre in order to demonstrate how prehistoric birds might have left footprints in the mud. They thought an Oxford professor should not behave in this way, demeaning himself and turning a lecture into a circus performance. Indeed, his very appointment had stirred up controversy, for the religious enthusiasts and the scriptural geologists asserted that the Bible recorded not only the Truth, but all that was needed to be known about the distant past; so what was the point of a Professor of Geology, other than to attack the Bible?

When Buckland heard about the bones in Kirkdale, he dropped everything and travelled at once to North Yorkshire, where in December 1821 he spent what must have been an uncomfortable week in the cave. He wrote a detailed account of what he found, which was published by the Royal Society in February 1822.

The Kirkdale Cave was a long tunnel, varying

between 2 and 5 feet wide, and extending horizontally north-east for about 100 yards. In only a few places was it high enough to allow him to stand up, and although there were a few side-tunnels, there was no other exit apart from the mouth, which had been exposed by the quarrying. On the floor of the cave was a foot of mud, and in this mud were the broken pieces of thousands of bones. The bones had come from a wide variety of animals, including giant deer, hippos, rhinos and even straight-tusked elephants. There were one or two teeth from lions and bears, and many bones from such smaller animals as rabbits and water-rats. Almost all the larger bones were broken, with jagged edges. But by far the most common bones in the cave were those of hyenas; Buckland found fragments from at least three hundred individual animals. In particular the lower jaws, with four savage molars, could not have come from any other species. The jaws in the cave were about one third larger than those of the 'modern Cape hyena', but otherwise identical.

For Buckland it was clear that the foot of mud was the residue of the Flood, but he was left with a real mystery; a cave in the middle of North Yorkshire full of the bones of animals normally thought to be tropical. How on earth had they got in there? There was no shortage of theories. All of them had to fit in with the 'known facts' – that the world had been created in six days in 4004 BC, and the Flood had happened only about ten generations later, as reported in the Bible.

One theory was that all these animals had been living in Yorkshire when the Flood happened. Terrified by the rising waters, they had all rushed into the cave for safety, and were drowned where they sheltered. The problem is, it's hard to believe that rabbits and deer would rush to shelter in a cave with three hundred hyenas, and anyway, as the entrance is only 2 feet high, no elephant or rhino could have squeezed in, however scared it was.

Another theory was that the waters of the Flood had been so violent that they swirled animals all around the world, and tropical animals had been swirled up from Africa to Yorkshire, where they had fallen into the cave through a hole in the roof. Unfortunately there was no hole in the roof.

Maybe, said a third theory, the Flood was so violent it smashed all the animals into pieces, which was how the big ones got in through the entrance, and why the bones were broken. But then surely they would also have been worn smooth, like the pebbles on a beach. The bones in the cave had sharp splintered ends.

Another theory suggested that the animals had indeed all lived in Yorkshire, but that food had become scarce. The hyenas had eaten all the other animals to extinction, one by one, and had then turned on one another, until there was only one left. The last hyena had eaten itself!

Although this last idea is absurd, the theory is not so far from the conclusion Buckland reached. He suggested that for hundreds or even thousands of years the cave had been a den for generations of hyenas, which had foraged for food in the neighbouring countryside. Hyenas will eat either fresh meat or carrion, and must have dragged whole carcasses or parts back into the cave, which would explain the great variety of bones. The fact that the bones were all broken would also fit in with this, for hyenas are known to crunch up their bones to reach the marrow. Buckland even found what he thought were teeth-marks on some of the bones, and to support his theory he performed a cunning experiment, of a kind that is rarely possible in either biology or palaeontology. When a travelling menagerie came to Oxford from Exeter, Buckland procured the hindquarters of an ox, and fed them to the hyena. The hyena, understandably surprised to be given lunch by the professor, performed admirably, not only crunching the ends off the bones, but even leaving tooth-marks identical to those found on the bones from the cave.

Buckland's conclusion – that the cave had been home to generations of hyenas, in a time when tropical animals lived in Yorkshire – caused a furore that rumbled on for twenty years, because he was describing life centuries before the Flood. This was dangerous ground and he was repeatedly attacked for his heretical views. The Dean of York said 'If Buckland be right, Moses must be wrong!'

The Kirkdale Cave turned out not to be unique. A similar collection of bones was found in a cave on Durdham Down near Bristol in 1842, while in Kent's

Hole in Torquay William Pengelly found bones of mammoth, woolly rhinoceros, cave-bear, cave-lion and the extinct sabre-toothed tiger, but Buckland's discoveries at Kirkdale started the trouble. The split between religion and science was developing. In 1840 another geologist, Professor William Whewell, wrote that a new name was needed for those who wished to study science for its own sake; he proposed they should be called 'scientists'.

The Kirkdale Cave is near the river 1 mile west of Kirkbymoorside, though the mud and the bones have gone, and the entrance is up a precarious and muddy cliff.

24 Edwin Budding and the Lawnmower

A lawn is a patch of grass that is always cut short. Two hundred years ago lawns were rare, because cutting the grass was such hard work; at Blenheim Palace fifty labourers were employed full time looking after the pleasure gardens and the lawns. They used to cut the grass every ten days in summer, a line of scythesmen or 'mowers' starting early in the morning when the dew was on the grass, for the scythe worked better when the grass was wet. Even skilled scythesmen left swirls or sear marks on the grass, because the scythe was swung in a half-circle, and the blade was often serrated.

In Britain today, the majority of houses have some sort of lawn, and large houses may have acres. Public parks have huge lawns, and cricket pitches, golf courses, tennis courts and football fields have all become practical. The difference has been brought about mainly by the lawnmower, invented by Edwin Beard Budding of Stroud in Gloucestershire.

Edwin Budding was born late in 1795, the illegitimate son of a farmer. He began to work for a carpenter, but moved into the iron foundries, and became a freelance engineer because he was good at solving engineering problems. Between 1825 and 1830 he developed a pistol that was allegedly better than Sam Colt's revolver of 1835. In 1843 he improved the carding machine, with the help of George Lister. He designed new types of spanner and lathe. But his great triumph was the mowing machine, which he invented in 1830. According to legend, he was working at the time in Brimscombe mill where a rotary cutter was used to trim the nap from woollen cloth. The idea came to him that a similar machine could be built to cut the nap off lawns. He went into partnership with John Ferrabee, whose job was to sort out the patent, the business and the marketing, and together they produced a 19-inch mower with a wrought-iron frame. One of the first machines went to the Regents Park Zoological Gardens, where the foreman Mr Curtis said, 'it does as much work as six or eight men with scythes and brooms . . . performing the whole so perfectly as not to leave a mark of any kind behind.'

The patent, no. 6081 of 1830, is clear and specific: the invention is 'a new combination and application of machinery for the purpose of cropping or shearing the vegetable surface of lawns', and the drawings show the precise construction. The main roller at the back provided drive via gears to the cutting cylinder, and there was a second roller in the middle for adjusting the height of the cut. The grass cuttings were thrown forward into a tray. Later versions were made with an additional handle in front to pull, with wider frames, and so on, but the basic design remains essentially unchanged to this day.

The patent also says: 'Country gentlemen may find in using my machine themselves an amusing, useful and healthy exercise.' In one sense that was the power of Budding's idea, for it enabled ordinary people to cut their own grass; they did not need to pay men with scythes. That's why so many people have lawns today.

By 1832 Ransomes of Ipswich were selling Budding machines. Their advertisements said: 'This machine is so easy to manage, that persons unpractised in the Art of Mowing, may cut the Grass on Lawns, Pleasure Grounds, and Bowling Greens with ease.' Meanwhile their instructions were rather simpler than those on many of today's gadgets: '. . . take hold of the handles, as in driving a barrow, . . . push the machine steadily forward along the greensward, without lifting the handles, but rather exerting a moderate pressure downwards . . .'.

More than a thousand were sold in the 1830s, but alas Mr Budding died of a stroke in 1846, so he probably didn't reap the full reward from his sharp idea. His partner John Ferrabee owned the Phoenix Iron Works in Thrupp, just outside Stroud, and that is where the first machines were made.

The Phoenix Mill has risen from the ashes and instead of mowing machines now produces wonderful books – including this one.

25 Edmund Cartwright and his Power Loom

The sleepy farming village of Goadby Marwood, a few miles north of Melton Mowbray in Leicestershire, does not look like a hotbed of technology, but Edmund Cartwright, inventor extraordinary, was the rector there from 1779 until 1786. He fancied himself as a poet and he invented a great variety of things from interlocking bricks to a cure for putrid fever, but he's best known for the power loom, patented in 1785.

Edmund Cartwright was born on 24 April 1743 at Marnham in Nottinghamshire. He went to Wakefield Grammar School and was sent off to Oxford to study for the Church. While he was at Oxford he published a long poem called *Armina and Elvira*, which was praised by Sir Walter Scott and others, and went through several editions. On the strength of this one good poem and a few mediocre others, he later called himself 'The Father of Poetry' – which seems more than a little presumptuous – and declared that all later poets were his children!

In 1784 Cartwright went up to Derbyshire on holiday, and visited Richard Arkwright and his amazing cotton spinning mill at Cromford. In 1769 Arkwright had patented the water-frame, and his mill was one of the first mass-production factories in the world. After seeing the Cromford mill, Cartwright went to a pub in Matlock and got chatting to some cotton men from Manchester; they reckoned that if a few more mills like Arkwright's were built, there would be more cotton thread than the weavers could cope with, and the spinners would have to start exporting the thread. Cartwright said 'Well, Mr Arkwright should invent a weaving machine, too.'

The others dismissed this as impossible, but Cartwright, who had heard about an automaton chess-player being exhibited in London, said if you could build a machine to play chess you could surely build a machine to weave cloth. In fact the chess-playing automaton, known as 'The Turk', was a conjuring trick. Built in Vienna in 1769 by the Hungarian engineer Baron Wolfgang von Kempelen, it created tremendous excitement when it took on all comers and won, moving the pieces with its left hand. The doors of the chest were opened before the performance, and the inside seemed to be full of intricate machinery, but in fact hidden inside was a very small, very skilful chess player, with a large bladder.

Not knowing it was a fake, Cartwright went home to Goadby Marwood and set about building a weaving machine! He had never seen anyone weaving, and had no idea how it was done, but he wandered about the house making shuttle movements with his hands, which sent his children into fits of giggles, and in the end he managed to construct a power loom, which he patented in April 1785. His patent and the drawing are exceedingly vague; you can tell he'd never seen a loom before. His machine wasn't a great success – two burly men were needed to make it work – so Cartwright set about improving the design.

First he went to see a weaver, and was amazed by the simplicity of the process, which had scarcely changed in centuries, apart from John Kay's invention of the flying shuttle in 1733. This allowed the weaver to throw the bobbin of weft thread from one side of the warp to the other with one hand, and more than doubled the rate of weaving.

Basically cloth is woven by passing one thread, the weft, backwards and forwards between the long warp threads that run from one end of the cloth to the other, and comprises three actions: shedding, picking and beat-up. Shedding is the making of a tunnel or shed between the warp threads for the weft to pass through. Picking is passing or throwing the weft through the shed. Beat-up is pressing the new weft thread down against the previous one to form a new edge on the cloth being woven. Until Cartwright's day these three actions were done by hand, and a good weaver could do perhaps 100 picks a minute.

Cartwright's second machine made all the actions automatic, and therefore enabled them to be much faster. Even a pedal-powered loom enabled a competent weaver to do 160 picks a minute. But clearly there was potential for using external power; Cartwright had been much impressed with Arkwright's water-powered spinning. He set up a weaving factory in Doncaster, powered initially by a water-wheel, and in April 1789 gave a dinner to his workforce of 120 people. They had a whole roast sheep, several pieces of beef, and about thirty plum puddings, and they drank at least eight toasts, so it must have been a good party.

But Cartwright wanted to go further. He planned to use a steam engine to drive his looms, and that's when he began to hit trouble. Thousands of weavers could see their jobs disappearing, and they took drastic action. Grimshaws set up a factory in Manchester, and planned to put in 400 looms, but received threatening letters: 'Sir, we have sworn together to destroy your factory, if we die for it, and to have your life for ruining our trade.' And when only twenty-four looms had been installed, the factory was burned to the ground. No one else dared try such an experiment.

Cartwright's loom was one of the major innovations of the industrial revolution, and in 1789 he patented a wool-combing machine that could do the work of at least twenty men. But again the workers protested; into the House of Commons poured petitions against its use from 50,000 wool-combers. After two great inventions Cartwright hadn't made a penny, but to his credit he kept on inventing.

In 1795 he patented interlocking bricks. He was worried about the fact that houses were built with timber supports, and were liable to catch fire, and he was trying to build fire-proof houses. His bricks were intended to make timber supports unnecessary. He made simple bricks for making a normal wall, and more intricate ones for building self-supporting arches and domes. They simply plugged together like pieces of a jigsaw puzzle – and indeed like the stones of John Smeaton's Eddystone lighthouse. Unfortunately, although these bricks were a brilliant idea, they were too expensive to be popular, and never caught on.

In 1806, Cartwright's last loom patent expired and rivals were free to make power looms without paying Cartwright a penny. So in 1807 a group of Manchester businessmen went to the prime minister and asked for money, on the grounds that Cartwright had spent £30,000 of his own money on inventions that were good for the country, but had made no money from them. In 1809 the government gave him £10,000!

He took the money, retired to a farm in Sussex, and continued inventing things that nobody would ever use. In 1823 he thought up an engine fired by gunpowder. Luckily, he died peacefully before he had the chance to blow himself up. He left behind countless useless inventions and one which made his name – the power loom.

Goadby Marwood is a lovely village, and well worth a visit, although there are no signs of Cartwright's incumbency, apart from a list in the church. The looms at the Bradford Industrial Museum show at a glance the extraordinary development of looms brought about by the self-appointed 'Father of Poetry'.

26 Sir George Cayley, Inventor of the Aeroplane

The world's first powered flight was achieved by John Stringfellow in 1848, but his aircraft was only a model. The first heavier-than-air flying machine to carry a person was built by another Yorkshireman, Sir George Cayley, and the epic flight took place in Brompton Vale in North Yorkshire in 1853.

In the little church in Brompton, poet William Wordsworth married his childhood sweetheart Mary Hutchinson on 4 October 1802. There is even a theory that his famous poem about daffodils was written not in the Lake District, as is generally supposed, but at Brompton, where there are also daffodils under the trees by a lake. William and

Mary must have noticed that just behind the little church is a great house, called Brompton Hall, but they probably didn't realise that even while they were being married, the squire was busy in his garden shed designing the world's first aeroplane.

George Cayley was born on 27 December 1773. His family had lived at Brompton Hall for generations. When he was nineteen his father died, and George became the sixth baronet – Sir George Cayley. So he had both money and time, although he also had an estate to manage. He was always interested in scientific observation. At the age of fifteen he was timing the beats of a crow's wing, and while he was at school he measured the rate of growth of his thumbnail; it grew just half an inch in one hundred days.

For many years he enjoyed a close relationship with his intelligent cousin Miss Phil, but in 1795 he married a difficult and brittle girl called Sarah Walker, the daughter of his tutor in Nottingham. Their relationship was generally uncomfortable, and he may well have come to build his aircraft because she made the atmosphere in the house so chilly, and his workshop provided a refuge.

By 1796 he was designing flying machines. From string, whalebone, and feathers he created little toy ornithopters that would fly when wound up. He went on to design toy gliders, modelling them roughly on the crow. He realised that flight involved two important factors – forward propulsion and lift

– and that the two could be tackled separately. He came to the conclusion – as did Stringfellow and Henson forty years later – that birds could get lift without flapping. After all, many birds glide for long distances without a single flap, and without plummeting to the ground. Cayley set about investigating lift by using a whirling-arm machine.

Aerodynamic experiments are hard to control, because you have to organise a steady flow of air or wind speed, and he did this by the ingenious use of a whirling-arm. He made his experimental wing of about one square foot, which he reckoned was the area of a crow's wings, and fixed it to the end of a wooden arm three feet long, pivoted near the centre on a vertical rod, and neatly counterbalanced at the other end. He wound a string round the rod, passed the end over a pulley, and hung a weight from it. When he let go of the weight it would fall, pulling the rod round and making the arm whirl. By doing this indoors he could be sure the 'wing' was always moving at constant speed through the air.

According to legend, his wife would not have this apparatus in the house; so he waited his opportunity. Their first child, Anne, was due in 1796 and Sarah went to stay with her mother in Nottingham for her confinement. George immediately set up his whirling-arm apparatus on the top landing in the great staircase of the Hall, so that the weight had a clear 20 foot drop to the ground. He tried various angles for mounting the wing, and reckoned he got maximum lift at an angle of 6°. Then he built a glider, with the wings set at 6° up from the fuselage, and went out to test it in Brompton Vale, the field behind the house.

He was so delighted by how well it flew that he waxed lyrical about the flying machines of the future. He reckoned a glider would be the ideal way to get people down mountains: 'It was very pretty to see it sail down a steep hill, and it gave the idea that a larger instrument would be a better and safer conveyance down the Alps than even the sure-footed mule.'

He went on to design the best aerodynamic shape for slipping through the air, and planned an internal combustion engine to provide power. 'When we can get a hundred horsepower into a pint pot,' he wrote to *The Times*, 'man will be able to transport his family and possessions as readily by air as he now does by railway.' He asserted that flying was the future, and that we should all come to use 'that uninterrupted navigable ocean which comes to the threshold of every man's door. . . . We shall be able to transport ourselves and our families with their goods and chattels more securely by air than by water, and at a velocity of from 20 to 100 miles an hour.'

Unfortunately, for many years he was too busy to pursue flying. He invented rifling for the barrels of big guns. He suggested that passengers on trains should wear seat-belts. He designed a net like a cow-catcher to attach to the front of trains so that any workmen on the line would be scooped up rather than run over. He designed an 'Artificial hand for working men', and became MP for Scarborough. But in the 1840s he returned to aeronautics. He built a triplane which carried a boy off the ground on a downhill flight. And finally, in 1852, he built his New Flyer.

Cayley described his New Flyer in some detail in the *Mechanics* magazine of 15 September that year, although for some reason he gave the article the title 'Governable parachutes'. It was a monoplane with a kite-shaped wing and a tricycle undercarriage. In order to keep the weight down, Cayley had devised wheels with small rims and spokes of string in tension; in other words he had incidentally invented the bicycle wheel!

The following year, 1853, saw the first flight. Sir George was by now seventy-nine – rather old to be the world's first test-pilot – so he volunteered his coachman, probably one John Appleby, to take the tiller. The aircraft was launched from the grass field on the high east side of Brompton Vale by half a dozen farm hands running and pulling on ropes. It soared into the air, flew right across the valley – about 200 yards – and landed heavily on the grass the other side. The coachman clambered out of the wreckage, and said: 'Please, Sir George, I wish to give notice. I was hired to drive, not to fly!' Nevertheless, this was the world's first flight of a heavier-than-air person carrying aircraft.

When the Wright brothers flew their aircraft Flyer I at Kittyhawk in North Carolina on 17 December 1903, they paid tribute to Cayley: 'About 100 years ago an Englishman, Sir George Cayley, carried the science of flying to a point which it had never reached before and which it scarcely reached again during the last century.'

In Brompton, 7 miles west of Scarborough, there's a pub called the Cayley Arms. Although Brompton Hall is now a school there is a plaque on the back of Cayley's workshop, visible from the road.

27 John Clayton and the Discovery of Coal Gas

For hundreds of years people must have been digging coal out of the ground and burning it for warmth. During all that time someone must surely have noticed that coal produces a flammable gas when it is heated. However, we have a precise date and location for the first scientific examination of the phenomenon, for John Clayton wrote an excited letter about it to Robert Boyle and the Royal Society published it in their *Philosophical Transactions*.

Within two miles of Wigan, he says, he found a ditch wherein the water seemed to burn like brandy, and the flame was so fierce that several strangers boiled eggs on it. What a wonderful discovery, on an afternoon walk, this assembly of egg-boiling strangers huddled around a ditch! Determined to get to the bottom of this, he drained the ditch, dug down, and found some 'shelly coal'. He lit a candle and lowered it down the hole, and 'the air catched fire, and continued burning'.

So he took some of the coal home with him, heated it in a retort over his fire, and watched with fascination. At first came only phlegm, then black oil – he was founding the chemical industry here – and then a gas which he collected and stored in bladders, and was able to ignite and amaze his friends. This flammable gas was coal gas which, when the technology became available, provided light and some power for Victorian England.

The evidence is patchy, but he may have been the same John Clayton who was Rector of Crofton near Wakefield from 1687 to 1694, and went on to become a bishop in Ireland. He repaired the church roof and the steeple in 1689 – and seems to have discovered coal gas in his spare time!

John Clayton's name is on the list of rectors of Crofton Church, south-east of Wakefield.

28 Eleanor Coade, her Stone and Buckingham Palace

Eleanor Coade invented, and for fifty years produced, the first successful artificial stone: a ceramic material so durable that 650 pieces survive to this day, in fireplaces, statues, ornaments and doorways. She made stone for George III and George IV, and received commissions from all over Britain, from North and South America, the Caribbean, Poland and Russia.

The Coade family came originally from Coad's Green in Cornwall. Eleanor (christened Elinor) was born in Exeter on 24 June 1733, where her father George was a prosperous wool finisher. Unfortunately, the wool business declined, and he went bankrupt first in 1759, and then again in 1769. The second time his house and belongings were sold, and he died soon afterwards.

Luckily Eleanor had already moved to London and established herself in business. In that same year, 1769, she set up in Narrow Wall, Lambeth (now Belvedere Road) as a maker of artificial stone. Her mother joined her there, and there has been much confusion because she also was called Eleanor. Furthermore, the daughter called herself Mrs Coade for respectability in business. In fact she never married, partly perhaps because she was an ardent feminist and was reluctant to allow her husband to acquire all her possessions and her business, as he would have done until the Married Women's Property Act of 1882. In her will she left money to several widows and spinsters, and to some married women, on condition that their husbands could not touch it, and that contrary to normal practice, they signed for the legacies themselves 'notwithstanding their coverture!' She also left £100 to the Girls' Charity School at Walworth, but only £50 to the Boys'.

Her factory flourished from the beginning in 1769 until she died in 1821, and indeed carried on into the 1830s in the hands of the man who had been her manager. Several patents had been taken out for artificial stone before she came on the scene, but none of the processes really worked. We do not know how she found a winner, but she certainly did, and her product was ceramic – a type of pottery.

There are three kinds of pottery: earthenware, which is weak and porous and used for flowerpots; stoneware, which is stronger and used for casseroles; and porcelain, which is very strong but impossible to work in large quantities, because the stuff is almost liquid before firing. Eleanor made stoneware; she used ball clay from Devon and Cornwall, mixed it with 10 per cent grog (crushed stoneware), 5–10 per cent of flint, and 5–10 per cent of fine sand. The mixture was rolled out like pastry, pressed into moulds, finished or fettled, and finally fired at 1100–1150°C. Pressing the cold wet clay mix into the moulds was tedious, fiddly work, and she probably used children to do it: some very small fingerprints have been found in the stone!

Robert Adam had come back from Italy in 1758 bursting with enthusiasm for neo-classical architecture, so elegant stonework was popular. He used loads of Coade stone, and many others followed. Her stone was used for fancy doorways, for statues, for urns and other stone ornaments, and for commemorative pediments; its one great advantage was that, unlike real stone, Coade stone did not erode – it was impervious to weathering.

Among surviving examples of Coade stone some can still be found in Buckingham Palace, St George's Chapel, Windsor, the Royal Naval College at Greenwich, and even the entrance to the zoo in Rio de Janeiro. The best-known pieces are the huge lion on the southern end of Westminster Bridge and the tomb of Captain Bligh. There is a wonderful river god at Ham House in Surrey, and an impressive doorway at Schomberg House, half way up Pall Mall.

Eleanor's uncle Sam had lived in Lyme Regis, and in 1784 he gave her his house, which was then called Bunter's Castle, and is now called Belmont; it is still dressed with her stone. The secret formula of her stone was finally worked out by analysis of a fragment from the top of one of the gateposts.

Very few women managed to establish successful businesses in the eighteenth century; she must have had three exceptional talents: for discovering such a successful formula for what she called 'Lithodipyra' and making it work; for either being or employing a fine artist and making attractive statues which appealed to the public; and for being a brilliant businesswoman and entrepreneur.

The easiest pieces of Coade stone to see are the lion on the south end of Westminster Bridge and the doorway of Schomberg House, half way up the south side of Pall Mall. But Alison Kelly's book lists hundreds of others. Eleanor used a horse-mill for grinding the stone. This was discovered in 1950, and the bed of the mill – the bottom stone – is now set into the paving by the river bank in front of the Royal Festival Hall, although there is no plaque. The best news is that Mrs Coade's secret formula didn't die with her; in Dorset, Philip Thomason has analysed her stone, worked out the recipe and is now making Coade stone again.

29 William Cookworthy's China

Broadly speaking, there are three types of pottery – earthenware, as used in flowerpots; stoneware, as in casseroles; and porcelain, used for the finest teacups. The difference between earthenware and porcelain mugs or cups is obvious if you drink from them; the porcelain is smoother and finer and feels colder. Until the early eighteenth century the only porcelain available in Britain was imported from the Far East, and was therefore called china. Because it was clearly of better quality than the material most people had, there was some enthusiasm to crack the secrets of the mysterious east and make porcelain in Britain.

The man who did it was William Cookworthy, born in Kingsbridge in Devon on 12 April 1705, the eldest of seven children in a Quaker family. When he was thirteen his father died, and the next year

William was apprenticed to a firm of chemists and druggists run by Silvanus Bevan in London. About 1733 he established a wholesale chemist's business in Plymouth. He married Sarah Berry – they eventually had five daughters – and he became a Minister for the Society of Friends, which meant that he travelled a good deal around Devon and Cornwall in order to preach.

He was always interested in geology, and he may have read a book about the manufacture of porcelain in China, even though the recipe was still secret. His brother had been to China, and may well have brought home first-hand accounts of the business. The critical clue came in 1745; Cookworthy describes in a letter of 5 May to a surgeon friend how he had recently met an American who discovered china clay – kaolin – in Virginia. Cookworthy reckoned that if it existed in Virginia it might well exist in Cornwall too; so he started searching in earnest, and in due course he found deposits of the right sort of minerals at Tregonnin Hill in the parish of Germo, near Helston. Then he found better and more accessible deposits at St Stephen near St Austell, on the property of Lord Camelford, who was interested, and helped with the development.

Cookworthy took samples back to Plymouth and there began his experiments. When he heated one sample to white heat in a crucible he obtained 'a beautiful semi-diaphanous white substance'. He soon discovered that all he needed was 'china stone' or petuntse which was quarried as a local building material and 'china clay' or kaolin, which was used to line the smelting furnaces. So much for the 'secret ingredients'!

Progress was slow, but in 1768 Cookworthy took out a patent for the manufacture of porcelain, and with Lord Camelford's help opened a factory at Coxside, Plymouth, where he employed fifty or sixty people, including an experienced porcelain painter and enameller from Sèvres. However, the business was quickly in financial trouble; Cookworthy had difficulty maintaining a consistent product, and the cost of coal for firing the kiln was a serious problem. There was great demand for porcelainware, but unfortunately he could not make it profitably, so a few years later he sold his patent to his partner, Richard Champion of Bristol. At the same time they applied for an extension of the patent, but this was bitterly opposed by Josiah Wedgwood and other Staffordshire potters, who wanted to make porcelain themselves. Champion also ran into financial problems, and in 1777 sold the business on to a company in Staffordshire, where the coal was cheaper.

William Cookworthy was described as a tall, venerable man, with a three-cornered hat and bushy, curly wig, a mild but intellectual countenance, and full of conversation. He became well known in the scientific world; in August 1768 Captain James Cook, Sir Joseph Banks and Dr Solander dropped in to dine with him just before they set off around the world in their second-hand coal barge to observe the transit of Venus. Cookworthy died in 1780; the Bristol factory closed in 1781; and by 1858 there were forty-two companies producing 65,000 tonnes of china clay every year.

The Cookworthy Museum at 108 Fore Street in Kingsbridge, South Devon, has a small display of Cookworthy material; 01548 853235. Try also the Plymouth Museum; 01752 668000.

30 William Coppin and the *Great Northern*

For thousands of years boats have been built of wood, and although one or two were made of iron in the eighteenth century, large iron ships were not built until the 1840s. One of the most famous was Brunel's *Great Britain*, but the first of the large iron ships was the *Great Northern*, built in Northern Ireland by Captain William Coppin.

William Coppin was born in County Cork on 9 October 1805, twelve days before the Battle of Trafalgar, and the sea was in his blood. At the age of fifteen he rescued six customs men when their boat capsized in the River Shannon, and when he finished school his parents sent him off to Canada to learn about boat-building.

He came back to Ireland and built a 100-ton ship – the *Kathleen* – when he was only twenty-four. Then he was commissioned to build a 600-tonner, the *Edward Reid*. He delivered it himself to a timber merchant in Londonderry. He loved the place so much that a few years later he went back to live there.

Coppin was a good sailor, and captained a number of other ships in the next eight years, including paddle-steamers to Philadelphia and passenger ships to Liverpool, before buying a boatyard on the River Foyle below the soaring battlements of Londonderry. There he built many ships, of every size and kind. The most spectacular, and the most famous, was the *Great Northern*, which was launched on 23 July 1842. At 220 feet long, and with a displacement of 1,750 tons, she was the biggest ship ever built in Ireland. She was rigged as a 50-gun frigate. She had three masts, and carried a full set of square-rigged sails, and a huge 370 horse-power steam engine which drove an Archimedes screw propeller, 12 feet in diameter, thundering round at a stately 88 rpm. The launch was such an event that twenty thousand spectators gathered to watch, crammed on every bit of dock, on the roof-tops, and on sixty boats offshore. Even the Donegal Grand Jury insisted on coming, and the court was closed for the day!

Coppin sailed her round to London, because he hoped to sell her to the British Government.

Unfortunately this was the only voyage the *Great Northern* made, for after a long and expensive delay, while Coppin sat in dock biting his nails, the British Government said 'No thanks'; perhaps they thought it would be unwise to buy a warship from Ireland. Coppin, now almost bankrupt, had to sell the ship for scrap to pay the harbour dues.

In his later life Coppin turned to salvage. Lots of ships sank, and in deep water they were extremely hard to reach. But they often had on board not only valuable cargo, but expensive steam engines, well worth recovering. So William Coppin thought hard about how to get down to the wrecks and bring them up. In 1876 he patented an amazing new diving suit. It was revolutionary in two ways: when you dive down more than a few feet in the sea, you are subjected to great pressure – go down to 30 feet and you have double the pressure at the surface, at 60 feet, three times the pressure, and so on. Coppin's new diving suit had two waterproof rubber skins, separated by tough ribs that would withstand some of this extra pressure, and so make life easier for the diver. It was the first attempt at a partially armoured suit. He also invented a better system for breathing out. Before then, divers had had to exhale straight into the water, which meant they had to breathe out against all that pressure. Coppin's new suit brought the used air back to the surface, so he could control the pressure at which they breathed out. With his brilliant new equipment, Coppin claimed he could go down to 120 feet and stay there for an hour – which was a great advance on what had been possible before.

He developed a cunning technique – to plug all the holes in a boat with clay, and then fill the hull with air, so that it floated to the surface. Coppin had realised that bubbles of air under water have immense lifting power. Archimedes' Principle says that the uplift is equal to the weight of water displaced. So if you fill a large ship with air, when it's under water, the uplift should be almost a ton for every cubic metre – more than enough to float the ship to the surface!

Coppin was a prolific inventor. In 1886 he patented an electric fish-catching apparatus – which looks like a winner, if you can believe the picture on the box!

However, the strangest Coppin tale is not about the captain, but concerns his young daughter Louisa, known to the family as 'Weesy'. She was born in 1846, and died on 27 May 1849, aged only three and a half. Six months later a ball of bluish light appeared in one room of the house. Curiously, the other children weren't frightened; they said it was just Weesy, come back to visit them. They used to chat to Weesy's ghost, and ask it questions. One day they asked what had happened to Sir John Franklin, the great explorer, who had gone off past Newfoundland to look for the north-west passage to India. He had set sail two years earlier with the ships

Erebus and *Terror*, and no trace of the expedition had been seen since. The blue ball of light apparently produced a map on the wall, which showed the whereabouts of the ships and the expedition. Coppin noted the details and in May 1850 went to see Lady Franklin, who was so convinced that she launched another expedition to search for them in the spot identified by Weesy's ghost.

William Coppin's grave is in St Augustine's churchyard, high up near the battlements of Londonderry. His home down the hill at Ivy House – 34 Strand Road – has become a pizza restaurant.

31 Moses Bruine Cotsworth and his Rational Calendar

Our calendar is a mess. We have seven months with thirty-one days, four months with thirty days, and one with twenty-eight or twenty-nine. Only February ever has an exact number of weeks. All this would have been sorted out if only the world had accepted the ideas of Moses Bruine Cotsworth.

Cotsworth, born at Acomb near York in 1859, worked as a goods clerk for the North Eastern Railway in York, but he was obsessed with numbers. He became a statistician, and used to get up at 4 a.m. to work on his calculations before going in to the NER. This led to various books of calculations and ready-reckoners, but his *magnum opus* was the

	S	M	T	W	T	F	S	S	M	T	W	T	F	S	S	M	T	W	T	F	S	S	M	T	W	T	F	S
Jan	1	2	3	4	5	6	7	8	9	10	11	12	13	14	15	16	17	18	19	20	21	22	23	24	25	26	27	28
Feb	1	2	3	4	5	6	7	8	9	10	11	12	13	14	15	16	17	18	19	20	21	22	23	24	25	26	27	28
Mar	1	2	3	4	5	6	7	8	9	10	11	12	13	14	15	16	17	18	19	20	21	22	23	24	25	26	27	28
Apr	1	2	3	4	5	6	7	8	9	10	11	12	13	14	15	16	17	18	19	20	21	22	23	24	25	26	27	28
May	1	2	3	4	5	6	7	8	9	10	11	12	13	14	15	16	17	18	19	20	21	22	23	24	25	26	27	28
Jun	1	2	3	4	5	6	7	8	9	10	11	12	13	14	15	16	17	18	19	20	21	22	23	24	25	26	27	28
Sol	1	2	3	4	5	6	7	8	9	10	11	12	13	14	15	16	17	18	19	20	21	22	23	24	25	26	27	28
Jul	1	2	3	4	5	6	7	8	9	10	11	12	13	14	15	16	17	18	19	20	21	22	23	24	25	26	27	28
Aug	1	2	3	4	5	6	7	8	9	10	11	12	13	14	15	16	17	18	19	20	21	22	23	24	25	26	27	28
Sep	1	2	3	4	5	6	7	8	9	10	11	12	13	14	15	16	17	18	19	20	21	22	23	24	25	26	27	28
Oct	1	2	3	4	5	6	7	8	9	10	11	12	13	14	15	16	17	18	19	20	21	22	23	24	25	26	27	28
Nov	1	2	3	4	5	6	7	8	9	10	11	12	13	14	15	16	17	18	19	20	21	22	23	24	25	26	27	28
Dec	1	2	3	4	5	6	7	8	9	10	11	12	13	14	15	16	17	18	19	20	21	22						
																						bd	23	24	25	26	27	28

Moses Bruine Cotsworth's Rational Calendar.

Rational Almanac published in 1904. All the information you needed was in the table inside the front cover of his book, but he actually wrote 471 more pages, to justify the idea.

Cotsworth said the first day of every month should be a Sunday, and every month should have exactly four weeks. There should be thirteen months in the year. He proposed to use the existing months, and add an extra one called 'Sol', the month of the sun, between June and July. Thirteen months of four weeks each makes fifty-two weeks, or 364 days. Christmas Day would always be on Sunday 22 December, and he proposed that the following day, Boxing Day, should simply be another Sunday. Then New Year's Eve would be Saturday, and everything would fit. Leap years would be catered for the same way – with two consecutive Sundays. The result is a wonderfully simple year planner. Any particular date will always be the same day every month – and every year. The 13th would always be a Friday, and birthdays would always fall on the same day of the week.

Cotsworth was passionate about his rational calendar. He spent years promoting it, travelled to more than sixty countries, and was appointed to the League of Nations Committee on Calendar Reform, and became Director of the International Fixed Calendar League. Despite all this, he failed to change the world, but he did convince George Eastman, head of Kodak, and until a few years ago all Kodak employees were paid in thirteen monthly instalments.

32 Humphry Davy's Gases for Health and Laughter

As you drive into Bristol from the Cumberland Basin a magnificent city panorama unrolls. Dominating the left-hand side of the view is the Avon gorge, spanned high above the river by the delicate-looking Clifton Suspension Bridge, Isambard Kingdom Brunel's showpiece (although the money kept running out, and it was not finished until after he died).

Almost underneath the eastern end of the Clifton Suspension Bridge is St Vincent's Rock, from the bottom of which, during the seventeenth and eighteenth centuries, came gushing out warm murky water – 60 gallons a minute at 76°F. This was Hotwells Spa. The water was believed to be medicinal, and people came here from far and wide to take the waters, including Catherine of Braganza in 1677. She set the trend for everyone who was anyone, and by the 1780s Hotwells was one of the most fashionable and most crowded watering places in the kingdom.

Many of the people who came to take the waters lodged along the road in Dowry Square, and so Dr Thomas Beddoes set up his brand new Pneumatic Institution at no. 6. This was funded by private subscription – they had £1,000 from potter Josiah

Wedgwood, for example – and its aim was to find out whether the various gases that had just been discovered by Priestley, Lavoisier and others had any useful medicinal value. Dr Priestley, for example, said that breathing oxygen made him feel invigorated; would it perhaps be useful for patients who were ill, especially with diseases of the lungs?

The Institution could take eight in-patients and up to eighty out-patients. Many of them suffered from tuberculosis, which was a major killer, and all sorts of gases were tried in the attempt to find a cure. Beddoes apparently believed they might benefit from the gases produced by cows. It is unlikely that he actually took the cows into the ward, but he certainly kept a small herd in the garden next door, and piped the gases into the bedchambers. These gases, you understand, were what the cows breathed out, as well as what came from the other end. . . .

If this had been effective, Beddoes would surely have been delighted, since the gases from the cows must have been produced at minimal expense! However, I imagine there was quite an incentive for the patients to say they were better and discharge themselves! Beddoes was the mastermind, but naturally he did not actually run the Institution; for that he hired a young Cornishman called Humphry Davy.

Humphry Davy was born in Penzance on 17 December 1778. He went on to run the Royal Institution in London; he was knighted, and became incredibly famous. But he was just nineteen when he came to Bristol in October 1798 as Medical Superintendent! The following year he heard about the new electric battery that had been invented by Volta in Italy. Volta said he made electricity just by holding dissimilar metals together. Davy was excited by this, but disagreed with Volta. He said you never got something for nothing; there must be a chemical reaction going on. He and Beddoes built a huge battery in the Pneumatic Institution in order to test out their ideas.

What's more, Davy argued that if chemistry could produce electricity then the same thing should work the other way round, and electricity should be able to produce chemistry. Thus he conceived the idea of electrochemistry, and later he went on to use electrochemistry to isolate the new metals, potassium and sodium. The paper he wrote for the Royal Society about this was probably what got him invited to the Royal Institution in 1801.

But his real job in Bristol was to investigate gases. He made a variety, and tried them all out on himself. He almost died inhaling carbon monoxide, but he had a wonderful time when he found out how to make nitrous oxide, which came to be called laughing gas. The Department of Anaesthesia at the Bristol Royal Infirmary is named after Sir Humphry Davy, partly because nitrous oxide has become one of the most useful of all gases in medicine. When mixed with oxygen it is called 'gas and air', and it has a range of uses: it's used as a painkiller in childbirth; it's carried by paramedics in ambulances; and it's used by dentists.

When you inhale it, as a 25 per cent mixture with air, the effect comes on within about four breaths, or 30 seconds. I found I felt tingling in my fingertips, which then went numb; I could jab them with a pin without worrying. Nitrous oxide also reduces anxiety – which helps medical staff to give injections. There seems to be some argument about whether it really reduces pain or merely makes you not care about it. But perhaps that does not matter!

Being under the influence of nitrous oxide feels like being slightly drunk – having two large glasses of wine one after the other. Colours seem to get brighter – or the contrast increases. When you decide to move your head the view you see takes some time to catch up; there's a delayed response. Yet these effects disappear within a couple of minutes, and you can then drive a car safely! As long as you have oxygen as well you can take gas and air for hours. You will stay awake and lucid, although if the concentration is high enough, any joke may produce uncontrollable laughter.

Humphry Davy used to wander around Clifton breathing nitrous oxide from a green silk bag. He tried it out on all his literary friends, who loved it and danced in the streets. Samuel Taylor Coleridge said it made him feel as warm as when he came home to a fire after a walk in the snow. Southey wrote to his brother: 'O Tom! Such gas has Davy discovered . . . it made me laugh and tingle in every toe and fingertip. Davy has actually invented a new pleasure for which language has no name!'

The Pneumatic Institution was at 6 Dowry Square, an elegant private house in Hotwells, Bristol.

33 Nicholas de Chemant's Stove-cum-Dining Table

London's Soho district is packed with good restaurants and was probably a good place to eat 200 years ago, but Nicholas Dubois de Chemant seems to have been bothered less by the food and more by his cold feet. He was a surgeon dentist, and he lived in Frith Street.

Eating dinner even in posh homes must have been a chilly affair in the 1790s; central heating had not been invented, and a fireplace on one wall wouldn't be much use unless you happened to be sitting right next to it. As an expatriate Frenchman de Chemant wanted to have warm, cosy dinner parties. So he invented a combined stove and dinner table, and because he took out a patent on it, we know his plans in detail. The table could, he said, be round or oval or square, but the crucial features were a hollow centre and a passage through the side. In the middle he put a stove – he said that any stove of about the right size would do. The smoke from the stove went round a long curly flue pipe before it reached the main chimney. And this long curly pipe ran between the legs of the table, so that all the diners could rest their feet on it.

Result: warm feet, cosy chat, intimate social intercourse – just the thing for the eighteenth-century dinner party. Meanwhile the passage through the side of the table allowed one of the servants to get in and stoke up the fire in the stove, if anyone felt even the faintest chilliness of the feet!

These days the Frith Street restaurants are heated, and de Chemant's stove is no longer needed.

34 Arthur Doodson's Pendulums for Tide Prediction

Arthur Thomas Doodson (1890–1968) was the son of a Lancashire cotton mill manager, and was one of those people who loved not only mathematics but actually performing calculations. In an age before computers, his prodigious ability was used to defend London from Zeppelins, to ensure the perfect timing of the D-Day invasion, and to design and build the best tide-predicting machine in the world.

The port of Liverpool had more interest in the tides than most. Apart from being one of the great ports of the Empire, Liverpool's situation at the end of the fairly shallow Mersey estuary made the pattern of the tides particularly tricky. But the safety and efficient running of the port depended upon being sure when ships could move in or out. So it was not too difficult to persuade Liverpool ship owners to pay for a Tidal Institute, which was eventually based at the observatory on Bidston Hill, a magnificent landmark on the Birkenhead side of the harbour entrance. Indeed Bidston Hill was well known to the shipping companies because it was here that a primitive early-warning system was operated in the days before radio made it possible to know precisely where your ships were. On the hill stood a series of flag-poles, and when a ship was spotted heading for the harbour the appropriate company flag was run up the pole so the dock could be made ready. So the Liverpool Tidal Institute was part of a great maritime tradition, and the man they recruited to sort out the calculation and prediction of the tides was Arthur Doodson.

A would-be teacher and keen piano player, Doodson's life changed when he became profoundly deaf. Being mechanically gifted, he made his own hearing aid long before portable hearing aids were generally available, and carried it around in an attaché case. He then thought about being a chemist, but switched to mathematics. He turned out to be particularly good at devising new methods for computing mathematical tables, and his tables were the best yet. He was so keen on computation that he could often be seen calculating away on buses and trams travelling to and from work, and during his lunch hour. In 1916 Doodson's delight in this high-precision but repetitive work singled him out for the ballistics department of the War Office – but here he ran into a problem. He was a deeply religious man – the church seems to have been his main social activity – and a conscientious objector. Apparently he was persuaded that calculating trajectories for anti-aircraft guns targeting the Zeppelins over London was defensive work, but it must have been uncomfortable for him working in a place dedicated to waging war. Nevertheless, his vision was such that he replaced cruder methods with his own firmly mathematical approach, and ended the war as head of the section. It must have been a relief to move on to the work that dominated the rest of his life – the tides.

At first sight, tides seem quite simple. The water of the oceans is pulled up towards the moon by gravity, forming a 'hump' of deeper water on one side of the globe. There is a corresponding hump on the other side where the water is 'thrown out' by the motions of the earth and moon. As the earth rotates, each place passes under the high and low 'humps' and we experience tides. But the sun also pulls on the water of the oceans, reinforcing (spring tides) or decreasing (neap tides) the effect of the moon, depending upon whether the sun, earth and moon are in line or not. This is just the start of the complexity. If you actually sat in a harbour recording the height of water for a year (as people did), the resulting graph is often very complicated, not least because there are often local effects caused by tidal currents flowing round the land or up shallow estuaries like the Mersey.

So how can you predict the tides for places where you might not even know what the local influences are? Rather than go back to first principles, it was clear that you should start from the actual tides – hence the man recording the height of water for a year. Then a mathematical trick is used. The impossibly complex and apparently irregular tidal curve can be reproduced by adding together several quite regular curves – sine waves. The idea is that if you choose enough regular curves, and get their height and frequency right, you can reproduce any tidal curve, no matter how complex. Then if you run all the regular curves together and add up the results, you should be able to predict the tides into the future.

These principles had been worked out by the 1870s, but Lord Kelvin, charged with reporting to the Tides Committee of the British Association, couldn't work out a neat way of doing the fiendish calculations. He travelled to the British Association meeting of 1872 by train and found himself in a carriage with Mr Beauchamp Tower, a well-known inventor. Kelvin discussed the problem of adding together many regular movements, all of different sizes and travelling at different speeds. Tower suggested that if you could mechanically represent each regular movement – which is quite easy – then perhaps the sum could be done mechanically as well. He proposed that if the regular movements could be represented by pulley wheels moving up and down, then simply passing a wire over all the pulleys would add up their movements; if you attached a pen to the end of the wire, it would draw the resulting line. Kelvin realised this was the answer, and presented his solution to the meeting. The machine could add up ten regular tidal 'constituents' and, as he reported, 'the machine may be turned so rapidly as to run off a year's tides for any port in about four hours'.

By the time Doodson became involved with tides in the 1920s, tide-predicting machines had been around for fifty years. But the results were not always very good, especially for unusual ports. Doodson looked very carefully at the tides at Newlyn in Cornwall, and soon devised new methods. It became clear that for good predictions the tides had to be separated into more than forty constituents, each represented in the machine by a moving pulley. The new machines he devised were finally good enough to analyse tides anywhere in the world, and eventually the Liverpool Tidal Institute became responsible for supplying tide predictions for every major port in the Commonwealth.

Arthur Doodson's greatest moment of glory was once again associated with warfare. The government often consulted Doodson as the world's greatest expert in tidal prediction. During the war, it was not unusual for them to supply him with tidal information and ask for a prediction, but concealing where the information came from. The *Express* headline on this occasion was: 'The doctor solves Problem X: Tide wizard's £3000 robot makes its greatest forecast.' Problem X turned out to be calculating the precise tides for the invasion beaches in Normandy on 6 June 1944 – D-Day.

Arthur Doodson's wonderful machine is still on Bidston Hill, but is now run only occasionally.

35 Cornelis Drebbel and his Submarine

Cornelis Drebbel was born in 1572 in Alkmaar in Holland. He started his working life as an engraver and glassworker, but his interests soon moved into alchemy and science. He published a book called *The Nature of the Elements* (i.e. earth, air, fire and water). He also ground lenses, invented a force pump for a fountain, a new type of chimney and a clockwork motor that could allegedly keep going for 100 years. He came over to England in 1604 at the request of King James I, who had heard about Drebbel's claims to have made a solar-powered perpetual motion machine.

The king gave Drebbel an income and lodgings at Eltham Palace in south-east London. In the 1400s Eltham was an important hunting lodge and country escape for the royal family, who often went there for Christmas. What's more, dignitaries from abroad, heading for London, would pop in for a wash and brush up before seeing the king. Unfortunately, in the seventeenth century the place became a ruin; all that remains now are the moat, a few walls and the magnificent great hall.

At Eltham Drebbel produced all sorts of extraordinary devices, including a compound microscope, a thermometer, a telescope, a machine that produced lightning, rain, thunder and extreme cold, a still for obtaining fresh water from salt water, wind-powered musical instruments and toys, an incubator, a thermostatically controlled oven and an extraordinary pump.

About 1620 Drebbel set about making a submarine. We have no accurate contemporary description, but it was probably like two rowing boats, the second clamped upside down on top of the first, and the whole thing covered in greased leather. There was a watertight hatch, a rudder and four oars. There were two things that were really clever about Drebbel's submarine: first, how he got it to sink and then to resurface; second, how the passengers and crew breathed under water.

His solution to the first problem was to put under the rowers' seats large pigskin bladders, connected to the outside by pipes. When the bladders were flooded, the boat would sink; when the water was squeezed out again, the submarine would surface. When the submarine set off, the bladders were empty and tied shut with rope. When the crew wanted to dive they untied the rope, allowed the bladders to fill with water, and down she went. When they wanted to surface the crew squashed the bladders flat, squeezing the water out.

Drebbel was so satisfied with his submarine that he built two more, each bigger than the last. The final model had six pairs of oars and could carry sixteen passengers; the hull was strengthened with iron bands, and even had windows. This model was demonstrated to the king and thousands of Londoners. It could apparently stay submerged for three hours and had a range of 6 miles – allegedly they rowed in three hours from Westminster to Greenwich and back, a distance of about 6 miles (which seems highly unlikely!). The submarine cruised about 15 feet below the surface, at which depth the water pressure would have been about one and a half times normal atmospheric pressure.

To stay under water for three hours, they must have had a supply of oxygen, but this is a bit of a mystery. One account claims Drebbel had tubes to the surface and a set of bellows to circulate the air. Another suggestion was made by Robert Boyle in 1662. He wrote that he had spoken with 'an excellent mathematician' who was still alive and had been on the submarine. According to Boyle's account Drebbel had a 'chemical liquor' that would replace that 'quintessence of air' that was able to 'cherish the vital flame residing in the heart'.

Did Cornelis Drebbel know about oxygen? If so he took his knowledge to the grave. Boyle said that 'when [Drebbel] perceived that the finer and purer part of the air was consumed by the respiration and steames of those that went in the vessel, he would by unstoppering a vessel full of liquor, speedily restore the troubled air'. Another account, by someone who was actually there, claimed that the substance in Drebbel's flasks was a gas. If this was true, we have to believe Drebbel had jars full of oxygen in his submarine – a full 150 years before Joseph Priestley officially discovered oxygen in the 1770s! And now we step into the realms of unknown history. What we do know about Drebbel is that he was friendly with other famous alchemists of the time.

One of his friends was a man called Sendivogius. They probably met in 1619, while Drebbel was in Prague, tutoring the children of the Holy Roman Emperor. Sendivogius had come up with his Central Nitre Theory, and probably talked to Drebbel about it.

Sendivogius's theory revolved around saltpetre, or potassium nitrate. He said it was the food for life. You could feed plants with it, and if you heated it you got aerial nitre, which was food for people. He said that without this stuff 'no mortal can live, and without which nothing grows or is generated in this world'.

If we can believe that he used Sendivogius's aerial nitre, then Cornelis Drebbel was not only the first submariner, but also the first person to put oxygen gas to use. Unfortunately, alchemists were very secretive and Drebbel never told anyone what was in those jars. He died in November 1633 – in his only real source of income at the end of his life, a pub under London Bridge.

Nothing remains of Drebbel's submarine, but Eltham Palace is still worth a visit.

36 John Boyd Dunlop and the Pneumatic Tyre

This is the apparently straightforward story of the vet who transformed cycling comfort by ripping up one of his wife's old dresses, nailing it to a wooden disc and thus inventing the pneumatic tyre. Unfortunately, Dunlop's claim to this great invention turns out to be rather controversial.

John Boyd Dunlop was born on 5 February 1840 in Dreghorn in Scotland. He studied animal medicine, and went to Belfast to set up as a vet in 1869. For twenty years he ran a successful practice in Gloucester Street. He had a son, Johnny, who rode to school on a tricycle and liked to race with his friends. But the streets in Belfast were rough – they were made of cobbles, with tramlines crossing them, and in those days bicycle and tricycle tyres were made of solid rubber. Anyone who has tried solid tyres will confirm that it would have been most uncomfortable. Young Johnny complained that his bottom was sore.

His dad John Boyd wondered if he could smooth the ride by putting a cushion of air between the bike and the road, and he decided to build a prototype. Apparently he was for some reason or other used to handling and using rubber, so he got hold of a thin rubber tube and glued the ends together with rubber solution. To inflate the tyre, he incorporated a valve from a football, and so made himself an inner tube. The next challenge was to fix the tyre to the rim of the wheel, and he achieved this, and protected the delicate rubber tube, thanks to one of his wife's old dresses, which he ripped into strips and wrapped over the inner tube, nailing it into his prototype wooden wheel.

Then, rather brilliantly, he conducted a scientific test. He took his prototype wheel, and a similar one with a solid tyre, and rolled them along his cobbled back yard. The solid one soon fell over, but the pneumatic tyre rolled to the end and bounced off the back wall. So he made pneumatic tyres for the back wheels of Johnny's tricycle, and sent him off to school. The first field reports were highly favourable: Johnny could now beat his friends in races – and in comfort!

What was surprising was that the new tyre was not only more comfortable, it actually went faster. The reason the pneumatic tyre works so well is that the air cushion in effect irons out the little bumps in the road. Technically, it reduces the 'unsprung weight' to zero. When the solid wheel goes over a bump, the whole wheel (and thus the whole bike) is thrown into the air, which is uncomfortable for the rider and also uses energy. When the pneumatic tyre goes over the same bump, the tyre squashes a bit but doesn't rise. So you hardly feel a jolt, and although some energy is lost – and goes to heat the air inside the tube – it loses much less energy than is necessary to lift the bike and rider off the ground. The squishiness of the tyre does increase its rolling resistance, because every movement of the tyre on the road deforms the rubber – it's like riding up a very slight hill all the time – but you lose much less energy like this than you do if you have to lift the whole bike and rider on every bump.

John Boyd Dunlop thought there might be money in his tyre, so he demonstrated it to some Belfast businessmen, and then applied for a patent in July 1888. He got tyres made in Edinburgh, with bikes from Edlin and Co. in Belfast, who had made Johnny's tricycle. There were some real technical problems to be overcome, like getting special forks made to fit his chunky tyres. But the biggest problem was the macho attitude of cyclists; many serious cyclists thought only namby-pambies would ride on safety bicycles as opposed to the fast but deadly 'high bicycle' or penny-farthing, let alone on cushioned wheels. So Dunlop went straight to the top. Willie Hume, Captain of the Belfast Cruiser Cycle Club, had had a terrible fall from a penny-farthing so he rode safety bikes. Dunlop persuaded him not only to ride on pneumatic tyres but to enter a race with them. The great race happened on 18 May 1889, on the Queen's College playing fields. Everyone laughed at Willie Hume when he turned up on his inflatable tyres, but they stopped laughing when he won the race. Two of the losers in that race were the Du Cros brothers. They managed to get hold of bikes with pneumatic tyres, took them over to England, and in the summer of 1889 they won every race they were allowed to enter.

Their dad was William Harvey Du Cros, a Dublin paper merchant. He saw the potential for these tyres, and in 1896 he bought the business for three million pounds. After various deals and struggles it became the Dunlop Rubber Company, with the white-bearded portrait of John Boyd Dunlop as its logo. Tyres were at first still fixed to the rim of the wheel – conventionally spoked now, rather than wooden – by wrapping canvas impregnated with rubber solution round the inner tube and rim, permanently fixing the tyre. This skilled job was done by the company, so cycle manufacturers from England who wanted pneumatic tyres had to send men over on the ferry with bare rims to be fitted up. Dunlop himself took no part in the business, moving to Dublin where eventually he had an interest in a drapers. So although he lived comfortably, it was not Dunlop who made the real money from his invention.

This is where you have to be rather careful, because there is a dispute as to whether it is really 'his' invention at all. To the distress of the company, it turned out that Dunlop wasn't the first person to invent the pneumatic tyre; one had actually been patented forty-three years earlier by another Scot called Robert Thompson. So what are the facts? The titles of the patents reveal what the two men were trying to do. Thompson's patent is dated 10 December 1845, and is for 'An improvement in carriage wheels which is also applicable to other rolling bodies'. Dunlop's patent of 31 October 1888 is for 'An improvement in Tyres of wheels for bicycles, tricycles, or other road cars'. Thompson's wheels were big and heavy, intended for carriages. The problem was they were so cumbersome that the idea didn't catch on. In Dunlop's day the bicycle as we know it was just becoming available, and he saw this as the important area. Perhaps Thompson was just ahead of his time.

Both men described the use of a rubber tube encased in canvas, though only Dunlop specifies in detail how it is to be attached to the wheel, or how air is to be introduced (through a non-return valve). Thompson merely says that air is passed through a pipe 'fitted with an air-tight screw cap'; he doesn't say how you stop air escaping as you tighten it. In summary, the idea of a pneumatic tyre was clearly patented first by Thompson, although we have Dunlop to thank for the word 'pneumatic'. Dunlop thought of applying it to bicycles and other light vehicles, where Thompson had rather generally applied it to locomotives, carriages and other road vehicles. Dunlop subsequently modified his patent, to make it clear that he was claiming the method for making and using the tyre, not the idea of using air.

So Dunlop's invention looks a little tainted – especially if you believe the claim of some supporters of Thompson that the families actually knew each other in Scotland. But it seems unlikely Dunlop would have applied for a patent knowing that someone else had already taken one out – indeed you might have expected the Patent Office to have picked this up. In the end, it was Dunlop rather than Thompson who brought the world the pneumatic tyre, thanks in part to his sore-bottomed son.

The premises of John Boyd Dunlop's veterinary practice have become a car park, but the pneumatic tyre is everywhere.

37 Thomas Edmondson – Just the Ticket!

Some inventions look so obvious with the benefit of hindsight that it seems extraordinary that they took so long to appear. A good example is the printed railway ticket. Railways began to provide serious transport in the early 1830s, and to start with every ticket was written out on paper by hand and every passenger's name written down in a big book in the booking office. This was a laborious business, and for any complex journey distributing the money was a nightmare, since there were more than fifty different railway companies.

The breakthrough came in 1837 at Brampton, 12 miles east of Carlisle, where the railway station was built a mile and a half out of town so that it would not interfere with the horse trade. The man with the vision was the station-master, Thomas Edmondson.

Edmondson was born in Lancaster on 30 June 1792. He was always fiddling with things, and when he was a small boy his mother, seeing that he could never be kept out of mischief, taught him to knit so that he would at least be quiet and useful. Later he connected the baby's cradle to the butter churn, so that when anyone was making butter they rocked the baby at the same time. He became a cabinet-maker and went into business in Carlisle, but it failed, and he became bankrupt.

So at the age of forty-four he joined the Newcastle & Carlisle Railway and became station-master at Brampton – and had to suffer all the inefficiency of manual ticketing. One day, walking across a field, he had a vision: the process could be mechanised. Tickets could be printed for particular journeys, numbered, dated, and finally clipped when they'd been used. The whole system apparently came to him in one single flash of inspiration.

Unfortunately the Newcastle & Carlisle Railway said there would be no demand. Luckily for Edmondson – and us – in 1839 the brand new Manchester & Leeds Railway offered to double his salary if he would go and work for them and introduce his system. Within a few years it was in use not only throughout Britain but all over the world. And his system was so effective and so simple that it wasn't bettered for 150 years – until computers came along.

He did well from his invention, by patenting it and charging a royalty of 10*s* per mile per annum – in other words any railway company using his system paid him 10*s* a year for every mile of track; so if they had 30 miles of track they paid him £15 a year. And according to the history books 'he worked out his invention with skill and patience, enjoyed its honours with modesty, and dispensed its fruits with generosity'.

Trains still stop at Brampton Station, 12 miles east of Carlisle, although it now has neither buildings nor a stationmaster.

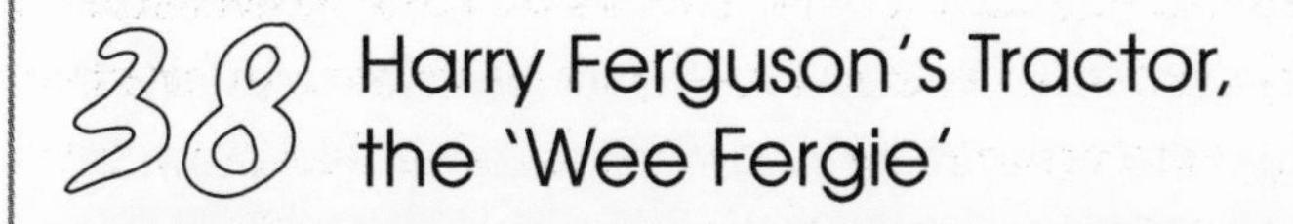

38 Harry Ferguson's Tractor, the 'Wee Fergie'

Some people become Local Heroes by a single shattering stroke of brilliance, others by a string of elegant theories. One Ulsterman will be remembered for neither of those reasons, but because for forty years he designed agricultural machinery better than anyone else in the world. His name was Harry Ferguson. He was born on 4 November 1884 in Growel, near Hillsborough, County Down, the fourth son in a family of eleven children. At the age of fourteen he went to work on the family farm. Later he went to Belfast to join his brother repairing cars and bikes. Then he caught the flying bug – Blériot had just flown across the Channel – and became the first man in Ireland to build his own plane, which he managed to fly on 31 December 1909.

In 1913 he started selling cars and tractors from May Street in Belfast, and it was there, in what is now a pub, that in 1917 he designed his first plough. It must have seemed a bit boring and down to earth – literally – after flying about in a plane, but this was where his fame and fortune lay. In 1916 there had been a desperate food shortage, and the Irish Board of Agriculture asked Ferguson to improve tractor ploughing methods, and increase productivity – and that is exactly what he did for the rest of his life!

He and his designer Willie Sands travelled extensively around Ireland demonstrating tractors to reluctant farmers, who thought they would never replace the horse. As a result Ferguson and Sands learned a great deal both about ploughing methods and about what types of tractors and ploughs were available. The tractors were great big monsters with simple tow-bars at the back. If you wanted to plough, you hitched your heavy plough on to the tow-bar, and pulled it across the field. Basically, the tractor was designed simply to replace the horse and pull things.

There were two major problems with this. First, you had little control over the depth of ploughing. The plough ran on its own wheels, and you had to preset the depth. It all had to be extremely heavy to keep the ploughshares down, and it simply sank in according to its weight and the softness of the ground, so your furrows would be much deeper in the softer bits of the field.

Because the plough was so heavy, the tractor needed tremendous power to pull it along, and the only way to get more power in soft ground was to make the tractor immensely heavy too. Many weighed more than 3 tons. As a result they were unwieldy and inefficient, and used masses of fuel just getting themselves about. Worse, the tractors and ploughs were dangerous. If your plough hit a large rock under the surface, the nose of the plough would dig in, the back wheels of the tractor would keep turning; the whole thing would jack-knife and the tractor would turn right over backwards. Many tractor drivers were killed in this way.

Harry realised that he could make the system much safer by using a three-point linkage. The main towing force was transmitted by two bottom links, as before, but he introduced a rigid top link. This solved both the previous problems. First, when the plough hit an obstacle it couldn't dig in, and the tractor couldn't tip over backwards, because the top bar prevented any jack-knife. All that happened was that the back wheels spun until they lost grip. Second, the driver could control the depth of the furrow with the top link. Extend it a bit, and it pushed the ploughshares down into the earth; pull it, and it lifted them nearer the surface. It was a really brilliant innovation, and formed the basis of what came to be called the Ferguson System.

Armed with this basic idea, Ferguson set about redesigning the whole mechanism. Instead of having a tractor and a whole lot of things to tow behind it, he thought of the tractor and plough as a single unit. There was no need to have wheels on the plough; just think of it as an extension of the tractor. He devised a hydraulic link to adjust the plough in mid-furrow, and he made both the tractor and the plough as light as possible – he got them down to about half the weight they had been before.

Harry Ferguson was a stickler for detail. Even in the early days he insisted that everything in the workshop had to be in exactly the right place. If even a single nut and bolt was misplaced then he refused to begin work. Vehicles in the garage had to be lined up precisely on chalk marks, and the whole premises were kept scrupulously clean. Every mechanic had to wear clean overalls, and would be reprimanded for not changing them during the day if they got dirty.

Later, he made all his employees carry pencil and paper at all times, in case they suddenly had a useful idea. The notebook had to be in the left jacket pocket, and the pencil within easy reach of the right hand. Ferguson often stopped people in the corridors and asked to see their notebooks.

In 1936 Harry Ferguson went into partnership with David Brown of Huddersfield, and 1,250 Brown-Ferguson tractors were built. However, Ferguson was stubborn and dogmatic, and Brown found him too difficult to work with, so the partnership broke up.

Ferguson went off to America and showed his tractor and plough to the king of cars, Henry Ford. In 1919 Ford had offered him a job, but Harry refused; Ferguson was not for hire. However, when he went back in 1939 they went into partnership, on an unwritten handshake agreement, and between 1939 and 1947, 300,000 Ford Ferguson tractors were built in Dearborn, Michigan. Every serious farmer had one, even President Franklin Delano Roosevelt. Unfortunately, when Henry Ford died, his grandson Henry Ford II refused to recognise the unwritten agreement, and cut Ferguson out. Ferguson sued him for $340 million. Four years and $3 million later, he accepted an out-of-court settlement of $9.25 million.

In 1946 Ferguson started making his own TE20 tractors in Coventry. This tractor, the 'Wee Fergie', was the most successful of all; in the next ten years, half a million were made. They became the basic piece of equipment on almost every farm in Britain – easy to drive and maintain, small enough to plough the tiniest field.

Ferguson insisted on simplicity in every aspect of his machines. Every bolt and nut and shaft on the Wee Fergies had a diameter of either $\frac{11}{16}$ in or $1\frac{1}{16}$ in. Each tractor was supplied with a spanner $\frac{11}{16}$ at one end and $1\frac{1}{16}$ at the other. The spanner was 10 inches long; this was the standard distance between furrows, so the farmer could use the length of the spanner to check his ploughshares. And the spanner was marked in inches and centimetres, so that among other things he could use it as an accurate dipstick to check the fuel – there was no other fuel gauge.

In 1953 Ferguson went into partnership with the Canadian firm Massey Harris to form the agricultural giant Massey-Ferguson. Massey-Ferguson tractors formed the basis of the Sno-cats that took Sir Edmund Hillary to the South Pole, and the company has been important ever since.

There's a twist in the tail of this tale. In 1948, wanting to promote his new TE20, Ferguson ordered some scale models from Nicholas Kove, who had just started using the first injection-moulding equipment to make plastic combs. Kove had no new materials – this was just after the war – so he made the model tractor bodies from old fountain pens, and the rubber tyres from the insulation taken from waste electrical cables. They came out in whatever colours had been available – red, cream, blue. Furthermore, Kove could not afford to assemble them, so he sent the tractors out in kit form. Nicholas Kove's company was called Airfix, and the Wee Fergie was the very first Airfix model.

Harry Ferguson summed up his philosophy in one sentence: 'Beauty in engineering is that which performs perfectly the function for which it was designed, and has no superfluous parts.'

He was a hero because he revolutionised world agriculture by application of simple scientific principles to the art of ploughing.

Wee Fergies are still used on thousands of farms, and perhaps the most fitting memorial to Harry Ferguson comes from Wales: in the Welsh language, the word for 'tractor' is *fergie*.

39 Robert Fitzroy, Inventor of the Weather Forecast

Most of us take the weather forecast for granted. It appears daily in the papers, hourly on the news, and on television it has its own cable channel. For most of us, predictions of tomorrow's weather are of mainly academic importance, but for farmers, pilots and fishermen, knowing the weather in advance is crucial. The first person to attempt systematic weather forecasting was Robert Fitzroy. He was a naval man, a brave and gallant sea-captain and a brilliant sailor but, as Charles Darwin discovered, he was a difficult man to live with, and he came to a tragic end.

Robert Fitzroy was born at Ampton Hall, a few miles north of Bury St Edmunds in Suffolk, on 5 July 1805 – three months before the battle of Trafalgar. He was the second son of the second son of the 3rd Duke of Grafton, and his mother died when he was five years old, so he probably had rather a tough and disciplinarian childhood. He went to naval college, and then to sea, and when he was only twenty-three the captain of his survey ship died, and Fitzroy was appointed to take command. The ship was the *Beagle*.

For her second voyage to South America in 1831 he decided he should take along a companion – some well-bred gentleman to share his day-cabin and to dine with. After much thought, he decided the right sort of person would be a scientist, who should bring on board culture and interesting conversation.

The *Beagle* was only 90 feet long and 24 feet wide, but carried a total crew of seventy-four, including a carpenter, a blacksmith, and a missionary. After a curious selection process Fitzroy offered the post of ship's naturalist to a young man called Charles Darwin, who jumped at the chance, even though his father objected at first, and the cabin was so small he could not stand upright in it. Neither of them knew the voyage would last five years, nor that Darwin would as a result of it write his wildly controversial book *On the Origin of Species.*

Fitzroy was neurotic and irascible, and sharing a cabin with him for five years must have been a considerable ordeal. Nevertheless, the voyage was a major success. When they returned, Fitzroy wrote an account of the voyage in two volumes; Darwin wrote a third volume which came to be called *The Voyage of the Beagle.*

In 1843 Fitzroy became Governor of New Zealand, but left under a cloud a couple of years later, and returned to England. His difficult character stood in the way of his landing a senior naval or diplomatic post, which is probably why in 1854 he took up the curious position of Head of the Meteorological Department of the Board of Trade. He was determined to make a success of the job, and a name for himself, and in 1861 he invented the weather forecast.

First he asked ships' captains, once they reached port, to post him details of the weather they had encountered. Then he saw the potential of the new electric telegraph, which would allow him to gather information much more rapidly and reliably. In order to ensure it was accurate and consistent, he set up twenty-four observing stations around the country, and issued each with a standard barometer and instructions on how to use it. Each day he compiled a summary in the form of a synoptic chart or weather map.

Every year in the early 1850s about a thousand ships were wrecked and some thousand lives lost near the British coast. At three in the morning on 26 October 1859 the sailing ship *Royal Charter* sank in a gale off Anglesey, with the loss of 400 lives and half a million pounds' worth of gold bullion. Fitzroy wrote a report about the disaster, and pointed out in words of one syllable that the storm could have been predicted at least twelve hours in advance using the information he had gathered. If the captain had been warned, he could have avoided the storm and saved the ship.

Fitzroy was therefore encouraged to issue storm warnings, and he invented a simple display system. A solid black cone point downwards – a 'south cone' – warned that a southerly gale was imminent; a 'north cone' – point up – warned of a northerly gale. These cones were used in every port, and provided useful warnings to sailors for more than a hundred years.

Encouraged by the success of his storm warnings, Fitzroy went further, and in August 1861 began to predict the weather. People knew a good deal about weather – for example, Cristoph Buys Ballot's Law said that if you stand with your back to the wind in the northern hemisphere then atmospheric pressure is lower on your left than on your right; and many 'experts' were happy to predict what they thought would happen locally the next day, but no one before Fitzroy had seriously tried to forecast the weather for the whole country. From 1862 his weather forecasts were printed in *The Times*.

They aroused considerable interest. The British have always been fascinated by weather, and when people saw forecasts in *The Times* they were amazed and delighted – except that the forecasts were often wrong. Today we are used to inaccurate weather forecasting. We know that even with the help of vast computers the meteorologists cannot be perfect, since the great engine of the atmosphere is too complex to be described by the models the forecasters use. Mathematical chaos ensures that the minutiae of meteorology will always be unpredictable.

However, in Fitzroy's day, people did not understand this, and he became the butt of terrible complaints and jokes. In 1864 questions about his forecasts were asked in the House of Commons. Even *The Times* said 'we must . . . demand to be held free of any responsibility for the too-common failures which attend these prognostications. During the last week Nature seems to have taken special pleasure in confounding the conjectures of science.'

As a fundamentalist Christian, Fitzroy had been seriously offended when Darwin's *Origin of Species* was published in 1859, since it seemed to suggest that God had not designed all creatures great and small – and it was all because he, Fitzroy, had taken Darwin on the *Beagle*. Now the most important people in the country, far from being impressed by his skill and ingenuity in predicting the weather, were pouring scorn on his incompetence. On 30 April 1865, Admiral Robert Fitzroy took his razor, cut his own throat, and died.

Fitzroy barometers are still preserved in a few maritime museums around the country.

40 Dennis Gabor and the Hologram

This book is a monument to ingenuity and invention. One of the intriguing aspects of the subject is how people have original ideas – specifically where and when their flashes of inspiration arrive. Sometimes the genius tells us, and the occasions are varied and curious. William Watts dreamed up how to make lead shot while lying in a stupor by his local church. Edward Berthon was sketching on Lake Geneva; Isaac Newton was allegedly sitting in his garden 'in contemplative mood', and there are many other examples. Perhaps the nearest we can get to a common set of conditions is that the person is doing something rather ordinary, something that takes time but little mental effort, so that the brain is free to roam. . . . The Greek scientist Archimedes had one of his brilliant ideas in the bath, and leapt out shouting 'Eureka!'. Unfortunately he was in the public bath in Syracuse, and he must have caused a few heads to turn as he ran home stark-naked. On the morning of

12 September 1933 Leo Szilard was waiting for the traffic lights to change so that he could cross Southampton Row on the corner of Russell Square in London. As he stepped off the kerb he suddenly realised, in a flash, how it might be possible to start a nuclear chain reaction, and so make atom bombs.

Dennis Gabor said he got most of his ideas while he was shaving, and he supposed that men with beards have fewer ideas, but the inspiration that won him the Nobel Prize came to him in 1947 while he was sitting at St Andrews Tennis Club in Rugby, waiting to play tennis with Winifred Smith. The previous players finished, and gathered their things. Miss Smith got up expectantly, but Dennis muttered something about having to check out an idea, and wandered off, leaving her without an opponent!

Gabor had just conceived the idea of the hologram – that a coherent light beam would carry three-dimensional information when it reflected from an object, and so in principle could produce a three-dimensional image. Unfortunately there was no practical coherent light source in 1947, so holograms could not be made until the laser was invented more than ten years later. Yet now we have holograms on every credit card, thanks to that flash of inspiration by a tennis court.

Every credit card hologram is a tribute to Dennis Gabor. St Andrews Tennis Club in Bilton Road, Rugby, is now a funeral parlour, but there is a plaque on his house at 47A Bilton Road.

George William Garrett's 'very nearly successful' Submarine

We were both intrigued and sympathetic when we first heard about a steam-powered submarine that was 'very nearly successful'. It was designed and built by an Irish vicar, George William Garrett.

Garrett was born in Dublin and went to Trinity College. He became a curate in Moss Side, Manchester, and later an honorary commander in the Turkish Navy – Pasha Garrett. But what endears him to us is that in 1878 he established the Garrett Submarine, Navigation, and Pneumatophore Company, and in 1879 he designed and built the world's first mechanical submarine – powered by steam. She was 45 feet long and carried a crew of three. The boiler was stoked while she was on the surface, and then the fires were damped down and she submerged, using diving rudders. In theory she could stay under water for four hours, and do 10 miles at two or three knots, using latent heat to supply power. Garrett had a dream that hundreds of his submarines would form a defensive ring around the British coastline.

The Navy recognized her potential, especially in view of the impending hostilities against the Russians. They offered Garrett £60,000 if the submarine passed marine trials in Portsmouth. So he organised a parish fête to raise funds, built his submarine, and launched her from Birkenhead. Unfortunately the weather was seriously bad and she ran into a storm off Rhyl in North Wales. The crew were taken off by lifeboat, and the submarine sank. She was called *Resurgam*, which is Latin for 'I will rise again' – but unfortunately she never did.

However, at Christmas 1995 divers found the submarine lying about 50 feet down on the seabed, with the hull intact and apparently in good condition. She has been declared a Maritime Treasure; so perhaps one day she will live up to her name.

Resurgam lies in 50 feet of water off North Wales.

42 George Green, the Mathematical Miller

In 1928 Albert Einstein sent a telegram to the University of Nottingham to commemorate the centenary of the publication of a remarkable essay in mathematical physics. Two years later, in June 1930, he visited Nottingham in person to give a public lecture in the evening, but during the afternoon he planned to go and pay homage at the grave of George Green, the author of the essay. Unfortunately he missed his train, and never saw the grave. However, he delivered his lecture to all the assembled ladies and gentlemen of Nottingham, on one of the hottest evenings of the year. Wearing full evening dress, Einstein spoke for two hours in German on General Relativity, which must have been unintelligible to almost the entire audience. So who was George Green, and why did his essay so impress Einstein?

George was born in Nottingham on 13 July 1793. At the age of eight he went to school, but eighteen months later he left, in order to join his dad in the bakery. In 1807 George's father decided to cut out the middle man, and make his own flour; so he built himself a windmill at Sneinton. It was one of the first brick mills in the area. Beautifully restored, Green's Mill is still making flour today.

A miller was employed to run the mill, and the miller's house was built on the side of the mill itself – the traces of plaster from the front room are still visible on the exterior brickwork. George was fourteen when the mill was built, and he probably played with the miller's daughter Jane, who was a few years younger. He never went any further to do his courting; George and Jane produced seven children, and are buried side by side in the churchyard below the mill. However, for some reason they were never married; perhaps his father threatened to disinherit him if he married the miller's daughter!

So George Green was comfortably established, with a partner and children and a prosperous business, but he wanted more; he wanted to leave his mark on the world. And so, astonishingly, he decided to become a mathematician! No one knows why he took this decision, nor how he got hold of the books, but apparently he went up to the top of the mill and studied mathematical textbooks 'in the hours stolen from my sleep', as he put it.

Most of the great advances in mathematics have been achieved by people in their late teens or early twenties; the barely adult brain appears to be the best cradle for brilliant steps forward in the most abstract of sciences. Newton, for example, made all his great discoveries in 1665–6, when he was aged twenty-three or twenty-four. There's a famous story of the 21-year-old French genius Evariste Galois, who discovered group theory; in 1832 he was challenged to a duel. He sat up the night before writing down his ideas on group theory so that they would not be lost, and died in the duel in the morning. Yet George Green left school at the age of nine and did not even start thinking about mathematics until he was in his thirties, so the fact that he discovered some astonishing new ideas is all the more remarkable.

As far as we know he had no colleagues or friends with whom he could discuss his notions, but in 1828 he wrote a long original paper with the snappy title *An essay on the application of mathematical analysis to the theories of electricity and magnetism.* He had this privately printed in Nottingham, and sold copies at 7*s* 6*d*. There were just fifty-one subscribers, mostly family and friends.

This slim volume almost sank without trace. No one heard about it in far-off Cambridge or London.

But luck was on George's side, for twenty years later a seventeen-year-old Irishman called William Thomson came across a reference to 'the ingenious essay by Mr Green of Nottingham', and managed to get hold of a copy the night before setting off for Paris. He read it on the stagecoach, with growing excitement, and told all his French physicist friends about its conclusions. They were stunned, for they discovered that this dusty essay had already solved several of the problems that were holding them up. In fact the essay could hardly have fallen into better hands; Thomson was himself a genius who made many advances in several branches of physics. He became Lord Kelvin, and was Professor of Natural Philosophy at the University of Glasgow for fifty-three years.

The gold in this essay lay in two nuggets, which came to be called Green's Functions and Green's Theorem. Green's Functions are a complicated mathematical trick that helps to make physics problems possible to solve, essentially by knocking off a dimension. Measuring the surface area of Australia on a three-dimensional globe would be difficult, but if you could knock off a dimension and measure it on a flat map it would be much easier. Green's Functions have been useful in the fields of gravity, superconductors, semiconductors, magnetism and many other branches of high-powered physics. That's why Einstein was so impressed. And these amazing ideas were conjured up by a middle-aged mill-owner, in the hours stolen from his sleep!

There's a science centre and coffee shop at George Green's windmill, which still makes flour at Sneinton, east Nottingham; open Wed–Sun, 10–5; 01602 503635.

43 Sarah Guppy's Tea and Toast

Dr William Oliver was an eminent physician who settled in Bath in 1725 and developed a rich and successful practice. He helped to build – and for many years ran – the Royal Mineral Water Hospital. During the course of his work he invented a biscuit with a special recipe as part of a diet he regularly prescribed. Before he died, on 17 March 1764, he gave the secret recipe for his biscuit to his coachman Atkins, along with £100 and ten sacks of the finest wheat flour. Atkins opened a shop on Green Street, marketed the biscuit as the Bath Oliver, and made a fortune. Buy a packet today, and you can see the portrait of Dr Oliver stamped on every biscuit.

Yet perhaps the most ambitious of the domestic inventors was Sarah Guppy of Bristol. Thomas Guppy was an iron founder, who was a colleague of Isambard Kingdom Brunel, and in particular cast for him the pipes for the South Devon atmospheric railway (*see* page 95). Tom's brother Samuel Guppy was a successful merchant with smart premises in Queen Square. He took out several patents for the manufacture of soap and nails, and it seems that his wife Sarah decided that this patenting business was good fun – and could be lucrative – so she had a go too, and altogether took out three patents.

Her first, in 1811, was ambitious; she patented the Suspension Bridge. Now suspension bridges had been built for some hundreds if not thousands of years – for example by the Incas in Peru – although the major suspension bridges in Britain, including the Menai Bridge, the Conwy Bridge, and the Clifton Suspension Bridge all came later. Presumably Telford and Brunel claimed earlier precedents and avoided paying Mrs Guppy for the right to use her ideas.

In 1831 – after her husband had died – Sarah Guppy patented an ingenious bedstead with special steps which slid out from below the sides of the bed; these both made climbing in and out easier, and prevented dust from gathering under the bed. But the bedstead also had 'a set of springs and rollers to be used for exercise when in bed'. Her idea seems to have been to do pull-ups without having to get up in the morning!

Her simplest and most alluring patent, however, was that of 1812, for 'Certain improvements in tea and coffee urns'. She is fairly precise about the construction; she makes her tea urn in any of the 'usual forms and constructions', but she cunningly modifies it with a simultaneous egg-boiler – a basket suspended from the lid so that the eggs sit in the water.

Her genius didn't end there, though, because in the lid of the urn she made 'an elegant and convenient support for a plate or dish or other vessel to contain toast or other article of food or refreshment'. In other words, Sarah Guppy's modified tea urn allows you to make tea and boiled eggs in one operation, and keeps your toast warm at the same time. How can we survive without one?

William Oliver's portrait hangs in the main staircase of the Royal Mineral Water Hospital in Bath, which he helped to build.

44 Goldsworthy Gurney: Bright Light, and Exhausting Hot Air

Candles and gas lamps produced a feeble, yellowish, flickering glow, just about bright enough to read by, but hardly enough to fill a large room with light. The first really bright light was invented by a Cornishman called Goldsworthy Gurney. He was an enterprising and energetic man, who was born on 14 February 1793 at Padstow, had a medical practice before he was twenty, married a farmer's daughter the next year, and moved to London in 1820. Thereafter he divided his time between London, where he could be part of Society, and the north Cornish seaside town of Bude, where in the early 1830s he built himself a castle. It's still there, standing on a concrete raft on a sand dune, close to where the canal empties on to the beach. Today it's the town hall.

Allegedly he lit the whole of his castle with a single central lamp, reflecting light into every room with carefully placed mirrors. This was clever, but what was really revolutionary was the light itself, for it was far brighter than any lamp had been before. Gurney achieved this by blowing oxygen into the flame, thus ensuring rapid and complete combustion of the fuel. In 1823 he had been awarded the Isis gold medal of the Royal Society of Arts for his invention of the oxygen-hydrogen blowpipe, and his 'Bude Light' was really just a practical extension of the same idea, though he did not patent it until 1839.

Bude Lights were used to brighten the streets of London – notably Trafalgar Square and Pall Mall – and in 1839 Gurney was invited to improve the lighting in the House of Commons. He did so in a dramatically simple way, by removing 280 candles, and replacing them with just three Bude Lights, which successfully lit the place for sixty years, until electricity came along around the turn of the century. But Gurney's bright thoughts went further than this, for in 1864 he wrote a paper outlining how seamen might identify lighthouses; he proposed that each lighthouse should have a Bude Light in a revolving frame, so that from anywhere out at sea it would flash on and off at regular intervals. By varying the number of flashes and the intervals between them, each lighthouse could have its own signature; thus a sailor who was sailing along the coast at night could quickly work out his exact position. Now, for example, the Eddystone Lighthouse shows two flashes every ten seconds, while the Bishop Rock Lighthouse shows two flashes every fifteen seconds.

Gurney's most spectacular invention – and the one that cost him most money – was the steam carriage. He had come up with the idea of the high-pressure steam jet, probably as yet another by-product of the oxygen-hydrogen jet, which greatly increased the efficiency of steam engines, and was apparently adopted by the Stephensons in their famous locomotives. Gurney, however, decided to use it to build a steam carriage, which he patented in 1825. He simply removed the horses from the front of an ordinary coach, and replaced them with a steam engine. At first he put the boiler under the passenger seats, but realised this might inspire terror, and in 1828 designed and built a Drag – a separate engine to pull the coach.

In 1826 he gave up his successful medical practice to develop the Gurney Steam Carriage Company, and in November 1827 *The Gentleman's Magazine* announced 'A steam-coach company is now making arrangements for stopping places on the line of road between London, Bath, and Bristol, which will occur every six or seven miles, where fresh fuel and water are to be supplied. There are fifteen coaches built.'

In 1829 Gurney was asked by the Quartermaster-General of the Army to lay on an official demonstration, in the shape of a journey from London to Bath and back. They set off at the dead of night on 27 July for what proved to be quite an adventure. After less than a mile, while crossing over a temporary bridge, they managed to collide with the Bristol mail-coach, and had to repair the damage in Reading. They were attacked by a Luddite mob in Melksham and had to cover the last few miles to Bath under guard. After four days' rest they returned home, completing the round trip at an average speed of 15 mph, much faster than the mail-coach. This was the first long journey at a maintained speed by any mechanised vehicle.

Two weeks later, on 12 August, the Duke of Wellington, then Prime Minister, asked for a demonstration in Hounslow Barracks, where the Drag first pulled the duke's carriage around the yard, and later a wagon carrying twenty-seven soldiers.

Sir Charles Dance started a regular steam carriage service between Cheltenham and Gloucester – covering the 9 miles four times a day – which ran for five months in 1831 until it was sabotaged by the mail-coach owners. However, despite this and other triumphs, the steam carriage failed to carry the day. The government decided to back the rapidly developing railways with an Exchequer Loan of £100,000, but rushed through a series of Turnpike Bills which put prohibitive tolls on horseless carriages. Gurney protested, and petitioned Parliament, but in 1832 his business failed; he had to abandon the whole thing, and lost £232,000.

One thing Gurney must have known as well as anyone was that politicians produce a great deal of hot air. In the 1850s MPs kept falling asleep, and in 1854 Gurney was appointed Inspector of Ventilation at the Houses of Parliament. He sorted them out with one of his steam jets, and went on to develop the Gurney Stove for warming and moisturizing air; it was used in many cathedrals.

His steam jets were also used to put out a fire in a coal mine at Clackmannan that had been burning for thirty years, and to clean out a revolting sewer at Friar Street.

In 1863 he was knighted by Queen Victoria, and in 1875 he died. His daughter, a fanatical supporter, donated a memorial chiming clock to the church at Poughill on the north side of Bude. It's a pretty stone church, with chickens in the graveyard, the nice blue clock on the tower, and a strong bell-ringing tradition. There's an excellent plaque inside the church above the door, describing with only slight exaggeration why he was a hero: 'His inventions and discoveries in steam and electricity rendered transport by land and sea so rapid that it became necessary for all England to keep uniform clock time.'

Goldsworthy Gurney's castle is now Bude Town Hall.

45 Joseph Aloysius Hansom and the Hansom Cab

You might have thought that a man whose invention becomes so well known that it takes his name would be a pretty good bet in business – think of the Duke of Wellington and his boots. But going into business with Joseph Aloysius Hansom, architect and inventor of the Hansom cab, would almost certainly have been a disaster.

Joseph Hansom was born in York on 26 October 1803, the son of a joiner. Although he worked in his father's business for a while, he showed enough promise as a designer for his articles of apprenticeship to be allowed to lapse, and he took out new ones with a firm of architects. He went to night school to improve his education, and was soon doing pretty well. He married and joined a firm in Halifax, where he first became enthusiastic about the Gothic style which became his trademark. A staunch Catholic, he specialised in churches.

His big break came in 1831, when he won the competition to design Birmingham's Town Hall. This should have been his moment of triumph, but it turned to disaster. As well as designing the town hall, he was contracted to build it, which he did in 1833 – but the terms of his contract meant that he personally had to stand bond for the builders.

Something went wrong, and he was declared bankrupt.

Hansom must have been a resilient character, because in the following year he applied to patent the 'Construction of Carriages'. In fact the carriages that appear in Patent 6733 aren't the ones you see in Sherlock Holmes films, with the driver at the back; those were modified carriages invented later, but the original safety cab was such a novel idea that the name of its inventor became attached to the more successful versions that followed. Hansom states his aim: that 'the wheels be of much larger dimensions, and the body parts of the carriages situated much nearer the ground, than has been hitherto conveniently possible'.

Not only was such a specification not 'conveniently possible', it was quite contradictory: if you make the wheels of a carriage bigger, the body will have to be further from the ground. Hansom got around this problem by dispensing with the axle and attaching the wheels instead to the sides of the body, which was strengthened for the purpose. He could then specify enormous wheels, which sailed smoothly over the rutted streets of London and other cities, and yet lower the centre of gravity of the carriage by setting the body closer to the ground, making it more stable than a conventional small-wheeled carriage. He also invented a wagon of a similar type, in which the whole body could be detached from the wheels – a forerunner of the container system used by lorries today.

There was a slight problem in Hansom's eyes: getting in and out. A conventional carriage was boarded from the side, but the Hansom's sides were entirely obscured by its huge wheels. In fact, it proved quite possible to arrange for access from the front, but Hansom had a more daring plan. In the patent he suggested that 'in certain cases the wheels be dispensed with altogether'. What he had in mind was not dragging the cabs around, but a new sort of wheel in which the centre remained stationary, and only the rim moved on roller bearings. In the centre of the wheel was a door, so that passengers actually entered the cab through the wheel. Not surprisingly, this more radical Hansom never caught on. But the basic design did, and Hansom sold it for £10,000. Not a penny of this was ever paid, as the firm got into difficulties. Eventually Hansom himself stepped in to sort things out, got the firm back into order and received a fee of £300 – the only money he was ever paid for his invention.

He turned instead to publishing, feeling that the building trade needed a journal. *The Builder* first came out in 1842, but there was not enough capital in the project and Hansom had to withdraw, taking a small fee from the publishers. He returned to architecture, and especially churches. His most famous are St Walburga's Church in Preston, Lancashire, with its 306 foot high spire, and Plymouth Cathedral, though there are many others all over Britain and also in Australia and South

America. Hansom died on 29 June 1882, a successful architect of the new Gothic style; but think how much more successful he would have been with a little more luck – or judgement – in business.

Hansom cabs are rare, but look out for his churches – and note the temple-like Birmingham Town Hall.

46 John Harrison's Marine Chronometers

A few miles from the southern end of the Humber Bridge stands an elegant house called Brocklesby Park, the home of the Earl of Yarborough. The stable block no longer holds many horses, but its little tower houses a magnificent clock, built in 1724 and still keeping perfect time today. The man who made it was a village carpenter called John Harrison.

Every part of the Brocklesby Park clock seems to embody a clever idea. The whole thing is made of wood, even the cogwheels. We would have expected them to be wearing out after 275 years of continuous running, but Harrison made the cogs of hardwood, with the grain running up each tooth for maximum strength, and there are several anti-friction mechanisms to avoid abrasion of the wood. The clock is a remarkable machine, and the man who built it was equally remarkable.

John Harrison was born in 1693 in a small village

on the Nostell Priory Estate near Wakefield in Yorkshire. His father Henry was a carpenter on the estate, and also repaired clocks. In 1700 the family moved to Barrow-upon-Humber, close to where the south end of the Humber Bridge is today. John helped in his father's workshop and became fascinated by machines on wheels. He was never able to express his ideas clearly in writing, but he was so interested in science that he borrowed a copy of the lecture notes on natural philosophy by Professor Nicholas Saunderson at Cambridge, and copied them all out, including the diagrams.

On 22 October 1707 there was a naval disaster. Admiral of the Fleet Sir Clowdisley Shovell, returning home from the Mediterranean, made a navigational mistake and in the middle of the night sailed full tilt into the Scilly Islands. Three ships were wrecked, 200 men drowned, and Sir Clowdisley himself, after staggering injured through the surf to the shore, was murdered by a woman for the ring on his finger.

Queen Anne was appalled that such an experienced seaman was unaware of his position. Her advisers explained that the problem was about longitude. When you are out of sight of land, finding out how far north or south you are – your latitude – is fairly easy as long as you occasionally see the sun or the stars. But finding out how far east or west you are – your longitude – was a difficult problem, and no one had yet found a solution.

So, in 1713, Queen Anne proclaimed a reward of £20,000 for anyone who could solve the problem of longitude or, more precisely, could find a method by which sailors could determine their east–west position to within 30 miles.

This was a massive amount of money, and dozens of suggestions were sent in, some of them more sensible than others.

One idea was to anchor a ship every 100 miles across the main oceans. Each of these ships would fire a cannon every day exactly at noon. Then any other ship within sight or hearing would be able to work out its position. Another suggestion was to supply each ship with a wounded dog. The bandage from the wound would be removed and kept on shore. At precisely noon every day some trusted person on shore would sprinkle on the bloody bandage a little of the famous 'powder of sympathy' discovered in the south of France by Sir Kenelm Digby, and the animal, feeling the psychic connection to its injury, would howl. Then the sailors would know exactly when it was noon in England. No one was quite sure whether this would work when the animal was thousands of miles away, and it was callously suggested that the animal might have to be wounded several times during the course of a long voyage.

The Astronomer Royal, Nevil Maskelyne, believed that the longitude problem would be solved by astronomy, using precise tables of the eclipsing of the moons of Jupiter, or some such data. Since he was a member of the Board of Longitude, whose duty it was to award the prize, the Board came to be rather biased in favour of an astronomical solution.

However, when word of the prize reached Barrow, John Harrison believed he could solve the problem with a simple clock, adapted for use at sea – a marine chronometer. His idea was to use time to measure longitude. Suppose your watch is set to Greenwich time. At noon the sun will be at its highest point in the sky. Now go across the Atlantic: at noon in New York the sun will again be at its highest point in the sky, but your watch won't say noon, it will say about five o'clock. In other words, when it's noon in New York it's five o'clock in London; thus, New York is five hours behind London. Or in other words, it takes that long for the sun to cross the Atlantic.

The sun takes twenty-four hours to go round the world, so New York is five twenty-fourths of the way round the world. Obviously that's one way of measuring how far west New York is from Greenwich. If you are navigating a ship, you need to be much more accurate than that, because if you were one minute wrong, then you'd be 17 miles out east or west; you could easily miss a small island – or crash into the Scillies. But by 1730 John Harrison reckoned he could make a clock that would be accurate to within one second a month, and with that he was sure he could win the prize.

He designed one in 1728 and took his drawings to London, but was advised to make a model to convince the Board of Longitude. So he went back to Barrow and started building. Seven years later he came back with a huge clock, standing about four feet high, with amazing springs bouncing out of the sides like arms.

He asked for a trial run, and the Board sent him on a voyage to Portugal and back, even though their own rules had specified the trials should take place on voyages to the West Indies. While he was in Portugal the captain died; the mate was delighted to have Harrison's assistance in navigation during the home voyage, and indeed Harrison's reckoning proved to be far the more precise. His clock was well within the precision required. However, the Board of Longitude said that because the same captain had not presided over both outward and inward voyages, and because the clock had not been to the West Indies, Harrison could have only £500.

In 1739 Harrison built a smaller and better clock, and in 1749 he produced a third, even more precise than the others. These came to be called H1, H2 and H3. He pressed the Board for further trials, but they prevaricated. Meanwhile he continued improving his machines, and in 1759 produced H4, which proved to be by far the most accurate clock in the world, and was small enough to hold in the palm of his hand. He was immensely proud of H4, and said

> Verily I may make bold to say, there is neither any mechanical or mathematical thing in the world that is more beautiful, or curious in texture, than this my watch, or timekeeper for longitude, and I heartily thank almighty God that I have lived so long as to in some measure complete it.

H4 was sent to Jamaica and back, and in four months lost less than two minutes, equivalent to 18 miles, but the Board still refused to pay. Harrison took it to Barbados, and throughout the voyage determined the longitude to within ten miles, but the Board still said he had not passed the test. He appealed to Parliament, and finally to King George III, who took his side and ordered his government to pay up.

John Harrison finally got his prize money in June 1773, when he was eighty years old, and had been working on the problem for fifty years. He died three years later. However, his skill lived on. A replica of H4 went on Captain Cook's third voyage around the world. Cook didn't survive the trip – he was murdered by a mob on a beach in Hawaii – but the chronometer came back less than a minute wrong after three years at sea! The problem of longitude – a deadly problem for sailors around the world – was solved by a brilliant village carpenter.

John Harrison's four clocks, H1–H4, are on display in the National Maritime Museum at Greenwich.

47 William Harvey's Bloody Revolution

In medical science great advances are rare, but one of the most dramatic discoveries of the last five hundred years was how blood circulates round the body. In the early 1600s, the world expert on blood-flow was the great Fabricius de Aquapendente, at the University of Padua. Fabricius had invented the Anatomy Theatre, where even students in the seventh row were only 25 feet from the cadaver being demonstrated.

Although Padua University was a centre of revolutionary scientific thinking, the up-to-date authority on the circulation of the blood was Galen, a Graeco-Roman physician who had worked in the second century AD – some 1,400 years earlier. No new theory had emerged. Part of the problem was that proper printing was only about a hundred years old, so ideas didn't travel quickly. It was also the done thing to celebrate classical authority, even though to a modern eye there was plenty of evidence to suggest that the doctrine of the ancients might sometimes be faulty.

There were two quite separate blood circulations, said Galen: the venous and the arterial. Venous blood was made in the liver and nourished the body. The blood constantly ebbed and flowed, being replenished by seeping through pores from the right to the left side of the heart. Generally, the blood moved out to the body during the day, and then was attracted back to the heart at night. The arterial circulation contained air from the lungs, which got rid of the heat from the heart, and was then breathed out.

Fabricius was interested in little lumps he could see in the veins; indeed he was credited with discovering them although in fact they had been known for some time. Since blood was supposed to be moving down the veins from the heart, what were these strange structures? He said their purpose was to restrict the flow and stop it reaching the extremities too quickly.

His students in the Anatomy Theatre included two young men – Galileo Galilei from Pisa and William Harvey from England. Galileo had done his experiments on falling bodies, but had not yet become famous over the moons of Jupiter. Harvey seems to have been born in Folkestone, Kent, in 1578, the twentieth year of the reign of Elizabeth I, probably on 1 April. His father was a merchant and had some inherited property, which made him wealthy enough to send William to the best local school, the King's School in Canterbury. We don't really know much about William's boyhood, but he may have already fixed on a medical career when he left school, because he enrolled in Caius College, Cambridge, founded by Dr John Caius, a distinguished but rather old-fashioned anatomist.

In 1599 he suffered a nasty attack of 'quartian ague', what we call malaria, which was then a common disease in the marshy Fens. He must have made a pretty good recovery, however, because the next year, 1600, he went to Padua to study with Fabricius. Perhaps being a student with the brilliant and radical Galileo helped Harvey to think the unthinkable – that his teacher Fabricius might have entirely the wrong explanations for the valves in the veins, the function of the heart and the working of the circulation.

Harvey was a man of great brilliance, but also of great courage, because he had the nerve to say that 1,400 years of scientific thinking were wrong. He realised that the whole theory was nonsense. He experimented with veins from animals, and found that valves didn't just slow down blood flow from the heart; they completely stopped it. There was no way blood could flow down the veins; their only purpose, he said, was to take blood towards the heart. He also said that the arterial system was filled not with air, but with blood.

Anyone might argue with anatomical interpretations, but it's pretty difficult to refute simple arithmetic, which was Harvey's next weapon. He had dissected many living creatures, and realised that the heart was a pump, and that in humans it ejected 2 oz of blood every beat, 60 times a minute. So how much blood would Galen's venous circulation have had in it? With each beat the heart pumps 2 oz; so in a minute, it pumps 3.6 litres –

about 6½ pints. Harvey worked out that in just half an hour 83 lb 4 oz of blood would be pumped out of the heart. The liver could not possibly generate all this blood, and anyhow there was no room for it in the body. His conclusion was clear: this was the same small amount of blood going round again and again.

Finally he worked it all out. The heart is a pump with two chambers. The left side sends blood to the body via the arteries. It comes back through the veins to the right side of the heart, which then pumps it round the lungs to get rid of carbon dioxide and take on more oxygen. The refreshed blood returns from the lungs to the left side of the heart, where the cycle begins again.

This was utterly different from the theory which had been accepted for 1,400 years, but after he published his book, as Harvey himself said, 'It will be very difficult for anyone to explain in any other way.' He began to explore these ideas in lectures from about 1616, and in 1628 finally published his great book, *Exertiato De Motu Cordis et Sanguinis in Animalibus: Anatomical Essay on the Motion of the Heart and Blood in Animals.*

Harvey lived almost to the age of eighty. He had a distinguished medical career, becoming chief physician at St Bartholomew's Hospital, physician extraordinary to James I and physician ordinary to Charles I. Although he was renowned in his own lifetime, we don't know much about his private life, although there is a famous letter from him revealing that his wife owned a talking parrot, and that he is reckoned to have been one of the first people to have become addicted to coffee!

Harvey was buried at Hempstead in Essex, not far from Saffron Walden, where there is not only a magnificent stone sarcophagus in the church but also forty-nine members of the Harvey family in the crypt below. The notorious highwayman Dick Turpin was baptised in the same church, and is reputed to have been born in the pub across the road.

William Harvey did much more than simply work out a few facts about the circulation. He was one of the first people to believe that argument and experiment were more important then ancient authority. He was a true founding father both of medical science and of modern scientific thinking.

Harvey was buried – above forty-nine other dead Harveys – in a fine marble sarcophagus in the church at Hempstead in Essex.

Frank Hornby, Inventor of Meccano

Frank Hornby was born in Liverpool on 15 May 1863 at 77 Copperas Hill Road, which is now opposite Lime Street station, and just behind the Adelphi Hotel. He became a book-keeper at a company that imported meat and livestock at 17 James Street. He married Clara Godefroy in 1887, and within three years they had two sons, Roland and Douglas. As the boys began to toddle Frank made toys for them, using his few tools and lots of determination, apparently inspired by Samuel Smiles's book, *Self Help*, which recounts tales of the heroic feats achieved against massive odds by great engineers and industrialists through hard work and dedication.

Gradually, as the boys grew, the toys became more complex; Frank and his sons constructed miniature bridges and trucks from tinplate, but for each new model they had to start from scratch. What Frank wanted was to find a way of changing them – that is, making a variety of toys from one box of materials. He realised he would need parts that were interchangeable, and during a train journey he dreamed up the idea of using perforated strips. He developed the notion, and came up with a half-inch wide strip of metal with a hole every half inch. Combined with small nuts and bolts, thick wire for axles, and simple brass wheels, this made a flexible system suitable for the construction of a vast range of mechanical models.

He patented his idea in 1901, having to borrow the £5 patent fee from his employer, David Elliott. He called the kit *Mechanics Made Easy*, and sold the first sets for 7*s* 6*d*. They contained eighteen pages of instructions explaining how to build twelve models, including the Eiffel Tower and various bridges and cranes. Also included in the first booklet were eight pages of Hornby's introduction to the system. He claimed, 'The aimlessness of an undeveloped fancy will give way to an organised method, and from confused, hazy ideas will spring order and precision.'

A model-building competition was announced in the magazine *Model Engineer* in October 1903 and held in January 1904. The first production factory was opened in 1907 at 10 Duke Street, Liverpool, and Frank changed the name to Meccano. The kits steadily grew as he added gears, pulleys, cranks and clockwork motors. They became increasingly popular, and by 1920 he had more than 1,200 employees. This made Frank a wealthy man and he bought a big house in Maghull, Quarry Brook. In 1920 he introduced Hornby 0-gauge model trains, and in 1934 Dinky toys; in fact, he provided the same sort of enthusiasm and inspiration for young engineers as Arthur Ransome did for young sailors. In 1931 Frank Hornby became MP for Everton.

Frank Hornby died on 21 September 1936, and although children now spend much more time sitting in front of computer and television screens than they do making models, Meccano is still among the best-known and best-loved constructional toys, after almost 100 years.

Frank's grand house at Maghull, Quarry Brook, is now a convent school, but his real memorial is the Meccano that he invented in 1900.

49 Henry Hunnings's Telephone Microphone

York is an old Roman city, a centre of learning – and just the sort of place I expected to find heroic pioneers. Furthermore, in Victorian times clergymen often dabbled in science; they were well educated and reasonably well paid, and they often had time on their hands. However, I was surprised to discover that a major advance in telecommunications was made in the tiny village of Bolton Percy, a few miles west of York, by the curate there – a man called Henry Hunnings. Life in small villages often revolved around the church, and as curate Henry Hunnings was involved in weddings, funerals, and vital decisions such as whether to prevent the sexton from buying oil for the bells without the sanction of the churchwarden.

Meanwhile in Boston, Massachusetts, an expatriate Scot called Alexander Graham Bell was working with deaf people, and trying to develop hearing aids, such as the system of *Visible Speech* invented by his father. As an extension of this work, he looked for ways to transmit speech along wires, and in 1875 invented the telephone.

Unfortunately it didn't work very well to begin with, because at both ends he had what we would call a speaker, and speakers aren't really sensitive enough for the voice; so he had to shout as loud as he could to be heard in the next room and, although exciting, it wasn't very practical. Then along came Thomas Alva Edison, possibly the greatest inventor of all time, who produced a mouthpiece made out of compressed soot (known as lampblack). Unfortunately that didn't work terribly well either.

At this point Henry Hunnings had a brilliant idea. We don't know how he knew about the telephone and the problems of getting speech into it, but he thought that maybe Edison should have used not soot, but bigger chunks of carbon. So Hunnings got hold of some charcoal and crushed it to make big granules. He put the granules between two thin metal plates or diaphragms to make a sandwich, and connected a battery across the two diaphragms. The idea was that the pressure of sound waves from the voice would push the diaphragms together and lower the electrical resistance, so more current would flow in the circuit.

That's the principle of the Hunnings microphone. The compressing of the chunks of carbon lowers the resistance, so that each bit of voice causes a pulse of current to flow in the circuit, and this can be sent as a signal along a wire. The weird thing is that anyone who knew anything about electricity couldn't possibly have invented this, because it seems to be obvious that no voice pressure could be high enough – you'd never shout loudly enough to be able to move those great chunks of carbon about. However, he was confident enough to patent his device in September 1878.

Hunnings tested his microphone on the telegraph wires between York and Darlington, and held a public demonstration of the 'micro-telephone' (price 15 guineas) at Cleveland Institute of Engineers, and it turned out to work extremely well. So well, in fact, that Alexander Graham Bell sued Hunnings – and lost. Eventually Bell bought the rights from Henry Hunnings for a thousand pounds. Not bad for a humble curate living in Bolton Percy.

And what an invention! The carbon-granule microphone remained in use until it was replaced by electronic systems in the 1980s; thus, in every telephone handset, the improbable genius of Henry Hunnings lived on for more than a hundred years.

If you have a little electrical meter you can easily make a model to see how the carbon-granule microphone works. First make a teaspoonful of carbon granules from a barbecue briquette (or artist's charcoal) by bashing it with a hammer. Lay a thin layer of granules on a 2p or 50p coin. Lay another coin on top. Make a circuit with a battery, the two coin-diaphragms, and the meter, set to measure current at its most sensitive setting. Then, while watching the meter, press on the top coin with your thumb, and see how the current increases with the pressure.

Bolton Percy is a pretty village with a lovely church, and a phone box within sight, but there is no plaque to commemorate the forgotten curate.

50 Charles Hutton and the Invention of Contour Lines

In 1774 Nevil Maskelyne went to Schiehallion in the highlands of Scotland and spent four uncomfortable months measuring the positions of observatories north and south of the mountain. Using Newton's idea of the Attraction of Mountains, he wanted to calculate the mass of the Earth (*see* page 217). Because this required some tricky calculations he went for help to a mathematician, Charles Hutton.

Born in Newcastle in 1737, Charles Hutton became a coal-miner, but was so bright that they made him a teacher, and then Professor of Mathematics at the Royal Military Academy in Woolwich. He wrote a paper in 1778 'On the force of exploded gunpowder and the velocities of balls'.

Maskelyne's surveyors had measured the altitude of dozens of points on the ground on and around Schiehallion, and Maskelyne wanted to know the size and shape of the mountain. Hutton reckoned that his first task was to represent the mountain on a flat map. He had the brilliant idea of joining together all the points of equal height; he wrote in his paper that he did this with a very faint pencil. The result was remarkable; he could see at once the shape of the mountain. Where the contours are close together the mountain is steep, and there is clearly a long ridge running along the top. Hutton's lines are what we now call contour lines.

To measure the volume of the mountain he imagined the whole thing was made of hundreds of thin vertical columns of rock; then he used his contour lines to estimate the height of each column, which allowed him to calculate the volume of the mountain. To work out its mass he assumed the whole thing had a density of 2.5 g/cm^3, the same as the surface rocks.

Hutton's calculations gave a value for the density of the Earth of 4.5 g/cm^3, and for the mass of the Earth as about 5,000,000,000,000,000,000,000 tonnes, which was within about 20 per cent of today's accepted value. This was the first measurement of the mass of the Earth; twenty years were to go by before anyone did it better; and meanwhile Charles Hutton had invented contour lines, which have been used on maps ever since.

Schiehallion is south-west of Tummel Bridge – GR 272754; a plaque by the picnic area on the small road north-east of the mountain describes the great event.

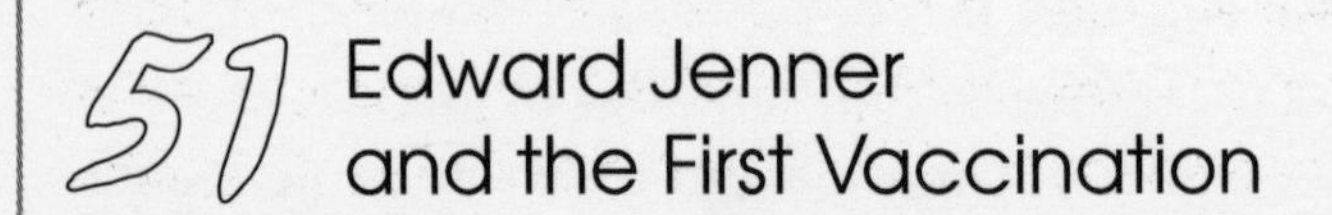

51 Edward Jenner and the First Vaccination

Finding out how diseases work and spread has always been difficult. Malaria was thought to be caught from bad air, which was why it was called by the name 'bad air' or malaria. Inventing useful treatments is even harder, and so I was surprised to find out that the killer disease smallpox was sorted out and dealt its death-blow before 1800, long before we had any effective plumbing or basic sanitation!

During the eighteenth century smallpox was a dreadful disease that almost everyone caught, and it killed one person in four; it was a worse killer then than cancer is today. It made millions blind, and those who didn't go blind got terrible scars on the face – the pockmarks from the pox. However, there was one group of people who never seemed to catch smallpox – milkmaids. These young women went around the farms milking the cows, and they were renowned for their prettiness; indeed it was enshrined in a popular song:

> Where are you going to, my pretty maid?
> I'm going a-milking, sir, she said.
> What is your fortune, my pretty maid?
> My face is my fortune, sir, she said.

One of the reasons they were so pretty is that their faces were not pockmarked, because they never seemed to catch smallpox. Most people thought this was just folklore, but some people took it seriously, and none more so than a young country doctor called Edward Jenner. He was born in Berkeley, in Gloucestershire, in 1749, studied medicine in London, and went back to be a doctor in his home town. For twelve years he was a medical journeyman – he had no permanent home, but rode about on his horse, staying either with his aunt or with any patient rich enough and willing to put him up for the night, and it was not until 1785 that he bought his own house, Chantry Cottage in Berkeley, for the princely sum of £600. It's now the Jenner Museum.

He was a scientist at heart, always asking questions. He was fascinated by hedgehogs, and measured their temperature when they were hibernating. He was also intrigued by cuckoos. He watched and described how the cuckoo chick pushed the rival chicks and eggs out of its nest. This work was so brilliant that he was elected to the Royal Society, and was invited to go round the world with Captain Cook. He didn't go; perhaps he wouldn't have enjoyed three years at sea. He was a bit of a dandy; he rode about Gloucestershire on horseback, complete with shiny black boots and silver spurs, and he certainly noticed how pretty the milkmaids were.

Jenner thought their apparent immunity was interesting, and started asking questions. The milkmaids told him that if they had caught cowpox, they would never get smallpox. Most people thought this was just an old wives' tale, but Jenner realized it might be a clue to saving the world from smallpox. Cowpox was a disease the cows sometimes caught; it produced nasty spots on their udders, and the milkmaids sometimes caught it, and got nasty sores on their hands. They usually felt ill for a day or two, but it wasn't serious. Jenner questioned milkmaids and doctors, and went on and on about his theory until he became a cowpox bore; so much so that he was banned from his local medical club.

People were so frightened of smallpox that many used to get themselves inoculated with it. That is, they were deliberately given smallpox. They knew they would get it only once, and they reckoned it was better to have it when they were fit and ready than if it came as a nasty surprise.

Jenner himself had been inoculated as a lad, and described the experience as really horrible. There were six weeks of preparation. He was bled to make sure his blood was fine; he was purged repeatedly until he became emaciated and feeble; he was kept on a diet, small in quantity . . . and so it went on. Then he was taken to an inoculation stable and 'haltered up with others in a terrible state of disease' – the whole thing was a nightmare, although he didn't see anyone actually die during his inoculation. However, there was a significant chance of dying simply from this inoculation, and Jenner was determined to stamp out the practice. His idea was that if cowpox protected the milkmaids, perhaps he could inoculate other people with cowpox, and that would protect them too. He suggested this to his friends and colleagues, and met with incredulity and disbelief. He was ridiculed – people thought they might turn into cows – and many doctors said he was mad.

The only way he could think of to prove his theory was by testing it. One problem was that cowpox was rare; the Gloucestershire farms suffered cases only every few years. But in 1796 a cow called Blossom got cowpox, and the milkmaid Sarah Nelmes caught cowpox via a cut in her hand. On 14 May Jenner carried out his critical experiment.

He chose a healthy young boy called James Phipps, eight years old, who had never had either smallpox or cowpox. He summoned the lad and the milkmaid into his study in Chantry Cottage, and with his little penknife he made two small cuts or scratches, about half an inch long, on James's arm. Then he squeezed some pus from Sarah Nelmes's cowpox sores, and rubbed it into the scratches. Sure enough, James caught cowpox. On the seventh day he complained of a sore arm, and on the ninth he became a little chilly, lost his appetite, and had a slight headache. But on the day following he was perfectly well.

Seven weeks later, on 1 July, James Phipps was deliberately inoculated with smallpox – but did not catch it. He was inoculated with the dreaded disease again and again, but never caught it. Indeed he lived to a ripe old age. And the fact that he failed to catch smallpox was critical. Jenner had his proof.

Jenner had managed to untangle three interlocked notions – first that the milkmaids' immunity was real, second that immunity against one disease – smallpox – could come from a different disease – cowpox – and third that cowpox germs could be collected from people – in this case the milkmaid Sarah Nelmes. You did not have to wait for the cows to come home. The Latin word for cow is vacca, and Jenner's technique came to be called 'vaccination'.

Jenner had to wait two years for another outbreak of cowpox, so that he could do some more experiments, and he had to wait for ten years before people really took note of what he had done. Meanwhile he built a rustic 'Temple of Vaccinia' in his garden, where he vaccinated the poor for free.

In the end he won due acknowledgement for his achievement. In 1806 he was given £20,000, in recognition of what was described as 'the most important discovery in the whole history of medicine'. By 1812 more than a million people had been vaccinated, and in 1978 the last case of smallpox was recorded in Somalia. As a result of the observations and deductions of a simple country doctor, the killer disease smallpox has been wiped off the face of the earth.

Jenner's House, Chantry Cottage in Berkeley, Gloucestershire, is now the Jenner Museum; open during the summer; 01453 810631.

52 John Mackereth's Pneumatic Bottom Corer

The Lake District is a strikingly beautiful area of Britain, with majestic hills separated by lovely lakes.

For decades the lakes have been used for recreation – they were the base for *Swallows and Amazons* and other Arthur Ransome sailing books. However, the lakes are also an important scientific resource, since they act as giant measuring and recording instruments. Flowing into Windermere, for example, are three rivers, and dozens of little streams. Together they bring down sediment from a catchment area of nearly 100 square miles. The mud on the bottom of the lake is formed partly from decaying aquatic plant and animal life, and leaves and insects that fall in, but mainly from all the silt that is carried down into the lake by these rivers. Each year a new layer is added to last year's sediment, until each year's mud is squashed down to a layer a fraction of a millimetre thick. So although the bottom of Windermere may look just like a sea of mud, in fact it's an ecological history book.

In order to read this book, ecologists need to take core samples. Essentially they push a hollow tube like a piece of drainpipe straight down into the mud, and then pull it up again with a core of mud inside. The mud is pushed out carefully on to a bit of guttering, and by looking along the core they can look back in time. Each part of this core carries a record of what has come off the hills in the years when it accumulated.

Look down about 14 inches, and this mud was laid down three hundred years ago – about the time of Isaac Newton. Go down 22 inches, and we're going back a thousand years – the Battle of Hastings.

A yard down, and it's almost three thousand years ago. Five yards down, and we're looking at the sediments of about fifteen thousand years ago, accumulated from the melting glaciers.

There are two clear discontinuities in the Windermere cores. There's a sharp change from pink mud to brown, which corresponds to the period when the glaciers finally disappeared from the Lake District some ten thousand years ago, and open tundra landscape gave way to trees and shrubs; after that there is more organic sediment, containing well-preserved remains of plants and animals. Then, towards the top of the sedimentary record, there is a rapid darkening, where the mud goes from brown to black. This happened between AD 1820 and 1850, when railways brought people into the area in ever larger numbers, and they began to pollute the lake with their sewage. But the lake has masses of other information locked away in its mud – the radioactive fallout from the nuclear weapons tests with a peak in 1963, for example, and from the Chernobyl explosion of 1986; both now used as markers to help date mud samples.

Over the decades many devices have been used to take core samples from lake beds, but one of the most spectacular and useful is the pneumatic corer invented by Frederic John Haines Mackereth. Born in Ambleside on 22 September 1921, he was educated at Windermere Grammar School. After gaining a chemistry degree from Manchester

University he spent a year in the Antarctic on a Norwegian whaler, but soon after the war he was back on the banks of Windermere.

One of the first things Mackereth did when he joined the staff of the Freshwater Biological Association (now the Institute of Freshwater Ecology) was to invent an instrument for measuring the concentration of oxygen in water. His gadget became the 'Dissolved Oxygen Meter', which is now the primary instrument that scientists use when they want to check the quality of water and the level of pollution. However, his most dramatic invention was the corer, designed in the late 1950s. The beauty of Mackereth's corer is that it needs little human effort, yet is able to collect an unbroken core 5 or 6 yards long and is light enough to be portable; so it can be taken to any lake where you can get a boat.

The corer is operated entirely by compressed air. The instrument is lowered to the bottom, and an air-lift pump used to pull the water out of the dustbin-like chamber, which forces it into the mud and clamps it to the lake bed. Then compressed air is pumped into the outer tube, forcing the inner tube over a fixed piston and down into the mud. When it reaches the end of its travel the air fills the chamber; the excess pressure lifts the seal off the bottom, and because the whole outer case is now buoyant with air it leaps out of the water like a huge salmon, and lands with a splash, the core safe inside the inner tube (which is in fact a piece of drainpipe). Then the corer can be towed back to land and the core pushed out of the tube for examination.

Only in recent decades have people realised what damage human beings can do to even the largest lakes. Even the land clearances of the earliest settlers enriched the lakes with woodland soil erosion; since then all sorts of sewage, fertilisers and other chemicals have been dumped in the lake. John Mackereth showed that lake sediment reflects the state of local soils, which were considerably enriched by all the minerals ground up by the glaciers. Mackereth also showed that magnetic particles in the lake mud can be measured, and line up with the Earth's magnetic field. Because the magnetic poles are always wandering around the true poles, the magnetism can be used to provide a check on the dates of the various layers.

So a big lake like Windermere provides scientists with a wonderfully sensitive instrument that both measures and records ecological history. And the best machine for collecting mud cores from deep lakes is the pneumatic corer invented by John Mackereth.

The Freshwater Biological Association is still at Ferry House, at the western end of the ferry-crossing from Ambleside.

53 Kirkpatrick MacMillan and the first Pedal-powered Bicycle

Courthill Smithy in the parish of Keir, about 14 miles from Dumfries, has more plaques on it than the average blacksmith's premises, and amazingly they all claim that right there Kirkpatrick MacMillan invented the bicycle. It is rather surprising to find that one person invented the bike, and more so that the invention came so late – in 1839, ten years after Stephenson's *Rocket* and thirty-five years after the first steam locomotives. What's more, tricycles were around in 1828 (*see* page 288). But did MacMillan really do it?

Kirkpatrick MacMillan was born in Keir in September 1812, and became a blacksmith like his dad. He probably went off to work on a neighbouring farm, got a job as a coachman, and at twenty-two became an assistant to the blacksmith of the Duke of Buccleuch. Eventually he returned to Courthill to assist his father and took over the business when his dad retired in 1851.

The story of the bicycle is a bit more complicated. Some people think it went like this: in Germany Karl von Drais had invented the hobbyhorse in 1817. It had no pedals, so you sat astride it and pushed with your feet on the ground and scooted along. This was a big craze for a few years, and it is quite possible that MacMillan saw one of these machines. Later, in the 1860s, pedal-driven bicycles were made by Michaux in Paris and were known as bone-shakers or velocipedes, depending on whether you were more impressed by their comfort or by their speed. The 'ordinary', high bicycle or penny-farthing came along in about 1870. But according to supporters of the Courthill blacksmith, Kirkpatrick MacMillan built the first powered bicycle much earlier, in 1839.

At this time the only bicycle around was the hobby-horse, and MacMillan's brilliant realisation was that it would actually be better to power the machine via some sort of mechanism, rather than using the feet directly on the ground. So MacMillan's machine was wooden like a hobbyhorse. It had wooden wheels with solid tyres but with a treadle-powered crank mechanism acting on the rear wheel. This consisted of two iron rods (he was an ironmonger, after all) hinged from just below the handlebar, one on each side. At the bottom of the rods were the pedals, which in turn were connected to the rear wheel cranks by a second pair of iron rods.

Riding it feels pretty peculiar to someone used to a modern bike – it's more like a foot-powered sewing machine. You have to get it rolling, and then push the pedals forwards, away from you, rather than downwards. It feels very heavy and steering is quite difficult because the cranks restrict the movement of the front wheel. Apparently the original machine weighed half a hundredweight, but in spite of this MacMillan frequently rode into Dumfries in less than an hour, which is impressive, to say the least. But it is without question a powered bicycle.

The critics say it is not the precursor of the modern bike. Drive to the back wheels didn't come into serious use for another forty years, and the treadles were a blind alley. However, we are used to pioneers who were ahead of their time. The more serious question concerns the evidence. And there isn't much evidence that MacMillan really built and rode such a machine – except a wonderful article in the *Glasgow Argus* of 1842 which reports that a gentleman of Dumfriesshire had ridden a velocipede 40 miles from Old Cumnock to Glasgow in five hours, and there among a crowd of spectators had mounted the pavement and knocked over a small child. Luckily the child was unhurt and the gentleman was fined only five shillings.

Unfortunately the article does not mention MacMillan by name, nor does it say that the velocipede was a bicycle, and by the social standards of the day he was not a gentleman. And it does say the wheels were turned by *hand*. On the other hand, in the area round Courthill, MacMillan's claim is recognised.

He didn't bother to patent the design and indeed seems to have done little with it, but others saw his bike, copied it and sold the copies for £6 or £7. Apparently Gavin Dalzell of Lesmahagow copied the

MacMillan machine in 1846, and his design became so well known that for years *he* was regarded as the inventor of the bicycle! So there is some controversy about who actually invented the bicycle. If it was Kirkpatrick MacMillan, the blacksmith of Courthill, he should surely be saluted as a mechanical genius who in the age of steam was the first to harness human power in a vehicle.

Courthill Smithy is now a private house, albeit with plaques on the wall. It stands a few miles south-west of Thornhill. There is a replica of the MacMillan bike in the Bicycle Museum, Drumlanrig Castle.

54 Margaret McMillan and the Invention of School Dinners

Green Lane First School in Bradford deserves recognition as an important historic site, because it was there that the first real school dinners were cooked and served in 1907.

Margaret McMillan was born in New York of Scottish parents on 20 July 1860, and later moved to England and into politics; in 1889 she began voluntary work for the Labour Party; in 1893 she went to Bradford to campaign for the Labour Party. The first thing she saw was the terrible state of the children; they looked puny, underfed and ill. Lord Shaftesbury had said the children of Bradford were so deformed they looked like the letters of the alphabet, although he didn't say which letters! Margaret McMillan spotted that this was good political territory and started her 'fight for the slum child'.

Her first campaign was to get the children clean, since many didn't change their clothes for seven or eight months. After much arguing she got the first school baths opened in Wapping Street School in 1897.

Poor people in Bradford usually sent their children to school in the morning without giving them any breakfast, and since there was no dinner at school the kids got hungrier and hungrier all day. Margaret was sure that lack of food and poor health were connected, and she persuaded Parliament to pass the Education (Provision of Meals) Act in 1906. As a result, the country's first school canteen opened in Green Lane on 28 October 1907, and was soon making nutritious meals not only for the Green Lane children but also for children in other schools all over Bradford.

For their school dinners today the Green Lane children get mainly Asian food – curries, samosas, and so on – because many of them are Asian. Ninety years ago they had not just dinner, but three meals a day. For breakfast they were given oatmeal porridge, probably with treacle, and bread and dripping. In the middle of the day they had stew and a sticky pudding, and then at teatime there was a slice of bread and margarine, and a cup of tea.

Margaret McMillan, once called 'Labour Prophetess of the North', died on 29 March 1931. She was a splendid campaigner and pioneer; she started the first nursery schools in Bradford, the first school medical inspections, and the first school baths, but best of all she started school dinners. In particular I remember her for the bread and dripping – I used to love it when I was at primary school.

Green Lane First School is flourishing, and the food there is delicious. Few people in the country can have escaped the gastronomic delights of school dinners!

55 George Manby and his Mortars

George William Manby (1765–1854) lived much of his life in the shadow of England's greatest maritime hero, Horatio Nelson, who had attended the same school as Manby in Downham Market, Norfolk. Manby claimed great intimacy with Nelson, but the dates don't quite add up – Manby was only five years old when Nelson, aged twelve, went off to sea, so in fact they can scarcely have known one another.

Although Manby spent most of his working life as a soldier, he was also an author, and he turned to literature when unspecified 'domestic troubles' caused him and his new wife to leave Denver in Norfolk, where he had been born, and move abruptly to Bristol. Most of his writing consisted of travel guides, but in 1803 he wrote a pamphlet entitled 'An Englishman's Reflexions on the Author of the Present Disturbances', in which he discussed the threatened invasion of England by Napoleon. This work attracted the notice of Charles Yorke, then Secretary at War, and in August 1803 Manby was appointed barrack-master at Yarmouth. It was there that Manby witnessed the dramatic and horrifying spectacle that was to change his life.

In February 1807 there was a great storm off the east coast, and a gun brig, the *Snipe*, went aground off Yarmouth. As usual word soon went around that a ship was wrecked, and people rushed to the spot. The *Snipe* was just 60 yards off shore, and was being smashed to pieces by the fierce wind and waves driving in from the east. Her passenger list included French prisoners of war, and many women and children. Although some escaped, sixty-seven people, including the captain, were drowned. All this happened within sight of Manby and the crowd on shore – but they were quite unable to do anything about it. Altogether that day a further 147 bodies were picked up along the coast. You can imagine Manby's horror, made worse by the feeling of impotence at having been so near and so unable to help. Incredibly, this was a far from uncommon incident. Manby resolved to make sure it couldn't happen again.

It is easy to see how disaster could strike a ship going aground in some remote location, but less easy to see why the *Snipe* and unfortunate vessels like it should be doomed to disaster so close to people who should have been able to help. The answer lies in the nature of ships and of storms. Sailing ships use their sails in two ways, like parachutes when 'running' with the wind behind them, or like wings to provide lift when the wind is in front. But the wing works only when it makes an angle with the wind, and so no ship can sail directly into the wind – it has to 'tack' back and forth at an angle to the wind to get the best out of its sails. So if a ship is driven on to rocks by an on-shore gale – where the wind blows from the sea directly on to the shore – it is truly helpless and thus doomed.

The ship cannot sail off again, because that would mean sailing directly into the wind – which is impossible. Worse, no would-be rescuers can sail in behind the wrecked ship, since they would be certain to end up the same way. The same problem affected the people on land: it was impossible to get a line out to the ship as this would mean throwing it into the teeth of the gale. Which is how sixty-seven lives came to be lost within 60 yards of the shore.

Manby's invention was inspired by a boyhood prank in which he had fired a rope over the roof of the church at Downham. He got hold of a mortar, essentially a small stubby cannon, and started experimenting. The mortar fired an iron ball about 2½ inches in diameter, to which a rope was attached; it had to be able to travel, with its rope, at least a couple of hundred yards if it was to do any good. The kick to do this came from the gunpowder charge in the mortar, and was so violent and explosive that the rope often broke or was burned. Manby tried using a chain between ball and rope, but the chain snapped. Eventually he settled on a leather strap attached to the ball, which absorbed some of the shock and didn't burn. He demonstrated his invention to the Suffolk Humane Society in the autumn of 1807. The first real trial came on 12 February 1808, when it was used successfully at the wreck of the brig *Elizabeth*. Soon after this, mortar kits, designed to be quickly carried to the scene of a disaster, were issued to coastguard stations up and down the country, with 302 sets eventually in place. Manby was awarded the very substantial sum of £2000 – pretty generous at a time when the price of a pint of beer was tuppence.

Manby's system is credited with saving hundreds of lives, and you might have thought he would have died happy. Following the mortar, he invented numerous other life-saving devices including the fire-extinguisher, a lifeboat, a jumping-sheet (for catching people leaping from burning buildings) and a device for rescuing people who had fallen through ice. All these were described in pamphlets published by Manby himself, but none met with the success of the mortar. Meanwhile, Manby's private life took a turn for the worse. He got into a fight with his wife's lover, which resulted in his being shot in the back of the head. He recovered, following an operation to remove from his skull the bullets and bits of his hat, and he carried these grisly souvenirs with him in a small box for the rest of his life.

Despite the money and acclaim, Manby ended his life in service to Nelson; he ran and lived in a museum dedicated to him at Yarmouth.

56 William Marwood's Long Drop

Before 1875 a prisoner sentenced to death was hanged by being suspended on a rope and allowed to die slowly by strangulation. This barbaric procedure was changed by William Marwood, who worked out how to break the victim's neck, causing instant death.

Marwood was a Lincolnshire cobbler, with premises at 6 Church Street, Horncastle. Over several years he repeatedly applied for permission to act as hangman, and was finally given his first commission in 1875, when on 21 December he hanged Henry Wainwright in Lincoln gaol.

Marwood did not hide this part-time profession. He used to go to fairs and show off his ropes for sixpence a time. He put up a big sign above his shop, and he charged high prices for his bootlaces; people came from miles around and bought them because they were the hangman's laces. He became famous, and was frequently mentioned in music-hall songs and jokes, such as 'If pa killed ma, who'd kill pa?' Answer: 'Marwood.'

Before Marwood, death was slow and painful: the pressure of the rope crushed the windpipe, cutting off the supply of air to the lungs. A typical victim lost consciousness after three or four agonising minutes, and died after about ten. Marwood's idea was to use a long rope and a trap-door high up on a scaffold, so that when the trap was opened, the victim fell seven or eight feet before reaching the end of the rope. Marwood tied the rope snugly tight, with the knot at the point of the jaw under the victim's left ear. This ensured that when the rope tautened it snapped the head back, causing a fracture dislocation of the atlanto-axial junction. The top vertebra, the 'atlas', sits on the second one, the 'axis'. A peg of bone sticks up from the axis into a socket in the atlas, and allows the head to swivel. Put your fingers to the back of your neck, and you can feel the atlas turn with your head, while the axis below does not move. When the head is snapped back by the long drop, the peg breaks, the neck kinks rapidly, the spinal cord is crushed, and the resulting spinal shock causes instant loss of consciousness, even before the heart stops beating. Because it caused immediate brain death, Marwood's long drop was more humane that the previous method; he used to say of his predecessors, 'They hanged 'em; I execute 'em.'

Marwood's shop is marked by a plaque at 6 Church Lane, Horncastle, Lincolnshire; it is now part of the next house.

57 Nevil Maskelyne Weighs the World

For thousands of years philosophers had wondered about the size of the world we live on. At about the end of the seventeenth century the radius of the Earth was calculated fairly accurately; it turned out to be about 8,000 miles or 13,000 kilometres – in strikingly good agreement with the size calculated by the Greek scientist, Eratosthenes, two thousand years earlier! The next question was, how massive is it?, or in other words, what is the density of the Earth? Is it made of the same sort of rocks all the way through, or does it, as some people suggested, have a hollow core? The first person to measure the mass of the Earth was Nevil Maskelyne, and his method was based on Newton's idea of the Attraction of Mountains.

In his famous book *Principia* of 1687 Newton said that if his law of gravitation was right, then on level ground a plumb-bob would hang straight down, vertically, because it would be pulled towards the centre of the Earth. However, if there was a mountain nearby, it would hang slightly sideways, because it would be attracted by the mountain as well as by the Earth. This idea came to be called the Attraction of Mountains. Most people thought the Attraction of Mountains was just a nuisance, because it prevented them from measuring an accurate vertical in mountainous places, but in 1772 the Astronomer Royal, Nevil Maskelyne, had a clever idea, which was to use the Attraction of Mountains to do two things – first to check Newton's prediction about the Law of Gravitation, and secondly, to weigh the world – or, more accurately, to measure the mass of the Earth.

Nevil Maskelyne was born on 6 October 1732, went to Westminster School and Trinity College, Cambridge, and became an astronomer after seeing an eclipse of the sun when he was sixteen. He was highly successful; he was sent to observe the Transit of Venus from St Helena in 1761, and he became Astronomer Royal in 1765. He suggested to the Royal Society the idea of an experiment to measure the mass of the Earth, and they were full of enthusiasm.

Charles Mason had just come back from surveying the Mason–Dixon line in America – this was the boundary between Maryland and Pennsylvania, or in other words it separated the land of slavery from the land of the free. Mason was sent off, at half a guinea a day plus expenses, to tour the highlands of Scotland on horseback to find a suitable mountain. After a long journey he recommended one north of Perth, which the lowlanders called Maiden-pap, but the locals called Schiehallion. It was large and symmetrical, and there were no other mountains close by; so the plumb-bob would be attracted only by Schiehallion.

The Royal Society then asked Mason to carry out the experiment itself, but even though they offered to double his pay to a guinea a day, he refused; perhaps he'd had enough of the highland weather. So the Royal Society went back to Maskelyne, and asked him to do it. He was not keen – he certainly didn't feel the Attraction of Mountains – and said he couldn't possibly go without permission from the King, but unfortunately the King said 'Go ahead.' So reluctantly he sent his assistant ahead with all the gear, and then followed, by ship from the Thames to the Tay, and about 45 miles on horseback into the mountains. At the end of June 1774 he reached Schiehallion.

First Maskelyne set up an observatory on the south slopes of the mountain. He had a 17-foot high parallelepiped tent of painted canvas that he had found in the basement of the Royal Society. Here he set up his equipment – a 'zenith sector' – basically a telescope fixed in the north–south plane, and a plumb-bob. He had plenty of time to get organised. The weather was so bad that three weeks went by before he could make a single observation, but finally, on 20 July, he was able to begin. His plan was to observe a number of chosen stars as each one crossed the meridian. So he lay on the ground, lined up his telescope precisely on each star in turn, and measured how far it was from the 'vertical' as shown by the plumb-bob. Because the plumb-bob was attracted by the mountain the angles were all slightly ‘wrong’, so he expected his observations to suggest he was a bit further south than his true position.

After six weeks he shifted camp to the north slopes of the mountain – the move took twelve men a week! – set up his bothy and observatory, and observed the same stars again. This time he expected the observations to suggest he was further north than he really was. From his observations, he knew he could work out the apparent difference in latitude between the two observatories – in other words, how far the northern one seemed to be north of the southern one. Meanwhile a team of surveyors had been squelching round through the heather with theodolites and chains, working out how far apart the observatories actually were, and also the exact shape and volume of the mountain.

Nevil Maskelyne spent four months on Schiehallion, and made 337 observations of forty-three different stars. When he finished his work, at the end of October, he held a party in his bothy both to celebrate and to thank the surveyors and the locals who had helped. It must have been quite a party, for a keg of whisky was consumed; the bothy caught fire, and the local fiddler’s violin was burned; Maskelyne sent him another from London.

On 6 July 1775 Maskelyne presented the Royal Society with the results. The real difference in latitude of the two observatories was almost exactly 1 mile; but from his observations he had calculated the distance to be 1 mile 480 yards. So there was a discrepancy of 480 yards. In other words, by the tiniest amount, the plumb-bob had indeed felt the attraction of the mountain. So Newton had been right – his theory of gravitation was confirmed – and Maskelyne was awarded the Copley Medal for his heroic experiment.

But what did his result tell them about the Earth? To work out the answer they hired a mathematician called Charles Hutton (*see* page 195). Hutton's calculations gave a value for the density of the Earth of 4.5 grams per cubic centimetre, and the mass of the Earth as about 5×10^{21} tonnes – that is five thousand million million million tonnes. In fact Newton had guessed a slightly more accurate value, and we now reckon it has a density of about 5.5 g/cm^3, and a mass of 6.6×10^{21} tonnes. However, Maskelyne's was the first measurement of the mass of the Earth; it was within about 20 per cent; and twenty years were to go by before anyone did it better. What's more, because relative masses had already been calculated, this single measured figure allowed Maskelyne and Hutton to work out the masses of the Moon, the Sun, and all the other planets in the solar system!

And the result did clear up one major dispute. Many people thought the Earth was hollow, but Maskelyne and Hutton utterly disproved that – indeed they suggested the Earth's core was very dense, and might even be made of metal. This was a triumph for the application of pure science and the Attraction of Mountains.

Schiehallion is south-west of Tummel Bridge – GR 272754; a plaque by the picnic area on the small road north-east of the mountain describes the great event.

58 John Metcalfe – 'Blind Jack' of Knaresborough

John Metcalfe, better known as 'Blind Jack', is buried in the pretty graveyard at Spofforth, near Wetherby in North Yorkshire. The gravestone carries a terrific heroic tribute, which begins:

> Here lies John Metcalfe
> One whose infant sight
> Felt the dark pressure of an endless night
> Yet such the fervour of his dauntless mind
> His limbs full sprung, his spirit unconfined
> That long ere yet life's bolder years began
> His sightless efforts marked the aspiring man.

It seems a bit over the top, but if ever a pioneer deserved to be called a hero, Blind Jack was that man. His ingenuity was matched by his personal bravery. Metcalfe was born in Knaresborough in 1717. When he was just six he caught smallpox and went completely blind. But he didn't let this stop him doing what all small boys do – climbing trees, leading apple-raiding expeditions in local orchards, learning to swim and even to dive. On one occasion at the High Bridge over the River Nidd in Knaresborough two men fell into the river. They sent for Blind Jack who dived again and again into the black water. One man was swept away, but on Jack's fourth dive he brought the other to the surface – sadly too late, as he had already drowned.

But Blind Jack was inventive as well as courageous and he became the first scientific builder of roads. In the 1750s the roads were scandalously bad. Although it is only 20 miles from Leeds to York, the journey by stagecoach could take eight hours; to get there for lunch you had to leave at four o'clock in the morning! On one occasion, Jack was in London and met his patron Colonel Lidell. The colonel kindly offered Jack a ride back to Harrogate in his coach, but Jack declined, claiming he couldn't afford the time. So they both set off for Yorkshire, the colonel in his coach and Jack on foot. Being completely blind, and having never walked the route before, Jack got seriously lost twice. It took him six days to walk home; the colonel in his coach took eight. So in 1765 Blind Jack decided there might be a future in building really good roads.

Clearly the difficult roads were the ones through boggy ground, and these were the ones Blind Jack tackled. Previously, road-makers either had to build roads around the bogs or, if that wasn't possible, they would dig the bog out. Unfortunately, this meant that the new road was lower than the surrounding wet ground and it acted as a drain. Jack invented a new system of floating the roads on rafts. First, he would dig trenches on either side of the proposed route, heaping the material dug out into the middle where it would dry out. He then collected heather for his raft, layering the twigs of heather first down the length of the road, then across. Finally he would put the stone roadway on top. Jack's attempt to build a road from Huddersfield to Saddleworth across the top of the Pennines became a public event. He employed up to 400 people, and crowds gathered to watch, confident that when the road opened the horses would sink into the mire. Instead they sailed across, and that stretch was the driest part of the road, working without repair for twelve years.

Although the roads themselves have now been overgrown, you can follow the routes Blind Jack laid over the Pennines, and at Devil's Clough near Marsden one of his wonderful dry-stone bridges survives. Jack's involvement in the roads was total: even though he couldn't see where he was going he surveyed the routes himself, a solitary figure 6 foot 2 inches tall and equipped with just a measuring wheel and stick. Yet he was able to describe in remarkable detail the routes he had planned, and the types of soil the road would pass over. In all he made 180 miles of road, earning £65,000.

Blind Jack led a pretty exciting life – eloping with a publican's daughter on the eve of her wedding, acting as recruiting officer on the king's side during the 1745 rebellion, smuggling, and earning money as a wonderful roving fiddle-player. Almost beyond belief were his horse-riding skills which he matched with his knack as a gambler to make quite a lot of money. He once bet that he could ride an unbroken horse at full gallop for 200 yards, and then bring it to a complete stop within 50. Naturally punters happily bet against this unlikely boast but Blind Jack had a brilliant plan. He took the horse to a bog, paced out 200 yards, pointed the horse towards the bog and let it loose. As he had promised it galloped for 200 yards and then came to an immediate stop in the bog, whence it had to be hauled out by rope.

There was an annual race in Knaresborough forest which involved riding round a circular 3-mile course marked by posts – not the most obvious challenge for a blind man. Again heavily bet against, Jack persuaded friends to stand by each post with a dinner bell. Jack was able to win the race by riding towards the sound of each bell in turn. Despite his spectacularly dangerous hobbies, Jack lived to be ninety-three, and left behind ninety great grandchildren.

You will find Blind Jack's gravestone in Spofforth churchyard.

59 John Michell and Black Holes

In the latter part of the eighteenth century the centre of scientific debate in the north of England was the Rectory at Thornhill, near Dewsbury in Yorkshire. The rector was the remarkable John Michell, who at the age of thirty-seven had retired from being Professor of Geology at Cambridge, where he also lectured on arithmetic, geometry, theology, philosophy, Hebrew and Greek. He used to hold entertainments for such friends as Joseph Priestley, discoverer of oxygen, John Smeaton, the engineer, Henry Cavendish, the silent physicist, and itinerant German musician, William Herschel, to whom he gave his telescope; Herschel went on to become a great astronomer.

Most people think black holes were invented by Stephen Hawking, or Albert Einstein. Not so. In 1783 Michell wrote to the Royal Society imagining a heavenly body five hundred times more massive than the Sun. An object falling towards it, he said, would eventually fall faster than light. In other words even light could not escape. John Michell was describing the black hole.

Towards the end of his life he devised a clever way of measuring the mass of the Earth. He fixed a small lead ball on each end of a long horizontal rod, and suspended it by a fine wire at the centre. Then he brought up two large lead balls, so that one was beside each of the small ones. Newton's law of gravitation meant the small balls would be attracted microscopically sideways by the large ones, so the rod would swing slightly clockwise from its normal rest position. Then he moved the large balls round to the other side of the small ones, so that the rod would swing anticlockwise. From the twist of the wire he could measure the gravitational force exerted on the small balls by the large ones, and from that he could work out the relative masses of the lead balls and the Earth. Unfortunately he died before carrying out the experiment, but he left the apparatus to his friend Henry Cavendish, who in 1798 measured the mass of the Earth at six thousand million million million tonnes – essentially the accepted value today. The unfair twist in the tale is that this is now called Cavendish's experiment.

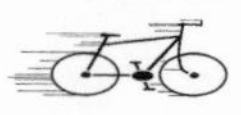

The old rectory at Thornhill, near Dewsbury, is across the road from the Church of St Michael and All Angels.

60 John 'Earthquake' Milne

In 1974 the Japanese ambassador to Great Britain made a pilgrimage to a tiny, rather nondescript village on the Isle of Wight. On a grassy bank he planted a cherry tree in memory of a local resident. This man, better known in Japan than in Britain, made the village of Shide the world centre for seismology. He was known as John 'Earthquake' Milne (1850–1913).

John Milne was born in Liverpool in 1850. At thirteen, he won a trip to the Lake District, and was so struck by the beautiful hills that he ran away to Ireland to see the scenery there. However, he soon buckled down to a career in geology, studying at the Royal School of Mines. He clearly had a taste for adventure, and despite his parents' misgivings undertook a dangerous expedition to Iceland in 1871. Having caught the exploration bug, he went to Newfoundland and Arabia, before his career really took off.

In 1875 Milne was offered the post of Professor of Geology and Mining at the Imperial College of Engineering, Tokyo. This was good news and bad: despite his adventurous streak, Milne got terribly seasick, and had to travel to Tokyo overland, through a Siberian winter. In 1875 there wasn't a railway, and he had to travel by carriage, boat, sleigh and even camel. On the night he arrived, there was an earthquake, and although his first job was to catalogue Japanese volcanoes, earthquakes really fascinated him.

Milne had two great achievements. First, he founded the scientific study of earthquakes (he is known as the 'father of modern seismology'). Secondly, he invented the instrument that made it possible, the horizontal pendulum seismograph. Milne's primary aim was to record how the earth moves in earthquakes. There were two rather obvious problems. You didn't know when, or where, the earthquake would occur. The first problem could be easily but tediously solved by recording earth movements all the time, just in case an earthquake happens. The second had proved insoluble: unless you are lucky enough to be near the epicentre of the earthquake, there are no discernible earth movements. Milne realised that in fact an earthquake would cause a disturbance at a distance, possibly all round the world, but that in most places the earthquake waves would be drowned by local effects, such as people walking about in the next room. However, he had defined the problem. It would be possible to detect earthquakes at a distance if there was something characteristic about earthquake waves that let you separate them from the bigger local disturbances.

Although the Chinese had used seismoscopes as long ago as AD 132, the first real seismometer was made by J.D. Forbes at Comrie in Perthshire in 1841, using an inverted pendulum. Milne also used a pendulum, but realised that earthquake waves would show up as sideways movements, so his was a horizontal pendulum. Essentially a pivoted arm with a weight on the end, suspended by a wire, he found that he could tune the seismometer by adjusting the length of pendulum arm, the size of weight and the tension in the wire. This brilliant device was able to pick up the characteristic earthquake waves, even when there were much bigger local vibrations. He made it into a seismograph, capable of continuously recording earthquakes, by attaching a pen to the end of the arm. Milne is a hero in Japan both because he put the study of earthquakes on a scientific footing, and because his understanding of earthquake waves allowed him to make the first serious suggestions about how earthquake damage to buildings could be prevented.

On 17 February 1895 Milne's house and observatory in Tokyo were destroyed by fire. He returned to England, setting up a new earthquake observatory at Shide Hill House. He caused something of a stir locally when he arrived with his Japanese wife Tone and assistant Mr Hirota. Reports flooded in from all over the world, and a steady flow of visitors came to see John and Tone, including Robert Falcon Scott – Scott of the Antarctic. The only visitors not welcome were members of the press, who camped on the door step whenever any large earthquake had been detected.

In contrast to his importance in Japan, in Britain he was virtually ignored by the authorities. The Post Office refused to supply him with a time signal (synchronisation of signals being vital to accurate measurement). Eventually, in 1900 the Eiffel tower began to broadcast time signals, and a Mr Shaw set up a crystal receiver for Milne with an aerial between two elm trees.

In Shide, Milne was able to detect earthquakes so clearly that it became the world centre for seismology. To correct for local effects, he established a second instrument on the Island at Carisbrooke Castle. Another series of experiments was undertaken at Ryde, to try to establish the tilting of the seabed at high tide. Every week the trace showed huge swings, which confused Milne. Eventually he discovered that the signals did in a way record the earth moving since they coincided with times when the butler and the housekeeper were off duty at the same time. He further claimed that from the traces taken at Shide he could tell how long the gravel trucks were stationary at the Barley Mow pub.

Shide Hill House is not as it was in Milne's day. Much has been demolished or rebuilt, and a new extension obscures the outside of the great observatory. However, there is one relic of Milne. Inside the house, in what is now a spare bedroom, a plaque has been found under the wallpaper. Originally on the outside of the house, it reads 'Earthquake Observatory 1900', the only clue that this was once a world-class laboratory. After Milne's death in June 1913, the station was kept running for six years, but then the house was sold and Tone returned to Japan.

John Milne's home and laboratory are now part of a private home in Shide, but across the road, by the river, is the cherry tree planted in his honour by the Japanese ambassador.

61 Samuel Morland's Megaphones

Samuel Morland was a member of the Secret Service. He was instrumental in restoring Charles II to the throne, and became his chief mechanic. Although he was vain and a bit of a fool, he pumped water higher than anyone had before, and conducted pioneering experiments in long-distance voice communication.

Samuel Morland, the son of a vicar, was probably born in Sulhampstead in Berkshire in 1625. At that time England was in political upheaval. By the time Samuel left Cambridge University, Parliament had thrown out the King, and Cromwell was running the country. Morland became a staunch supporter of the new government, and got himself sent to Sweden and France as a diplomat, doubtless because of his skills as a linguist.

Morland's character wasn't particularly attractive. He went to great lengths to keep in with people in authority, and was often regarded as a bit of a fool by those who witnessed his fawning. But he did have some very particular skills. He was the best man in Britain at opening, copying and resealing letters without detection; he claimed to have invented a method for quickly reproducing wax seals; and he could copy a page of writing in just a minute, probably by pressing a damp tissue paper over the surface of a letter. He could also forge handwriting. Not surprisingly, this led to a job in the Secret Service, privy to the secrets of state, a position which was to entirely change his beliefs – and his fortune.

One night in 1658 Morland was taking a nap at his desk when Cromwell came to see his boss, Thurloe. They discussed a plot to lure the exiled Charles II back to England – and then kill him. Cromwell suddenly noticed Morland, drew his sword and was about to run him through, but Thurloe said that he had been working through the previous two nights and was genuinely asleep. Morland was appalled by what he heard, and decided to switch support to the king, sending him money and details of the plot. Charles is supposed to have been pulling on his boots for the journey to England when the message arrived. In 1659 Morland went to Holland to see Charles, who knighted him. Sir Samuel made sure the king agreed to give him a huge pension as well.

Morland's talent for invention ensured his popularity with Charles II, our most scientific monarch, who went on to found the Royal Society, for many years the centre of British science. So it was to science rather than diplomacy that Morland turned in order to curry favour with the monarch, and his most famous invention, devised in 1670, went by the magnificent name of *tuba stentorophonica*.

The horn or trumpet was an ancient instrument, and had been used for ages to signal troops – Alexander the Great allegedly used one to give orders at a distance of 100 stadia (about 12 miles). But apparently Alexander's horn was a sort of musical instrument, played not unlike modern brass instruments, where the player makes a sort of refined 'raspberry' sound in the mouthpiece which the instrument amplifies. Morland wondered whether the trumpet could be modified for amplifying speech. He designed and made several trumpets of different shapes and materials, the first in glass in 1670.

It was about 32 inches long, 11 inches in diameter at the large end and 2½ inches at the small end. He then switched to more practical brass instruments, the next being much bigger at about 4½ feet long. This second instrument was the subject of two royal trials in St James's Park. In the first, the Lord Angier stood by the park wall near Goring House and heard Morland speaking from the end of the Mall near Old Spring Garden. In the second, the king, Prince Rupert and various dignitaries stood at one end of the Mall, and heard Morland speaking from the other – an impressive 850 yards.

Encouraged by his success, Morland began to think big. He took a 17 foot long copper instrument down to the river below London Bridge and, leaving it with a waterman, rowed down to near Deptford from where he heard the waterman clearly – a distance of 1½ miles. The fourth machine was the biggest he made, at an unwieldy 21 feet long. Both giant horns were heard from 'over against Faux-Hall, to the nearest part of Battersey over against Chelsey; And at another from Hide-Park-Gate to Chelsey-Colledge' – again 1½ miles. He judged that a conversation could be maintained at a distance of ¾ mile.

After this, the largest three were sent to Deal Castle to be tested. The Governor, Francis Digby, reported on 14 October 1671 that speech was heard at Walmer Castle, a mile away. The largest one was tried successfully between the shore and ships at anchor 2 to 3 miles out. Charles II ordered some *tuba stentoro-phonicas* for his ships, and they did create excitement at the time. Morland also made a hearing trumpet with an equally magnificent name – the *otacousticon* – but it is not clear how this would have differed from the speaking trumpet.

Although he invented many silly things, including a portable clockwork kitchen, his pumps were really good. He once sent a jet of water, coloured with red wine, over 60 feet above the top of Windsor Castle. One spectator called it 'the boldest and most extraordinary experiment that has ever been performed by water in any part of the world'. Charles II was so pleased with this that on 14 August 1681 he summoned Morland and presented him with a gold medal studded with diamonds, fastened to a green ribbon and bearing the inscription *Magister Mechanicorum* – Master of Mechanics!

Morland was spectacularly unlucky in love. His first four wives all died young, and his fifth marriage was a disaster. The woman was Mary Ayliff, an heiress – or so he thought. In fact, she turned out to be the daughter of a coachman, with no money at all, and she made Morland miserable and broke. Writing to Samuel Pepys he said, 'a criminal bound and going to execution is not in greater agonies than has been my poor active soul since this befell me', and signed himself 'your most humble but poor distressed servant, S. Morland'. Five months later, despite an appeal, a divorce was granted and he was rid of her.

Morland was clearly an ingenious man, but a bit of a fool. If he had persisted with any of his schemes he might have become a distinguished scientist. He is even recorded as devising a steam engine, having worked out that water turning to steam expands in volume two thousand times. This would have been the first working steam engine in Britain. Instead his reputation is summed up by the reception of one of his calculating machines at the Royal Society: Robert Hooke described it as 'very silly'. Indeed the memory of Morland might have sunk without trace had he not done one brave thing, and saved the king's life – and it is because of the gratitude of Charles II that we have heard of Samuel Morland, *Magister Mechanicorum*.

Morland's best memorial is the megaphone. Try making your own with rolled-up newspaper, and see at what distance it can be heard.

62 Henry Moule and the Earth-closet

In 1849 cholera struck Britain like a deadly tide, killing 55,000 people in a single year. Nowhere was worse hit than Dorchester, and in Fordington, just outside the city wall, the vicar worked tirelessly with the sick and the dying. On one day he held six funerals. They said Henry Moule stood between the living and the dead, boiling or burning contaminated clothes and bedclothes, and although he had not been popular, he gradually won the respect of the community. He also began to make the crucial connection between lack of sanitation and the spread of disease.

Moule described how, as he knelt beside a dying man, the overflow from the one privy shared by thirteen families trickled between his knees and the bed, and he saw the sewage bubbling up from the earth beneath the fireplace. Moule wrote to Prince Albert – the owner of the town – to explain the dreadful conditions; having written eight long letters without eliciting any sensible response, he set about his own methods of sanitary reform.

Henry Moule was born in Melksham on 27 January 1801, went to Cambridge, came to Fordington when he was twenty-eight, and stayed here for the rest of his life – more than fifty years. When he arrived with his wife Mary and two sons aged four and two, he found Fordington a sorry place. Thomas Hardy was to become a close friend of Moule's son Horace, and when he wrote *The Mayor of Casterbridge* Hardy used Mill Street, close by the vicarage, as the model for Mixen Lane – a slum of unmitigated horror, with gross overcrowding, appalling housing, poor sanitation and water; stinking ponds, crime, vice and prostitution.

Moule tackled his job with enthusiasm, making himself most unpopular with the parishioners by introducing a second fiery sermon in the Sunday service, and reforming the music until he drove the choir away. Moule even managed to get Dorchester races stopped. People jeered at his wife and children, and vandalised their lawn.

Undeterred, he ran the vicarage like a self-supporting commune, growing masses of vegetables, running a large hothouse, keeping cows, and earning some money by teaching not only his own eight children, but also seven paying boarders.

For some years he was chaplain to the troops in Dorchester Barracks, and he used the royalties from his 1845 book *Barrack Sermons* to build a church and also a school at West Fordington. He was an enterprising man; he took out patents for the steam heating of greenhouses and for a new kind of fuel for steam engines. This scientific attitude led him to a fascinating discovery.

In the summer of 1859 he decided that his cesspool was intolerably disgusting, not only to him but also to the neighbours. So he filled it in, and instructed his household to use a bucket instead. At first he buried the sewage in a trench in the garden, but he discovered by accident that in three or four weeks 'not a trace of this matter could be discovered'. In other words, the sewage had decomposed. He suspected dry earth was the active agent, and set about testing his theory. He put up a shed, sifted the dry earth beneath it, and mixed the contents of the bucket with this dry earth every morning. 'The whole operation does not take a boy more than a quarter of an hour,' he wrote, '*and within ten minutes after its completion neither the eye nor nose can perceive anything offensive.*'

So the dry earth deodorised the sewage and produced rapid decomposition. Moule's next step was to bring the earth into the house, dry it in a metal box under the kitchen range, and mix it in the bucket after every use . . . And in due course he developed a brand-new earth-closet – a sort of commode, with a bucket underneath the seat. Behind the seat was a hopper which he filled with dry earth. When he had finished using the closet, he pulled a handle, and a measured amount of dry earth was delivered into the bucket, to cover the offering.

He found he could recycle the earth, using the same batch several times, and he began to grow lyrical with rage at water-closets and praise for the earth: 'Water is only a vehicle for removing it out of sight and off the premises. It neither absorbs nor effectively deodorises. The great agent is dried earth, both for absorption and for deodorising offensive matters.'

And, he said, he no longer threw away valuable manure, but got a 'luxuriant growth of vegetables in my garden'. He backed up this last point with a scientific experiment, persuading a farmer to fertilize one half of a field with earth used five times in his closet, and the other half of it with an equal weight of superphosphate. Swedes were planted in both halves, and those nurtured with earth manure grew one third bigger than those given only superphosphate. Moule quoted a biblical precedent for his efforts, from a set of instructions about cleanliness in Deuteronomy, chapter 23 verse 13: 'With your equipment you will have a trowel, and when you squat outside, you shall scrape a hole with it and then turn and cover your excrement.'

Many people think the earth-closet is a bit of a joke, but Moule was convinced that it was the future. He worked out the implications; if used by a family of six, the earth-closet would need 50 kg of earth per week; so a town of 10,000 would need 17 tons of earth a day – but only borrowed!

He took out a patent in 1860, and set up the Moule Patent Earth-Closet Company Ltd, which manufactured and sold a wide variety of earth-closets, the expensive models made of mahogany and oak. They were even manufactured abroad under licence – in Hartford, Connecticut, for example, by the Hartford Earth-Closet Company.

Moule wrote a string of tracts and pamphlets, including *The advantages of the dry earth system,* and *Manure for the million – a letter to the cottage gardeners of England*. He also tried hard to get government support, with an 1872 paper on *Town refuse – the remedy for local taxation*. His main point was that to provide mains water and sewers was fantastically expensive, and the sewage still had to decompose somewhere. If everyone looked after their own there would be enormous saving in taxation, and much less spread of disease.

He managed to convince a lot of people: 148 of his dry-earth closets were used by two thousand men at the Volunteer encampment at Wimbledon in 1868; 776 closets were used in Wakefield Prison. The combination of economy and health was powerful. In 1865 the Dorset County School at Dorchester changed from water-closets to earth-closets, eliminated smells and diarrhoea, and cut the annual maintenance costs from £3 to 50p! Lancaster Grammar School also brought in earth-closets, but for less scientific reasons: the water-closets were always out of order 'by reason of marbles, Latin grammar covers, and other properties being thrown down them'.

For some decades in the second half of the nineteenth century the earth-closet and the water-closet were in hot competition. Almost everything Moule said was true, and much the same arguments are used today by the champions of bioloos and composting lavatories. Unfortunately, flushing does rapidly remove the sewage from the house, and as a result – in rich countries – the water-closet is winning, for the moment. . . .

Henry and Mary Moule lie in the top corner of the graveyard below the church in High Street, Fordington, right outside Dorchester. Moule Close is beside the church. There is an original Moule earth-closet in Dorset County Museum; 01305 262735.

63 William Murdoch – Soho by Gaslight

More than a hundred years after the discovery of coal gas the technology was invented to allow it to be exploited. The first person to suggest seriously that it should be used for lighting was an amazing but largely unknown Scotsman, William Murdoch. At home in 1772 he had apparently found that he could make coal gas by heating coal in his mother's teapot; he realised that in principle coal gas could be used to make bright reliable lighting. His chance came in Birmingham.

He was always inventive; as a boy he had built a wooden tricycle to ride to school with his brothers in Ayrshire – and this was decades before even the hobbyhorse. He designed a new type of lathe, and used it to make himself an oval wooden hat.

In 1777 he went to Birmingham to apply for a job with the great engineering firm of Boulton & Watt. Boulton would have turned him away, but Murdoch was wearing his oval hat – and got the job. Eventually he became the Third Man in the Boulton & Watt empire, and he stayed with the firm for fifty-three years. They sent him off to look after their steam engine interests in Cornwall, where he annoyed his landlady by hanging fish to dry all round his room. In 1784 he built a model steam locomotive, but Boulton

& Watt didn't want to know – in fact they actively discouraged him from pursuing such a frivolity – and his Cornish acquaintance Richard Trevithick built the first working steam locomotive about fifteen years later.

When Murdoch returned to Birmingham he lived in a cottage in the Soho foundry where they started making their own steam engines after Watt's patent had expired in 1800. There he picked up and developed his idea of gas lighting; he lit his house with it, and by 1802 he had installed gas lighting through the entire Soho manufactory. But still it came to nothing. Unfortunately Boulton refused to patent gas lighting; he said they had enough patents already what with their steam engines and so on, and so Murdoch never made a penny out of his brightest ideas.

William Murdoch's cottage, marked by a plaque, still stands in the remains of the Soho Foundry in Birmingham, now part of the Avery Works.

64 Matthew Murray and his Rack Railway

'This was the first instance of the regular employment of locomotives for commercial purposes' runs a line almost casually inserted in the *Dictionary of National Biography* entry for Matthew Murray. This comes as a bit of a shock because Murray does not feature in the usual list of railway firsts. His clearly wasn't the first locomotive – that honour goes to Richard Trevithick, whose Penydaren loco ran in 1804. Before that William Murdock had built a miniature high-pressure steam carriage perhaps as early as 1784. Yet most of us were brought up thinking that Stephenson's *Rocket* was the first proper loco to run commercially following its victory in the famous Raines Hill trial of 1829. So where does Matthew Murray fit in?

Murray (1765–1826) was born near Newcastle upon Tyne and was originally apprenticed as a blacksmith. In search of work when his indentures ended, he walked to Leeds, already a centre of the textile trade. He found work with Marshall's, famous as flax spinners. In the days before mechanised cotton-spinning, much of the cloth made in England was flax (linen) or a mixture of flax and cotton, in part because we couldn't produce hard enough cotton thread and also because imported cotton was expensive.

Nevertheless, mechanisation was becoming important and Murray proved to be a brilliant innovator. While at Marshall's he invented and patented several machines for spinning, carding and other stages in the preparation of cloth. He left in 1795 to set up on his own as Fenton, Murray, & Wood. They made flax machinery as before, but he began to spend more time on steam engines –

presumably huge stationary engines of the Watt type, which would have been around for over twenty years. Murray's works was called the Round Foundry and was organised so that all the machines could take power from a central shaft powered by a vast steam engine. He turned out to be rather good at engine-building – so good that he was regarded as a serious rival by the greatest engine builders of all, Boulton and Watt in Birmingham. To prevent Murray expanding, they quietly bought up all the land surrounding the Round Foundry!

This was the time of the Napoleonic wars, and the people of England were beginning to be hit quite hard. One example of the economic impact of war was the fact that horse-feed had become very expensive. A local businessman, Charles Branding, had begun to feel the pinch and wondered if it might be possible to do away with the horses altogether. He ran a coal mine up on Hunslet Moor – where the M1 motorway now leaves Leeds – and needed to transport the coal back into town. He operated a horse-drawn railway. These old railways had been around for years, and sometimes had wooden rails for trucks to run on. In other parts of the country cunning gravity-assisted systems used full trucks running downhill to pull the empties back up to the top. Branding turned to his manager, John Blenkinsop, who turned to Matthew Murray.

Blenkinsop planned to use cast-iron rails, and wondered whether Murray could build a locomotive to haul a wagon train along them. They realised that the materials available presented a serious problem. When a locomotive runs on smooth rails, it depends upon friction to get a grip. Indeed the pulling force of the locomotive is limited by friction – there comes a point where, no matter how powerful the engine, the friction is not great enough and instead of pulling the train, it spins the wheels. There is a simple way of increasing friction and thereby grip: increase the weight of the locomotive. And this is where Blenkinsop and Murray came unstuck: their cast-iron rails would crack if the locomotive weighed more than 5 tons. A 5-ton loco could haul only 20 tons of coal. Blenkinsop eventually solved the problem by laying a third, toothed rail. A cog on the engine engaged with this 'rack' to provide drive for the train, and so got round the problem of friction. Interestingly the limits of cast-iron rails cost Richard Trevithick dearly during trials of his machine. Because his 1804 locomotive broke the rails on its way out, he was unable to complete the return journey by rail and thus lost an enormous bet!

Blenkinsop and Murray did rather better. The *Salamanca* and the *Prince Regent* were put into service in 1811, with the *Lord Wellington* and the *Marquis Wellington* in the following year. This was the first commercial steam railway, four years before George Stephenson built his first locomotive. The rack technology worked extremely well. Instead of the 20 tons expected of a 5-ton locomotive, these power-houses were able to haul 90 tons. On one occasion they hauled thirty wagons at 3¼ miles an hour, an event of such note that it was witnessed by the Grand Duke Nicholas of Russia. We don't know if he was an early trainspotter, or simply didn't have anything better to do that afternoon. Murray's engines were also used in ships. Following consultations with the American ambassador in Liverpool in 1815, Murray supplied an order for the first paddle-steamer on the Mississippi!

Murray became a steam enthusiast, steam-heating his house and naming it 'Steam Hall'. Not everyone was as keen, and a group of Luddites visited the hall with crowbars one night, only to run into the formidable Mrs Murray, who saw them off with a brace of pistols. The railway ran for over twenty years, by which time materials had improved enough for cheaper, smooth rails to become standard. However, in the steep mountains of Switzerland, on Snowdon and even during construction of the Channel Tunnel, there is still a need for the rack railway, and locomotives for all these places have been built in Leeds by the Hunslet Engine Company – successors to Matthew Murray and John Blenkinsop.

The Middleton railway runs with steam trains in Matthew Murray's tracks.

65 John Napier: Logs, Bones and the Decimal Point

John Napier was born at Merchiston Castle in 1550. The castle is small, tall and elegant; in those days it was in remote countryside a few miles south-east of Edinburgh, but now unfortunately the castle is built into the middle of the concrete-and-glass Napier University, and the countryside is remote. John Napier, known as the 'Marvellous Merchiston', was regarded with awe. Locals said he could predict the future, and he kept a black cockerel that was supposed to be able to detect their secrets. Once, some valuables were stolen from the castle. Napier ordered his servants to go one by one into a darkened room in the tower, and there to stroke the cockerel, which he said would crow when it was touched by the guilty party. They all took their turns going into the room, but the cockerel remained silent. Then Napier took them into a lighted room and asked them to hold up their hands. All but one had black hands. The clean-handed servant was accused of theft; he hadn't dared touch the cockerel. In fact, Napier had covered the bird with soot.

Napier was keen on scientific agriculture; he experimented with various fertilisers on his fields. He devised a hydraulic screw for pumping water out of flooded coal pits. He also invented war machines to fend off any Spanish invasion. One was a metal chariot, propelled by those inside it, perforated with small holes from which they could fire pistols. 'The enemy', wrote Napier, 'meantime being abased and altogether uncertain what defence or pursuit to use against a moving mouth of metal.' Confused they would have been, meeting a tank in the sixteenth century.

But Napier's greatest love was astronomy. The air was clear then, before Edinburgh became 'Auld Reekie', and he liked to go up to his battlements and look at the stars. However, he found all the calculations tedious, and resolved to do something about it. For twenty years he laboured, and in 1614 published his *Mirifici logarithmorum canonis descriptio*, or Description of the marvellous canon of logarithms. Log tables allowed you to multiply numbers together by simply adding. Until the days of calculators, which arrived in the 1970s, they remained the best method for doing tedious calculations. Astronomers across Europe thought the technique wonderful, and log tables were rapidly adopted.

They certainly seemed like magic to Henry Briggs. Henry was born on 23 February 1561 at Warley, near Halifax in Yorkshire. He went off to London and then to Oxford, where he became Professor of Geometry. When he first saw Napier's book, he wrote to his friend James Ussher (who later became an archbishop and calculated the date of creation as 4004 BC) and said 'Napier . . . hath set my head and hands a-work with his new and admirable logarithms. I hope to see him this summer, if it please God, for I never saw a book which pleased me better or made me more wonder.' This reaction was not shared by all the schoolchildren forced to use logs in the subsequent centuries, but then Briggs was an unusual man. He did indeed travel all the way to Merchiston, and when the butler had shown him into the presence of the Laird, they sat for fifteen minutes without a word being spoken, lost in mutual admiration!

Briggs stayed with Napier for a month in 1615, and another month in 1616. He had planned a third trip, but Napier died on 4 April 1617, before the visit could take place. Briggs made an important contribution to the use of logs. Napier had worked all his out to base e, which is about 2.718, because that is how they drop naturally out of the series used to calculate them. These are called 'natural' or 'Napierian' logarithms. But Briggs pointed out that they would be more useful if they were to base 10 instead; so he proceeded to work out thirty thousand such logs to fourteen decimal places!

For a simple example of the use of logs (to base 10), suppose you planned to order a newspaper which cost 35p every day, including weekends, and you wanted to work out how much it would cost for a year – 365 days. Look up the logs of 35 (1.54407) and 365 (2.56229) and add them together to give 4.10636; then look up the antilog, and read off the answer: 12775p, or £127.75. All you have to do is one addition, which is much easier than multiplying.

Logarithms, however, were not the end of Napier's contribution to calculations; he also invented a pocket calculator. Despite his tables, Napier still felt that arithmetic was too hard for people to learn. In his book *Rabdologiae* ('Little rods'), which also covered such neat ideas as extracting square roots by moving counters around on a chessboard, he wrote, 'Some are accustomed to make arithmetic frightening through very love of the subject. This instrument provides a readily understood explanation.' His calculator comprised a set of square-section rods with numbers written down each of the sides. They were often made of ivory, and were consequently called 'Napier's Bones'. The Bones were massively popular for more than a hundred years. When the London diarist Samuel Pepys studied arithmetic in 1667 he wrote of his tutor: 'To my chamber whither comes Jonas Moore and tells me the mighty use of Napier's Bones.'

Today we have calculators, so the Bones are less useful. But another of Napier's inventions we use every day. When he was calculating his tables, Napier had to write down fractions of a whole number, just as we write pennies as fractions of a pound. There was no really good way of writing fractions down; so Napier invented one. We still use his invention today, and it's called the decimal point.

Merchiston Castle, smartly restored, is now part of Napier University, Colinton Road, 3 miles south-east of the centre of Edinburgh.

66 Thomas Newcomen and the First Working Steam Engines

Dartmouth, dominated by the Royal Naval College on the hill, has always been a seafaring town, made rich by traders from the sixteenth century onwards, and I wasn't surprised to learn that in 1749 Nathaniel Symons of Harberton tested his diving machine in the River Dart and, according to *The Gentleman's Magazine*, was lucky enough to come up again in 45 minutes; nor that in 1875 William Froude made a small steam engine there to use on steam yachts. But I was surprised to find that within a hundred yards of the quayside Thomas Newcomen invented and developed the first steam engine that really drained the mines. Indeed Thomas Newcomen, arguably the most inventive practical genius of all time, was born in 1663 right on the quayside.

He may have been apprenticed in Exeter, but it seems he went back to Dartmouth about 1685 and set up as an ironmonger, with John Calley, who was a plumber, as his assistant. In 1707 Newcomen rented a big house between Higher and Lower Streets. Unfortunately, the whole row of houses was pulled down in 1864 in order to join Southtown with the rest of Dartmouth. But at least the new road that forms the connection is called Newcomen Road.

Thomas Newcomen called himself an ironmonger, but in fact he was more like what we would call a blacksmith; he made tools for people. He probably visited mines and made tools for the miners, so he would have known about the problems of flooding. He realised that there would be a great future for anyone who could make a machine to drain the mines, and that was what he did.

Like Savery (*see* page 303), he condensed steam to make a vacuum, but whereas Savery had simply used that vacuum to pull the water up, Newcomen made his vacuum inside a cylinder, and used it to pull down a piston. Then a big lever transferred the force to the pump shaft which went down the mine.

Newcomen's engine was the first practical engine to use a piston in a cylinder. Casting the cylinders and getting the pistons to fit was just at the limit of existing technology, and the technique was generally to make the piston deliberately smaller than the cylinder by an inch or two, and to make a seal of wet leather or wet rope to close the gap. We have no idea how long Newcomen spent developing his engine, nor how many prototypes he built, although some rumours say the first effective one was built at Wheal Vor mine in Cornwall, but the first working engine of which there is good evidence was installed at a coal mine at Dudley Castle in 1712, twenty-four years before James Watt was born. That engine's cylinder was 21 inches in diameter and nearly 8 feet long, and it worked at the sedate pace of twelve strokes a minute, raising 10 gallons of water from a depth of 156 feet, which corresponds to about 5½ horse-power.

Newcomen engines worked day and night, as long as there was enough coal. They were less than 1 per cent efficient, and used a lot of coal, which was why they were installed first in coal mines where coal was free. But they were rugged and reliable.

Gradually the technology improved and they could be made with bigger cylinders, up to 6 feet in diameter. The one at Fresnes in France replaced a plant worked by twenty men and fifty horses. By the time Thomas Newcomen died in 1729 at least a hundred of his engines were working all over Britain, and also in France, Belgium, Holland, Sweden, Hungary, Germany, and Austria. They were manufactured for more than a hundred years. The Pentich engine was still working 127 years after installation – rather different from the engines we buy in cars today. A Newcomen engine was used in Barnsley until 1934.

In 1714 a Newcomen engine cost about £1,000. Most people couldn't afford this much, and one chap who tried said,

> That cursed engine pumped my pockets dry
> And left no fire to warm my fingers by!

The standard deal was to rent an engine for £7 a week – which is 35 per cent: a good rate of return for the manufacturer. But Newcomen didn't get rich. Savery's patent, which by the Fire Engine Act of 1698 had been extended until 1733, covered all engines that raised water by fire, and said:

> if any person or persons . . . shall at any time . . . presume to make, imitate, use, or exercise any vessells or engines for raiseing water or occasioning motion to any sort of millwork by the impellant force of fire, he or they shall forfeite to the said Thomas Savery . . . all and every such vessells and engines . . .

So Newcomen was forced to go into partnership with Savery, and seems never to have made much from his fantastic invention, although Savery did give him some shares. What's worse, the scientific establishment would not believe that a provincial ironmonger could have invented such an amazing machine, so Newcomen got no scientific credit at all. They said he had pinched other people's ideas and made advances by sheer luck. Whatever the establishment view, working out how to raise water by fire was one of the greatest technological advances of all time, made in the early years of the eighteenth century by Thomas Newcomen, ironmonger, of Dartmouth.

The Cornish countryside is studded with derelict engine houses, especially around Camborne and Redruth. In Dartmouth, Newcomen's house was demolished, but Newcomen Road runs up the hill where the house was, and has a small plaque on the wall. There's an attractive brass plaque on a slab of stone in the memorial gardens on the quayside, and in the back of the tourist information office is a genuine Newcomen Engine, which was bought second-hand in 1821 and used to pump water into the Coventry Canal; it can be made to run with an electric motor. A steam-powered modern replica of the original Dudley engine is on display at the Black Country Museum in Dudley, and runs occasionally (0121 557 9643).

67 Isaac Newton and the Colours of the Rainbow

Isaac Newton can't have enjoyed a happy childhood. Born at the full moon in the early hours of Christmas Day 1642 – the year that Galileo had died – he was so tiny at birth they said he would have fitted into a quart pot, and so sickly looking that he was not expected to survive the night. His father had died a few months earlier, and three years later his mother went off to marry a rich clergyman, leaving the baby in the not-so-tender care of her strict parents. When her new husband died she returned to the family home, Woolsthorpe Manor, but found Isaac an awkward lad. She wanted his help on the farm, but he was happier at the King's School in Grantham, where there is still an I. NEWTON carved in large crooked capitals on a window-sill in what is now the library. He was a dreamy lad, and the tale is told that usually he daydreamed on his way home from the market in Grantham. Everyone had to get off their horses and walk up Spitalgate Hill, but Isaac often forgot to get on again at the top, and would walk the 5 miles home, leading his horse.

He went off to Cambridge in 1661, but in April 1665 the University was closed because of an outbreak of plague. So Isaac went home, and with only himself for company, and his mind free to wander, he began the most productive and imaginative eighteen months of his life, 'for in those years I was in the prime of my age for invention, and minded Mathematics and Philosophy more than at any time since'. During that fertile period he not only invented the basis of calculus and solved several major mathematical problems, he also unearthed the basic principle of gravity, and set up in his head the fundamental laws of motion – although he did not write them down for another twenty years! And he solved the enigma of the spectrum.

We think we know how he set about this, because he wrote a wonderfully explicit letter to the Royal Society which describes in detail his experiments, his observations, and his conclusions. 'In the beginning of 1666,' he writes, 'I procured me a triangular glass-prisme, to try therewith the celebrated *phenomena of colours.*' Then, 'having darkened my chamber, and made a small hole in my window-shuts, to let in a convenient quantity of the sun's light, I placed my prisme at his entrance, that it might be thereby refracted to the opposite wall.' He was delighted at the pretty and intense colours, and he soon noticed that although his hole was round, the spectrum was five times as long as it was broad, 'a disproportion so extravagant, that it excited me to a more than ordinary curiosity of examining, from whence it might proceed'.

He first checked that this elongation was not produced by thickness or irregularity in the glass, or other similar simple anomaly, and then he wondered whether the rays of light were curving through the air, 'when I remembered that I had often seen a tennis ball, struck with an oblique racket, describe such a curve line'. But he satisfied himself that this was not the case. And so he was led to his crucial experiment: 'The gradual removal of these suspicions at length led me to the *Experimentum Crucis*, which was this: I took two boards, and placed one of them close behind the prisme at the window, so that the light might pass through a small hole . . . and fall on the other board, which I placed at about 12 feet distance, having first made a small hole in it also, for some of the incident light to pass through. Then I placed another prisme behind this second board, so that the light, trajected through both the boards, might pass through that also, and be again refracted before it arrived at the wall.'

What he found was that when he let a ray of red light through his second prism it was refracted again before it reached the back wall. When he let through a ray of blue light it too was refracted again, but much more than the red. Thus it was clear to him that light of different colours was refracted through different angles, the blue more than the red. Furthermore, each colour he let through did not break up into new colours, but 'obstinately retained its colour, notwithstanding my utmost endeavours to change it'.

He concluded that white light is not a single colour, but can only be a mixture of colours. Therefore the prism produces colours from white light because it refracts the different colours by different amounts, and so separates them one from another. 'Why the colours of the rainbow appear in falling drops of rain, is also from hence evident. For those drops, which refract the rays, disposed to appear purple . . . are the drops on the inside of the primary bow, and on the outside of the secondary or exterior one . . . those drops, which refract . . . red . . . are the drops on the exterior part of the primary, and interior part of the secondary bow.'

In the middle of this long letter he diverts for a page or so to explain why this varied refraction of light of different colours will lead to coloured fringes in telescope images, since the focal length of a lens must vary from colour to colour. And he goes on to describe the reflecting telescope he built to avoid this problem, and through which he had seen the moons of Jupiter. Thus the Newtonian telescope first appeared in print as an aside in his letter about the spectrum!

Much of this fascinating letter reads as though he has just come from the experiments on the bench; the descriptions are so simple and fresh. And yet this is far from the case. For one thing he says at the beginning 'I procured me a triangular glass-prisme' –

according to legend he bought it at Stourbridge Fair near Cambridge – but then a few pages later he introduces 'another prisme', so he can't just have gone to the fair and bought one. . . . What's more, he wrote this letter to the Royal Society in February 1672. The telescopic work was fresh, but six years had gone by since his first prism experiments, he had become Lucasian Professor of Mathematics at Cambridge, and he had delivered at least one course of lectures on optics; so by then the spectral ideas were firmly established in his mind, and there must have been plenty of hindsight to guide his precise descriptions.

However, when this letter was published, Newton was attacked by his rival Robert Hooke, who cast doubt on Newton's conclusions, and said the crucial experiment did not work. To be fair, the light becomes very faint after going through two holes and two prisms, so that making objective observations is extremely difficult; you can easily convince yourself that you can see what you want to see!

Newton was furious at being attacked in this way, and almost vowed never to publish his results again. Indeed he avoided publishing anything apart from a brief tract *Propositiones de Motu* until his great book *Philosophiae Naturalis Principia Mathematica* came out fifteen years later, in 1687. He published nothing more on light until Hooke had died, and his book *Opticks*, published in 1704, contains no mention of the phrase '*Experimentum Crucis*'!

Science is rarely simple, and even Isaac Newton could not solve the mystery of the colours of the rainbow without bitter argument. For most of his life, Newton was cantankerous and self-obsessive, but occasionally he produced bursts of charm. Writing a conciliatory letter to Hooke, he said: 'If I have seen further, it is by standing on the shoulders of giants.' And near the end of his life he said: 'I do not know how I may appear to the world, but to myself I seem only like a boy playing on the seashore, and diverting myself in now and then finding a smoother pebble or a prettier shell than ordinary, while the great ocean of truth lay all undiscovered before me.'

Isaac Newton's home, Woolsthorpe Manor, 5 miles south of Grantham, is open to the public on some days during the summer. Beware, there are two Woolsthorpes; Albert Einstein went to the wrong one! There is Newton Way and Newton Lane, and in Grantham the Isaac Newton Shopping Centre and material in Grantham Museum; 01476 568783.

68 Florence Nightingale: Sanitation and Statistics

The idea that cleanliness is next to godliness may have encouraged some members of the church-going fraternity to wash themselves, and medieval abbeys usually had lavatories – places to wash – but before about 1850 personal hygiene in this country was generally rare. Queen Elizabeth I astonished her courtiers by her enthusiasm for washing: she used to have a bath once a month, 'whether she needed it or not'!

Even though the Romans had organised extensive public baths in Bath and many other places, their example did not catch on. Until the middle of the nineteenth century there was little piped water in Britain; posh people washed their faces in bowls of warm water brought in by the servants; poor people used a stream or the village pond if they were desperate.

Cities without proper sewers were revolting, and people complained bitterly about the smell. In the hot summer of 1858, when the banks of the Thames were covered for miles with decomposing sewage, the 'Great Stink' was debated in Parliament, where the curtains had to be drawn and soaked in chloride of lime to allow the members to breathe.

However, most people failed to realise that lack of sewers and proper sanitation was a major cause of disease. In the mid-1800s, the infant mortality in English cities was 48 per cent; of all the babies born, only half lived to the age of five. They died from various illnesses – typhoid, cholera, diarrhoea – but basically they died because the sewage was not properly separated from the water supply.

The greatest advance ever made in human health was nothing to do with medicine, penicillin or surgery. It was the drive for simple sanitation, and it was brought about by such far-seeing doctors as William Budd and John Snow, and the remarkable

Florence Nightingale, reluctant debutante and brilliant campaigner.

William Budd, having caught typhoid himself and recovered, took a deep interest when the disease struck his own village of North Tawton in Devon. By following its progress from house to house there and later in Bristol, he proved that it must be spread mainly in drinking water. John Snow came to the same conclusion about cholera in London's Soho, and took dramatic action – he removed the handle from the pump in Broad Street, where he knew the water was contaminated, and stopped the outbreak dead in its tracks.

Florence Nightingale's posh background made her an unlikely candidate for a heroine, but with her sharp insights, wide experience and missionary zeal, she revolutionised both the nursing profession and the management of hospitals. Her family travelled widely; she was born in Italy on 12 May 1820 in the city of Florence, and that's where she got her name. Her father was a wealthy bookish man, but her mother Frances cared only for society – where she was going to be seen, and with whom, what she was going to wear, which parties were beneath her station, and above all what were the marriage prospects for her two daughters.

Florence was supposed to behave like a lady, and occupy her time with flower-arranging and tapestry. She horrified her mother by going off and investigating hospitals, not just in England but even abroad, and she worked for three months at a hospital for the destitute – the Institute for Protestant Deaconesses at Kaiserwerth in Germany – where she was amazed to find many of the deaconesses were only peasants!

In 1854 the Crimean War broke out, and *The Times* sent out a reporter, William Howard Russell, who was in effect the first ever special war correspondent. He wrote back vivid reports about the bungling incompetence of the army commanders, and the horrors of the Crimea. In particular he wrote that although the French hospitals were well organised, the English wounded were terribly neglected. 'Are there no devoted women among us able and willing to go forth to minister to the sick and suffering soldiers?' he wrote.

Florence Nightingale answered the call. On 14 October she wrote to the Secretary of State for War, volunteering her services; on the same day he wrote to her, asking her to go. Their letters crossed in the post. Just one week later she set off, with thirty-eight nurses. In the hospital at Scutari, they found appalling suffering. There were no bowls for water. No soap, no towels. No mugs, knives, spoons. No proper food. There were four miles of beds, and the soldiers lay in them with wounds, cholera, typhus, frostbite – all jumbled together. They died in their hundreds – mainly of disease. A thousand men died of disease before the first battle began. Florence would not let men die alone and uncomforted, so she sat beside their beds as they died; in the next couple of years she personally watched some two thousand soldiers die.

She applied basic common-sense ideas of sanitation and proper food, and in due course the death rate came tumbling down. In February 1855, just after she arrived, more than 50 per cent of the men admitted to hospital had died. By June, the figure was down to 5 per cent.

When she came back from the Crimea she was summoned to see Queen Victoria at Balmoral, and she began her task of persuading people that reform was necessary. Her main weapon, rather surprisingly, was statistics. Statistics had become all the rage.

Florence had collected statistics on everything in her hospital, from admissions, discharges, and causes of death, to the number of drains and the distance between the beds. She presented her results in striking graphics that she called 'coxcombs'. The

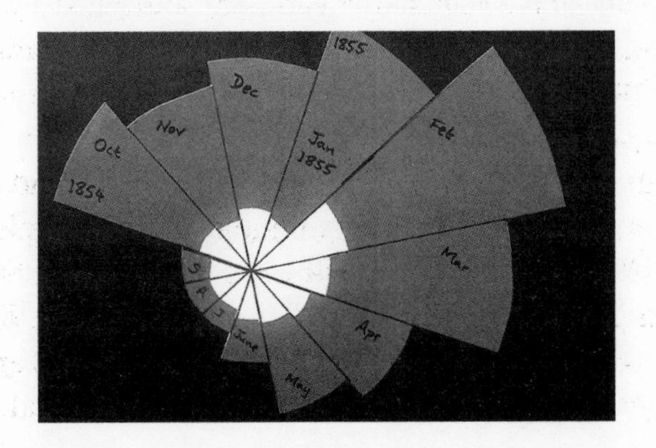

whole thing represents a year. Each segment is a month. The areas represent the number of deaths. The inner light parts represent deaths from wounds and the outer dark parts represent deaths from preventable disease. For every soldier who died of wounds, seven died from preventable disease. In her report to the Royal Commission she wrote that every year the army took the fittest young men, and managed to kill 1,500 of them with poor food and disease. They might as well have been taken out on to Salisbury Plain and shot. These were ideas that people could understand.

Florence Nightingale achieved two remarkable things. Before she came along, nursing was regarded as a menial job of drudgery; most nurses were illiterate women of loose virtue who liked their drink and had no concept of hygiene. She raised the status of nursing to that of a caring profession. She was hopelessly wrong in her theory of disease, but by a combination of common-sense, drive, plain speaking and sheer hard work, she managed to get through to the authorities and bring about massive reform in hospital management.

Yet when she was dying she refused burial in Westminster Abbey, and insisted on being buried without any special fuss in the family grave in East Wellow, near Romsey. On the big family memorial, where the other members of the family have their names carved in full, one on each face, her side simply says F.N.

Perhaps she would like to be remembered as the caring nurse. Remember those four miles of beds at Scutari? If she could not get round them all during the day, she carried on alone through the night, with her Turkish oil lantern – the woman they loved – the Lady with the Lamp.

Florence Nightingale was buried in the tiny churchyard of St Margaret's Church at East Wellow, near Romsey. The Florence Nightingale Museum is in the corner of St Thomas's Hospital in London; 0171 620 0374.

69 Joseph Paxton and the Crystal Palace

Although it sounds unlikely, giant lily leaves brought together the two best-known activities of Joseph Paxton, the extraordinary man who not only transformed the grounds at Chatsworth in Derbyshire, but also built the Crystal Palace for London's Great Exhibition of 1851. Joseph Paxton was born in Bedfordshire on 3 August 1801, the son of a poor tenant farmer who died soon afterwards. When he left school, Joseph was sent to work on his brother's farm, where he was beaten and starved, but not paid. When he was seventeen he ran away to be a gardener.

He was determined to better himself, and always made the most of every position he got into. He had a succession of gardening jobs, and at Chiswick

Gardens Arboretum became foreman, but because he earned only 18*s* a week, he had just decided to go to America to earn more, when one day he opened the door for the Duke of Devonshire, who owned Chiswick Gardens and lived next door. The duke took an instant liking to the lad, and although he was only twenty-three appointed him superintendent at his country home – Chatsworth House in Derbyshire. Wow! What a break!

On his first day at Chatsworth, Paxton was understandably nervous and keyed up. He arrived at 4.30 a.m., explored the grounds, climbed over the wall into the walled garden, set the men to work, watched the water-works in action, joined the housekeeper Mrs Gregory for breakfast, met her niece Sarah Brown and fell instantly in love – they eventually married and had a daughter – and all this before nine o'clock in the morning!

The Duke of Devonshire thought Paxton was wonderful, and more or less gave him a free hand with the gardens, so he set about building all sorts of magnificent display pieces. He made huge fountains, one of which spouts water up to 270 feet – twice the height of Nelson's Column. There is also a magnificent cascade of water down what is essentially a long flight of stone steps. The water for these displays came from a lake at the top of the hill behind the house. There are no pumps: gravity does all the work, and the high fountain can still be switched on just by turning a tap.

Paxton built an arboretum, a conservatory 300 feet long, and even a model village – Edensor. Apparently the duke was impressed by an architectural catalogue, and simply ordered one of each model! So every house is different. The duke adopted Paxton as a companion and confidant; they went everywhere together, and took one long trip around the Mediterranean.

In 1837 a traveller brought back from Guyana a fantastic new lily, but the experts at Kew Gardens were unable to get it to grow. Paxton got hold of a cutting, and designed a specially heated pool, using water-wheels to keep the water flowing. He managed to make the lily grow, and even he was staggered by its size. In three months it had eleven 5 foot leaves, and huge flowers. He named it *Victoria regia*, and gave Queen Victoria a bud. This lily was far too big to grow in most conservatories, and Paxton had to work out a way of designing bigger spaces. He wanted glass overhead, and he needed to dream up some simple structure that would hold up the glass. Inspired by the huge leaves of the lily, which were themselves a feat of engineering, he said, he tried floating his daughter Annie on a leaf and it worked.

So he designed a rigid structure made of radiating ribs connected by flexible cross-ribs. He tried it out, modified it, tried Mark 2, modified it again, and so on, until he got it to work. He used wood, because it was cheap and light, and he made the glass roof in ridges and furrows so that the maximum amount of light came in – even during the early morning and late evening light wasn't wasted by reflection. He designed special rafters that had gutters above the glass to collect rainwater and below the glass to collect condensation. For support he used hollow pillars that doubled as drainpipes. But the really brilliant idea behind the final design was that all the pieces were prefabricated, and simply bolted together on site. He designed the machines to make the parts, which were then manufactured in vast numbers.

In 1851 there was to be a Great Exhibition in Hyde Park in London. Clearly they needed a temporary building to house it, and a competition was held for the design of this structure. The judges included the great railway engineers George Stephenson and Isambard Kingdom Brunel, who rejected all 245 entries, and suggested their own plan, but this was so ugly it was turned down after a public outcry.

Joseph Paxton offered to put in a design, and was given two weeks. Within nine days he had on their desks a stunning version of his lily-leaf-supported greenhouse. It was simple to erect, it could easily be taken down again after the exhibition, and it was amazingly cheap – only £80,000 for a building big enough to hold twelve football pitches on the ground floor, and more than 100 feet high. Paxton raised the stakes by publishing his design in the *Illustrated London News*.

The building – the 'Millennium Dome' of 1851 – attracted great interest and disapproval in the press, and the magazine *Punch* sneeringly called it the Crystal Palace. Some authorities feared it would attract thieves and prostitutes, but the people loved it. In fact the whole thing was a phenomenal success, and Paxton was knighted, and became Sir Joseph Paxton.

There was a bit of a problem before it opened, because it was built with two huge elm trees inside, and a mass of sparrows came in out of the cold and nested in the elms, and made a lot of mess. How on earth could they get rid of the sparrows? Shooting was obviously impossible, with all that glass. The queen summoned the Duke of Wellington, and he, resourceful as ever, said, 'Well ma'am, you could try a sparrowhawk'. Biological control, in 1851!

The public lavatories in the Crystal Palace were installed by flamboyant plumber George Jennings, who decided to charge people a penny to go in. There was a storm of protest, but 827,280 visitors did indeed 'spend a penny' – which is probably where that expression came from! After the Great Exhibition, the Crystal Palace was taken down, piece by piece, and re-erected at Sydenham, where Paxton went to live. He became rich, famous, and Member of Parliament for Coventry, and died in 1865. The Crystal Palace was destroyed by a fire in 1936.

Chatsworth is open to the public, and has magnificent grounds, which still owe much to Paxton's inventiveness; in particular the great fountain and the water cascade are strikingly attractive, and there is a camellia planted in 1851 and therefore perhaps by him, in one of his original arboretums. There's also an excellent and reasonably priced lunch to be had in the restaurant.

70 Mikael Pedersen and Bikes Tied Together with String

The *Dursley Gazette* for 21 October 1893 reported:

> A NEW BICYCLE. Mr M. Pedersen of Dursley, with that ingenuity for which he is known, has recently constructed a safety bicycle of remarkable character. Its weight is only 19 pounds and the maker has tested the strength in an extraordinary way, he having ridden it up Whiteway.

Whiteway is the fearsome hill that rises through the beech woods to the east of Dursley in Gloucestershire. It is one of those hills that if you ride up it on a bicycle you wish you hadn't! In 1896 the Cyclists Touring Club instructed a local wheelwright to put up a sign on Whiteway reading: NOTICE TO CYCLISTS. THIS HILL IS DANGEROUS. Certainly I should not like to come down it without brakes and with my feet on handlebars, which was the style in Pedersen's day.

Mikael Pedersen was born on 25 October 1855 at Marbjeg, near Copenhagen in Denmark, the eldest of seven children. He became an apprentice in a local firm making agricultural equipment, and while he was there invented a self-clearing threshing machine and a new bicycle, the parts for which were made in the factory. He also invented a centrifugal cream separator, which made him money and got him invited to England by Mr Lister of Dursley. He moved over to England in March 1893, and in September the same year patented his new bicycle.

Behind his house he set up a small factory to make bicycles; the early machines were made of wood, but in 1897 he switched to metal. The startling new concept behind Pedersen cycles was that they were all in tension. The frame was made of many very thin tubes, most of which seemed to meet at a point behind the handlebars, and the ends of the tubes were tied together with fine wires. Even the saddle, instead of being perched on the end of a rigid saddle tube, was slung on a hammock-like strap, which provided the rider with soft suspension.

Soon these new cycles began to make their mark. On 14 November 1898 Harry Goss Green set a new record on a Pedersen from London to Brighton and back in 6 hours, 8 minutes and 11 seconds. In 1900 he broke several more records: London–Liverpool (203 miles) in 11 hours; World 100 miles in 4 hours 41 minutes; London–York (197.5 miles) in 10 hours 19 minutes; and World 12 hours, 225 miles.

Many other remarkable tales arose, such as that of the Revd Sidney Swan, who rode from his parish in Carlisle all the way to London (301 miles) in less than twenty-four hours, even though he was cut and bruised when knocked off by a dog near Towcester. Many thousands of Pedersen cycles were made in

Dursley, and some are still being made today, both in England and on the Continent.

In 1896 Mikael was President of the Dursley Star rugby football club and the Dursley Star cricket club. He married three times – to Laura, Dagmar, and Ingeborg. Unfortunately the business eventually failed, and he went back to Denmark, where he died on 22 October 1929. But his bones were brought back to Dursley in 1996.

A blue plaque marks Pedersen's house in Dursley, and Pedersen bicycles are still obtainable, both modern replicas and originals.

71 Liborio Pedrazzolli and his Swimming Umbrellas

People have always wanted to be able to flash through the water with more speed and more freedom; hence the attraction of flippers, snorkels and other swimming aids. Among the more splendid inventions in this area were the swimming umbrellas dreamed up by Liborio Pedrazzolli.

Mr Pedrazzolli came over to England from Italy in about 1880, married an English girl, and set himself up in business as a wholesale and export looking-glass manufacturer at 11 Hoxton Street in north-east London. He must have reflected carefully about improving the efficiency of his swimming, and reasoned that he got a good push on the water when he kicked with his feet, but his hands seemed to slip through almost without pulling him forwards. So in 1896 he applied for a patent for mini-umbrellas to hold in his hands and increase their grip on the water. His patent describes how they work: 'When the forward stroke takes place in swimming the apparati close up and thereby offer a minimum amount of resistance to the water, but when the return stroke is made the apparati expand in umbrella form, and the resistance thus offered enables the swimmer to pull or propel himself through the water at a speed hitherto impossible.'

There was only one way to test them; I made some myself. The result was interesting, although not conclusive. They certainly did give a good grip on the water, but only after about 12–13 inches of the stroke, because they were quite slow to open. Meanwhile they slightly impeded all hand movements, so my hands tired more quickly. After practising for half an hour I decided I would be better off without them – but perhaps if they had been lighter in construction, and a little longer, and I had persevered, I too might have been able to swim at a speed hitherto impossible!

What were Pedrazzolli's premises in Hoxton Street have become a school.

72 William Petty and the Catamaran

Having looked at the lives of so many pioneers, it is natural to fantasise about when in history it would have been most interesting to have lived. Two periods stand out: the beginning of the industrial boom at the end of the eighteenth century, when Boulton and Watt held sway in Birmingham; and the period just after the restoration of Charles II when science was at the centre of the nation's life, Isaac Newton was around, and the Royal Society was set up. Nowhere near as famous as Newton, Hooke and the rest, William Petty was nevertheless one of the founding fellows of the Royal Society. He was an anatomist, an economist, a cartographer and a naval architect, and in 1662 in Dublin he designed and built the fastest boat in the world.

William Petty was born on 26 May 1623 in a house in Church Street, Romsey, in Hampshire. Normally this detail wouldn't be of much interest, except that by an amazing coincidence another hero lived in Church Street, Romsey, who was also a boat designer! Indeed, Edward Lyon Berthon (1813–99) was Rector of Romsey Abbey, the magnificent church for which the street is named, and invented various nautical devices, most famously his folding lifeboats (*see* page 57), and although he wrote extensively, he never seems to have mentioned the other pioneer of Church Street. Petty's father was a clothier, and though his 'principal amusement was looking on at the skilled tradesmen', at an early age William went to sea. He was such a precocious child (brat might be a better word) that his fellow seamen left him deserted on a French beach with a broken leg.

William was a resourceful chap, and instead of returning home he made enough money teaching English and navigation to enter a Jesuit College at Caen, where he received a good general education. He clearly liked learning and went on to study at Utrecht, Amsterdam and Leyden in 1644, before finally returning to Oxford to finish his medical studies. It was here that he began regular meetings in his own rooms and those of Dr Wilkins to discuss experimental natural sciences. This group was a forerunner of the Royal Society.

He soon gained fame for reviving the 'corpse' of Anne Green, who in 1650 was sentenced to be hanged for murder. The execution was carried out on the morning of 14 December. After half an hour she was cut down and pronounced dead by the sheriff. Her body, like that of any executed felon, had been promised to Petty, the young anatomist, for dissection. Fortunately he immediately realised that she was not in fact dead. He revived her with a curious combination of medical techniques, including bleeding, warming by 'a buxom lady', and the digesting of 'powdered Egyptian mummy'.

Incredibly, Anne Green came back to life, was pardoned, became a bit of a celebrity and went on to have a happy family life. Petty's medical reputation was enhanced no end by this act of seemingly miraculous medicine, and he was appointed Professor of Anatomy at Brasenose College, Oxford.

His medical fame gained him the well-paid post of physician-general to Cromwell's forces in Ireland. It was here that he completely changed tack and gained fame for his 'Down Survey' of Ireland. The 1653 Act of Settlement meant that the soldiers and the army's financial backers, called 'adventurers', were to be paid with confiscated Irish land. Benjamin Worsley, the surveyor-general, was doing such a rotten job that Petty offered to do it himself, tendering to survey the entire country in thirteen months, providing accurate maps and borders, for £18,532. Instead of using skilled surveyors, he did the job using the now unemployed soldiers at a fraction of this cost, and made £9,000 for himself.

The unskilled soldiers managed this complex surveying task thanks to Petty's brilliance. He designed and had built simple instruments with which the soldiers noted the position of natural features and used the chain to measure distances. All the information was then laid on to gridded paper at a central office in Dublin by skilled cartographers. Petty's maps were used to sort out all the property wrangles of the following decades, and became the first complete and accurate map of Ireland.

In 1659 Charles II was restored and though Petty had worked for the Cromwellian army and was friendly with the Cromwell family, his great charm allowed him to remain on good terms with both sides. Indeed, far from being bitter, in 1661 Charles gave him the parishes of Kenmare, Tuosist and Bonane, and Petty became Sir William Petty. In 1662 Petty was a founding Fellow of the Royal Society (patronised by Charles) and that same year moved to Dublin. The family house was at what is now St Stephen's Green, on the site of the Shelbourne Hotel. This was where he began experimenting on his 'double-bottomed boat'.

He tackled the problem experimentally, trying out alternative shapes for the hull. Instead of building full-size ships, he modelled them 'in small' as he put it. Petty was the first to experiment with ship design on a small scale, and his results showed that long thin hulls were faster than broad hulls. There are a number of reasons for this. First, a submerged hull has to part the water in front of it. The wider the hull, the further the water has to go around the boat and this takes energy, slowing the hull down. Also, a short hull makes short waves, and at certain speeds these waves slow the boat down. The longer the hull, the faster it can go before these waves affect its speed.

Unfortunately, his tests also showed that thin hulls were very unstable and liable to tip over. So, to get the best of speed and stability, he joined two long thin hulls with a deck, and invented the catamaran. The result was stable, fast and highly original. We know now that the Hawaiians and Polynesians had huge double-hulled boats, but no record of them appears in any seventeenth-century writings. For Petty, and the western world, this really was a first.

Petty then built a larger boat, each hull 20 feet long by 2 feet in diameter. He called it *Invention*, but the locals named it *Simon & Jude*, as it was launched on the feast of St Simon and St Jude, 28 October 1662.

To prove his test results Petty organised a race in Dublin Bay, backed by the Royal Society. On Epiphany, 6 January 1663, he raced against a small collection of ships' boats and a 'black pleasure boate' and on the outward downwind leg, against the flood tide, covered the 2 miles in 'half a quarter of one hour' – a spectacular 16 knots. Though she suffered a broken rudder on the return leg, *Invention* comfortably won the silk flag of the Royal Society, inscribed 'Proemium Regalis Societatis Velociorum', and Petty must have thought the future was rosy for his 'double-bottomed boat'. He built bigger boats: *Experiment* was a 60-footer, carrying sixteen guns, which he sailed to Portugal and Spain, and just three years before his death he built the enormous *St Michael the Archangel*. This boat was a complete failure and Petty's hopes for catamarans disappeared with it.

Petty's main claim to fame was as a political economist – he was one of the first to analyse the nature of wealth and how nations might acquire it, realising that wealth was more to do with labour and land than gold and treasure. But when he died in 1687 he was still writing to friends, insisting that the catamaran was a winner. Although catamarans are spectacularly fast, they haven't really replaced conventional ships. However, if William Petty visited the site of that triumphant race in Dublin Bay today, he would be delighted to discover that the passengers, trucks and cars coming from Holyhead invariably travel at great speed and in any weather in a giant version of his 'double-bottomed boat'.

The high-speed ferry between Dublin and Holyhead is a catamaran, and the Shelbourne Hotel on St Stephen's Green in Dublin is on the site of Petty's house.

73 Alastair Pilkington's Floating Glass

Of all the materials that characterise the modern cityscape, glass is surely the most exciting. Breath-taking walls of clear, flat glass are draped over the world's most prestigious buildings, prompting us to wonder how something so solid could be constructed of a material so apparently light and delicate. Perhaps the fixation with vast areas of glass comes from it being a truly modern material: only fifty years ago the process by which most glass is made had not been invented. The man who solved a problem that had challenged technologists since Roman times was Alastair Pilkington – and the answer came to him while he was doing the washing up.

The use of glass in buildings has always been associated with wealth and status – at one time in England there was a window tax. But actually making the stuff flat, clear and in large sheets is a real challenge. Although the Egyptians used it, the Romans first mastered glass – working out how to blow it to make vessels. They discovered that you can't mould glass as you mould clay for pottery because if you touch the surface of molten glass, it loses its transparency. This is why making sheets of flat glass is so difficult – it would be nice if you could simply roll out a piece of glass like making pastry, but that would ruin the surface. So the first successful flat glass process was a development of blown glass, and the 'crown glass' process was used until the middle of the nineteenth century. At first the process looks like blowing a glass bowl. At a critical moment the bowl is put back into the furnace to soften it, and then is withdrawn, spinning fast. The centrifugal force opens the bowl out like a flower, and as the glass-maker keeps spinning it flattens out and stretches until it is perhaps 5 feet in diameter – a smooth sheet of glass with a 'fire finish' that comes from never having touched anything.

Unfortunately, right in the centre of the glass disc is a major fault – the bull's-eye, a nodule where the glass-maker's 'ponty' or iron rod was attached. So the glass is cut into sheets, avoiding the bit in the middle, which was thrown away until it became fashionable to put a bull's-eye into the glass of front doors. Because the disc is circular, rather a lot of the glass round the edge is also wasted. By the time Joseph Paxton came to design the Crystal Palace for the Great Exhibition of 1851, he could rely on a rather more productive process. The cylinder process was also based on glass-blowing and, as its name suggests, involved blowing a huge cylinder of glass, which was allowed to harden before being cut and flattened. Although machines blowing cylinders a few yards long were eventually produced, this was still very labour intensive and far from a continuous industrial process.

Lionel Alexander Bethune (pronounced Beaton) Pilkington, always known as Alastair, was born in India on 6 January 1920, and educated at Cambridge. The war interrupted his studies quite a bit; he was captured on Crete in 1942 and spent the rest of the war practising his clarinet in a prison camp. He finished his studies when he returned and joined the company which shared his name in 1947. It was with them that he put his mind to making the best flat glass in the world. St Helens was already the centre of the British glass-making industry, largely thanks to the Pilkington factory that had first opened over a century before. It is a curious fact that Alastair was not related to the Pilkingtons who owned the company.

By this time flat glass was made on an industrial scale but they still hadn't got it right. Plate glass was made by rolling the glass between metal rollers and then grinding and polishing away the ruined surface that resulted. The end product was good, but the process was hugely wasteful and expensive. More cunning was the 'window glass' process first tried in 1914. The idea was to draw a sticky ribbon of molten glass from the surface of the melted mass in the furnace, rather as you get a long string when you take your spoon out of a jar of treacle. As the ribbon rose, the surface cooled and eventually the glass set. It had the attraction of being continuous, and having an intrinsically good 'fire finish'. But 'window glass' could only be made thin and, worse, the way it cooled led to optical distortions – hence the name: it was all right for domestic windows, but not for anything fancy.

Alastair had joined Pilkingtons to work on the technical side of production, but soon rose into management. He claimed that it was because he was 'bored' that his mind became occupied with the problem of flat glass, and one day in 1952, while he was helping his wife with the washing up, he hit upon the answer. Glass is ruined if during manufacture it touches something solid; but what if the thing it touched was not solid? He realised that it might be possible to float molten glass on molten metal, just as oil floats on water. If you could control everything properly, it might be possible to allow the glass to cool enough to be lifted off the still molten metal as a sheet. Because the liquid metal would be perfectly smooth and flat, so would the glass. It turned out that tin was the metal with the right melting point and so on, but the rest of the process proved to be a bit of a nightmare.

Pilkington's account of how he made the float process work is very different from the way eighteenth and nineteenth-century lone inventors perfected their ideas. The principle of float glass was brilliant: glass would indeed float on tin and could be removed. But he needed a full-scale experimental plant, and had to get exactly right every detail of a process that had never been tried before he could get anything like saleable glass. Every month he would go to the Pilkington board to explain why it was taking so long, and to ask for another £100,000. Having invented the process in 1952, Pilkingtons did not announce it until 1959. In that time Pilkington had to solve chemical problems in the bath, to design spouts to pour glass on to the tin in a particular way, to devise a special atmosphere inside the float chamber, to work out how to cut and handle a continuous ribbon of glass. Most things that could have gone wrong, did, and for most of the development period no useful glass was made.

But they did have one bit of luck. When glass

floats on molten tin, it naturally forms a sheet 6 mm thick, which accounts for 50 per cent of the world market in glass! Finally in 1958 they got everything right, announced the process the following year, and then shut down the plant to prepare it for continuous production. When they started up again, the glass was no good and nobody knew why; it took fourteen very expensive months to fix. Today, however, thousands of tonnes of float glass are made every day thanks to the inspiration and perspiration of Alastair Pilkington.

There are now many float-glass factories, but Alastair Pilkington's real memorials are the world's millions of smooth glass windows.

74 Christopher Pinchbeck and his Nocturnal Remembrancer

When you wake up in the middle of the night you often experience a curious semi-conscious mental state, called the hypnopompic state by some psychologists. Often you have vivid images, and occasionally what seem to be brilliant thoughts. But by the morning they are all forgotten. The best way of trying to recall those flashes of genius seems to be to write them down; so you need to keep a pencil and paper by the bed. However, one potential problem remains; if you try to write down your pearl of wisdom in the dark, you might write on top of the previous idea, and thus render both illegible. This was the difficulty solved by the 'nocturnal remembrancer' of Christopher Pinchbeck.

Christopher Pinchbeck was born about 1710. His father – also called Christopher – made clocks and clever musical toys, and invented a new metal alloy, a mixture of copper and zinc that looked like gold and could be used in cheap jewellery; it is still called pinchbeck. Christopher Jnr was something of a mechanical genius. He won a gold medal for inventing a self-acting pneumatic brake for cranes; he made a very complicated astronomical clock with four dials, which found its way to Buckingham Palace; and he devised a candlestick which ensured that the candle always stayed upright, and therefore avoided spilling molten wax on the floor.

He patented his nocturnal remembrancer in 1768, and covered all manner of possible developments by describing it in fancy terms. Thus of the notepad he says, 'a set of tablets, whose leaves are of asses' skin, ivory, slate, and of every other material made use of for the leaves of tablets or pocket books, and whose case or outside is made of gold, silver, ivory, tortoiseshell, leather, and likewise of every material of which the outside or cases of other tablets or pocket books are made . . .'.

Basically, however, it was a notepad sliding up and down inside a case, and held in place by a spring-loaded catch resting in a notch. The case had a slot in the front, which you could feel in the dark, and through which you could write your brilliant idea; the front of the case masked the rest of the pad. When you had written down an idea, you slid the pad up the case to the next notch, so that your previous idea was covered by the case, and a fresh patch of pad exposed in the slot. Thus even in complete darkness you could write down your ideas and be sure of never going over something you had written before.

What is most amusing about this device is that even though it's really just a notepad he called it a 'nocturnal remembrancer', as though the gadget was going to do the remembering. I am reminded of those gadgets you buy by mail-order today that promise to do everything, and turn out to be just a piece of string and a pencil.

75 George Pocock's Kite-powered Charvolants – Evading the Tolls

In 1828 the citizens of Bristol were astonished to see a completely new vehicle sailing along the roads, over the downs and into the hills. 'After many experiments Mr George Pocock', according to the *Annals of Bristol*, 'invented a vehicle somewhat similar in form to the modern tricycle, and found that one of these, capable of carrying four persons, could be drawn by two kites of twelve feet and ten feet in height respectively – the speed attained with a brisk wind being about twenty-five miles an hour.'

George Pocock, brother of artist Nicholas Pocock, opened a school on St Michael's Hill in Bristol, and apparently had some problems with discipline, since he claimed to have invented a patent self-acting ferrule, or spanking machine. However, his kite-powered carriage was a far more humane device. He called the vehicle a charvolant, and demonstrated one to George IV at Ascot races that year. The charvolant would sail easily downwind and with slight modifications could be made to tack across the wind and even slightly into it. In 1836 the British Association for the Advancement of Science met in Bristol, and Pocock's charvolants were much admired. Among those who enjoyed a ride over the downs was Prince George of Cumberland, later King of Hanover.

Pocock also promoted the uses of kites for other things, including rescues. To demonstrate his ideas he put his young daughter Martha in an armchair and flew her from the beach up to the top of a high cliff. She survived the ordeal, and went on to become the mother of cricketer W.G. Grace.

The *Liverpool Mercury* recorded that Pocock used kites to pull a ferry boat across the Mersey, and said that with the largest kites and a good wind, a boat 'would be able to make the passage from and to Birkenhead, whatever might be the state and strength of the tide', and that the boat could be drawn in any direction 'less than five points from the wind'.

According to *A treatise on the Aeropleustic Art, or Navigation in the Air, by means of Kites or buoyant sails, with a description of the Charvolant, or Kite Carriage*, 'Mile after mile, in succession, has been performed at the rate of twenty miles an hour, timing it by chronometer in hand. A mile has frequently been performed, over a heavy road, in two minutes and three quarters. Let it be noticed, that the wind was not furious, neither were the kites additionally powerful for the bad state of the roads . . .

'That the swiftness of movement should almost prevent breathing, is certain, if going against the wind; but when travelling at such a rate, it is with the wind, and thus a perfect calm is enjoyed. One evil, however, it was supposed did arise from its velocity – loss of appetite; for on one occasion, when pulling up at a house of call seventeen miles from Bristol, some little concern was felt by the party when not one of them was disposed to take any refreshment. . . . However . . . on looking at the chronometer, they discovered that their travelling pace, up hill and down, had been sixteen miles within the hour: of course there could be little disposition to hunger so soon after a plentiful repast at home.'

The Pocock family travelled by charvolant for many years, and apart from the sheer fun discovered one great advantage over more conventional forms of transport on the turnpikes. The government had introduced heavy tolls on all carriages, partly to encourage people to use the railways which were then spreading across the country – the Great Western Railway reached Bristol in 1841. There were tolls laid down for steam carriages, for horse-drawn carriages and for ox-carts, but there were no tolls specified for charvolants, and so the Pococks used the turnpikes for free.

The Bristol Kitestore (0117 974 5010) has kite-powered buggies for sale, and sometimes also for hire.

76 Colin Pullinger and his Perpetual Mousetrap

Mice have always plagued people; ever since the first cave-dwellers began to store food in a larder, mice have been there to make the most of it. Whenever people move into any sort of home, mice move in right alongside; for thousands of years people must have been inventing ways to get rid of them. So the mousetrap has become a sort of symbol of human ingenuity – and this is just what *Local Heroes* is all about.

The earliest mousetraps were probably just holes in the ground; the advanced versions were bottles sunk into the ground, so that the mice could not climb out up the slippery walls.

Among the earliest known mechanical traps was the pit-fall trap, which was essentially a hole in the ground with a trapdoor, traditionally baited with a mixture of oatmeal and honey. The mouse came along, smelled the bait, stepped on the trapdoor, and dropped into the pit – or probably into a bucket of water.

Today the traditional bait is cheese; indeed poor-quality or plain cheap Cheddar cheeses are sometimes called 'mousetrap'. Most modern traps have metal springs; when the mouse touches the bait it releases a catch and a stiff wire loop snaps viciously down on the mouse's neck, usually killing it instantly. These traps are neat and powerful, but they have two disadvantages. First they are considered by some to be inhumane; occasionally the mouse is not killed, but injured and left in pain. Secondly, the trap can catch only one mouse at a time. Once it's sprung it's sprung, and other mice can come along and eat the cheese with impunity.

Both of these drawbacks were solved by Colin Pullinger, a Hampshire man, born in 1814 in Ivy Cottage in Selsey. Despite all the claims on his trade card, he eventually inherited his father's house and carpentry business, and then, about 1860, he invented a new mousetrap. This was a 'perpetual mousetrap' – one that would catch mouse after mouse – and the mice were not killed or even injured.

The trap had a hole in the middle of the top, for the mice to go in, attracted by the smell of the bait kept in a perforated bait-box inside. Below the entrance hole was the critical mechanism, a cruciform beam like a see-saw which the mouse would tip with its weight. Once the see-saw had tipped, the mouse could no longer reach the entrance hole; so its only way out of the small compartment was through a one-way door into the end of the box. Once it had gone through this door, there was no escape, and the trap was set ready for the next mouse, which would find its way to the other end of the box. Colin always stressed how humane it was; the mice were unharmed, and could presumably be set free in your neighbour's garden!

Colin Pullinger's mousetrap was incredibly successful, both operationally and financially. He claimed in his advertising that he had once caught twenty-eight mice in one trap in a single night, and that in nine months a farmer had caught nearly a thousand mice in one trap.

The factory grew until Pullinger employed forty men and boys; he was the biggest employer in Selsey. They had horse-powered circular saws and drills; they could make a trap in four and a half minutes, and they made 960 a week. By 1885 they had sold two million, at half a crown apiece, and mousetraps went on being made in Selsey until 1920.

The success of Colin Pullinger's enterprise lends support to the aphorism coined by the American writer Ralph Waldo Emerson: 'If a man write a better book, preach a better sermon, or make a better mousetrap than his neighbour, tho' he build his house in the woods, the world will make a beaten path to his door.'

Colin Pullinger's house, Ivy Cottage, still stands in Selsey, but there is no obvious trace of the yard where he made his mousetraps.

77 Robert Recorde, and the Invention of the Equals Sign

There's an age-old philosophical question, raised by Plato among many others: Was mathematics invented by people, or was it all out there in the world, waiting to be discovered? Some bits of mathematics are so familiar they seem almost to be part of nature. Take the equals sign, for example; it seems so natural you might almost expect to find one in the garden, but it was actually invented by a gentle soul and a brilliant teacher of mathematics. He introduced algebra to this country, he was the first to write about arithmetic and geometry in English, and his name was Robert Recorde.

Robert Recorde was born in 1510. His dad was the 120th Mayor of Tenby in the south-west corner of Wales. In those days Tenby was a busy port; the harbour was surrounded by large stone houses belonging to wealthy merchants. Robert went to Oxford, became a fellow of All Souls College, and lectured on mathematics, rhetoric, music and anatomy. Later, he went to Cambridge and to London.

His first book, *The Grounde of Arts* (1543), was a simple textbook of arithmetic, but so good it went through at least fifty editions. He followed this in 1551 with *The Pathway to Knowledge*, all about geometry; *The Castle of Knowledge*, in 1556, about astronomy; and finally in 1557 *The Whetstone of Witte*. In this last book he introduced not only plus and minus signs, but the equals sign.

Apparently this sign used to be an abbreviation for *est* (which means 'is' in Latin), but he formalised it in his book: 'to avoid the tediouse repetition of these woordes: is equalle to: . . . a paire of paralleles, or gemowe [twin] lines of one lengthe, thus: ═══, bicause noe. 2. thynges can be moare equalle.'

In his first book there are 2, 3, 4, and 5 times tables, but he reckoned the later ones were too difficult; so he taught a curious method of multiplication for digits from 6 to 9, using the St Andrew's cross.

Thus to multiply 7 × 9 he wrote

```
7
  X
9
```

Then he subtracted both numbers from 10 and wrote in

```
7   3
  X
9   1
```

Multiply the right-hand digits to give the right digit of the answer

```
7   3
  X
9   1
-----
    3
```

Then subtract diagonally (9-3 or 7-1) to give the left digit of the answer

```
7   3
  X
9   1
-----
6   3
```

Strange, but it seems to work!

Robert Recorde died in 1558, the year that Elizabeth became Queen, and five years before William Shakespeare was born.

St Mary's Church in Tenby has a lovely memorial and portrait in relief; Tenby Museum has three original Recorde books, although not on display; open 10–4.

78 Thomas Romney Robinson's Cup Anemometer

Armagh Observatory was built in 1790. Its director for almost sixty years, from 1823 to 1882, was a man of exceptional versatility and vitality, even among my heroes. He made significant contributions to astronomy, meteorology, electricity, magnetism, turbines, air-pumps, fog signals and balloons. He even stressed to ladies the importance of chemistry! In an address to the Royal Irish Academy in 1852 he said 'The person who cultivates only one branch of science cripples his mind, and does himself an injustice.' His name was Thomas Romney Robinson.

Thomas Romney Robinson was born in Dublin on 23 April 1792. He was a child prodigy, reading avidly by the time he was three, and having a book of poems published when he was only thirteen. He became rector of Enniskillen, and then director of Armagh Observatory when he was thirty-one.

The most worthy thing he did was to compile a catalogue of the positions of 5,345 stars – a huge task involving ten years of solid work for him and his assistant Neil McNeil Edmondson. When it was published in 1859 it won him the Royal Medal of the Royal Society, and he said proudly 'Already it has taken its place among the standard catalogues of reference'. But Mr Edmondson said, 'The fact is, Doctor, it has made old men of us.'

In 1849 Robinson read a paper in Belfast about his observations of the moon. He made a number of statements which show the depth of his understanding:

> We see only one side of the Moon, because it turns on its axis at the same rate as it revolves about the Earth; so the same side always faces us.
>
> It has no atmosphere, because stars going

behind it disappear suddenly, whereas if there were any atmosphere they would go slowly.

Things on the Moon's surface are light and spongy. A body weighing 6 lb on Earth would weigh only 1 lb on the Moon.

From the length of the shadows we know there are cliffs on the Moon 25,000 feet high, while on Earth there are none more than 500 feet.

He was always interested in anything that might upset his astronomical observations. Railways, for example: they shook telescopes and, by using his influence in the House of Lords, he managed to prevent people from building railways not only at Armagh, but also at Greenwich and Oxford.

Wind also rocked the telescope. What was the best way to measure wind speed? After much thought and consideration of various types of apparatus then in use, he invented the cup anemometer. He reckoned that hemispheres would be efficient and easy to reproduce – anyone could make them. He experimented, and decided that four arms were better than three or five. He calculated that if there were no friction, the speed of the cups would be exactly one-third of the wind speed, which turned out to be correct. And finally this elegant machine does not have to be turned round to face the wind. It works just as well wherever the wind comes from.

This was such a good piece of design that no one has bettered it yet. You've probably seen them in airports; meteorologists all over the world use cup anemometers, although they often make them with three arms.

But what really endears Robinson to us was the way he set out to find out where he was. At the 1834 meeting of the British Association for the Advancement of Science in Edinburgh, and at the 1838 meeting in Newcastle, he and others agreed to measure very accurately the longitudes of Cambridge, Oxford, Dublin and Armagh, basically to check the maps. We now assume our maps are absolutely accurate, but 150 years ago there was some uncertainty about the exact positions of places. So they wanted to measure their longitude, and they proposed to do it by two different methods.

They persuaded the famous clockmaker Mr E.J. Dent to visit them with fifteen chronometers. These were all synchronised at Greenwich, then Mr Dent carried them in a wooden box on his knee for 500 miles by train in England, 275 miles at sea by steamship, and 190 miles by stage-coach in Ireland. The whole journey took only a week, being performed, as Robinson remarked, 'with the marvellous rapidity of modern improvement'.

But Robinson also wanted to use direct observation, so his second method was to set up a signal that could be seen from both Armagh and Dublin simultaneously. Then they could be sure their clocks were exactly synchronised. There isn't a mountain high enough to be visible from both places, but the highest mountain between Armagh and Dublin is Slieve Gullion, and from Slieve Gullion they could fire rockets high enough for the explosions to be visible from both 18 miles away in Armagh and 51 miles away in Dublin.

Robinson sent his son up the mountain to organise the rockets, with assistance from Lieutenant Thomas Larcom of the Ordnance Survey, who provided them with maps, tents and, most important, rockets. They set up camp on the mountain on 13 May 1839. The Rector of Forkhill provided remarkable hospitality, even for Ireland, including food and two policemen in case of trouble. But the only trouble came from the weather; it snowed, and for two nights that week they couldn't fire any rockets.

Robinson sat in the observatory in Armagh; his friend William Rowan Hamilton sat in Dublin, and they both had to measure as accurately as possible the time of the rocket bursts. Robinson also trained three assistants by getting them to write down the times of shots from a flintlock pistol. Robinson sat in the dark by his telescope, and every now and then looked at the precise grandfather clock by the light of a candle, and he counted the seconds in his mind. 'Five past one, and 10 seconds, 11 . . . 12 . . . 13 . . . 14 FLASH – there it goes – 14.4 seconds – write it down.'

They started firing the rockets at 10 o'clock at night, since they could see the signal better in the dark. They fired fifteen rockets the first night, at five-minute intervals, thirteen the next night, and more at the end of the week. Each rocket provided one precise observation in Armagh and another in Dublin. Robinson and Hamilton both knew their own local time accurately, by observations. After watching the rocket explosions they could synchronise their clocks, and measure precisely the difference between local time in Dublin and local time in Armagh.

The result of this heroic set of experiments was completely to revise the difference in longitude between Dublin and Armagh from 1 minute 14.220 seconds to 1 minute 14.258 seconds. In other words, by letting off several pounds of high explosive into the night sky, Thomas Romney Robinson showed that Armagh was further west of Dublin than anyone had suspected by a distance of nearly 2 feet!

Armagh Observatory is a fine building with an original Robinson anemometer mounted on a tower; note how far west it is!

Nicholas Saunderson, Blind Mathematical Genius who Taught Others to See

One mile west of Penistone, high in the Yorkshire Pennines, lies the little village of Thurlstone, built dramatically on the sides of the hills, the cellar of one house being level with the roof of the three-storey house next door. Nicholas Saunderson's birth in January 1682 is commemorated by a plaque in Latin on the wall by the telephone box. When he was about a year old, Nicholas caught smallpox, and lost not merely his sight but his eyes as well. This boded ill for his future, since most of the people in the village lived by manual labour, and blind labourers were not much in demand.

However, he showed promise at the village school, and his parents sent him off to the Free Grammar School in Penistone, the seventh oldest school in the country, close to the imposing church in the centre of town. Here Nicholas found a great delight in studying the works of Isaac Newton, and turned out himself to have a gift for mathematics; but what call was there for blind mathematicians in rural Yorkshire?

In 1707 he decided to go to Cambridge, the centre of scholarship, and because he had no money to go as a student, he went as a teacher. His subject was Newton's Optics, of all improbable things, and he lectured so brilliantly that his lectures were always packed. Young John Harrison, the clock-maker, copied out all his lecture notes. However, Saunderson was not always successful; Horace Walpole, son of the first prime minister, wrote that he had been unable to learn his tables, and Saunderson had said to him, 'Young man, it would be cheating you to take your money; for you can never learn what I am trying to teach you.'

Saunderson became well respected, wrote a treatise on algebra, and in 1711 he was given an MA by special mandate from Queen Anne. He was elected Lucasian Professor of Mathematics, the position that Newton had held until 1703, and one of the most prestigious maths jobs in the world. But perhaps the most remarkable thing about this remarkable man was that according to legend he learned to read by feeling the letters on the gravestones in Penistone churchyard.

There's a plaque near the phone box in Thurlstone, and the churchyard at Penistone has gravestones that he must have read by touch.

80 Thomas Savery's Patent for Raising Water by Fire

The industrial revolution changed the world for ever. Some would argue that the intellectual drive may have come from the Lunar Society in Birmingham; certainly the idea of gathering a large workforce in a single factory was perhaps started by Richard Arkwright in Derbyshire; but what gave the whole thing momentum was the harnessing of power, and in particular the power of steam.

Most people think the steam engine was invented by James Watt, but in fact the first practical machine was patented forty years before Watt was born – in fact, in the year that James Watt's father was born – 1698. What's more, that machine was invented not in London, nor in Manchester, nor in Birmingham, but at Shilston Barton in South Devon, by Thomas Savery.

Thomas was born about 1650 into a wealthy family. They bought a medieval manor house and built on a huge extension. As the younger son of a younger son, Thomas was a gent, but had no land to work, so he devoted his mind to engineering and invention. In 1696 he patented both a machine for polishing glass and marble and another for 'Rowing of ships with greater ease and expedicion then hath hitherto beene done by any other'. This seems to have been a capstan attached to paddle-wheels – a sort of seventeenth-century pedalo. In those days all patents were issued by the king. Luckily Savery knew William III – William of Orange – and William liked his rowing machine, so Savery got a patent – but the navy turned it down, which made him really cross.

He seems to have been a military engineer, and he must have known about all the mines being worked nearby, especially the tin mines in Cornwall. The miners had a real problem. The surface seams had been worked out, and when the miners dug down, the mines filled up with water. To begin with they baled it out by hand, then they used horses, but deep mines were difficult to keep from flooding.

One evening after dinner, so the story goes, Savery threw his wine bottle on the fire, observed the last of the wine inside turning into steam, and in a flash of brilliance realised the steam must be pushing the air out of the bottle. He grabbed the bottle, and thrust the neck into a bowl of water. The steam inside condensed, the water slowly rose up into the bottle, and Savery reckoned that if a wine bottle could pull water up out of a bowl, then a bigger bottle could pull water up out of a mine.

So he made himself a model, showed it to the king, and got himself another patent – for 'raiseing water by the impellant force of fire'. He also demonstrated his machine to the Royal Society on 14 June 1699. The patent has no diagram, nor even a description of the engine, but in 1702 he published a book called *The Miners Friend; or, an Engine to raise Water by Fire, Described. And of the manner of Fixing it in Mines. With an Account of the several other Uses it is applicable unto; and an Answer to the Objections made against it.*

The book is a wonderful mixture. First, there's a crawling letter to the king, in very large print – perhaps he was worried that the King had poor eyesight, then one to the Royal Society, and a ten-page sales pitch to the Gentlemen Adventurers in the Mines of England. Then follows a diagram and detailed instructions – just as you might get for a video machine today. First installation, then operation; for example, page 15:

> Light the Fire at B. When the water in N boils, the Handle of the Regulator mark'd Z must be thrust

> from you as far as twill go, which makes all the steam rising from the water in L pass with irresistible Force through O into P, pushing out the Air before it, through the Clack R making a noise as it goes. And when all is gone out, the Bottom of the Vessel P will be very hot.

In his book, Savery describes vividly what happened when the machine worked:

> On the outside of the vessel you may see how the water goes out, as if the vessel were transparent. For as the steam continues within the vessel, so far is the vessel dry without, and so very hot as scarce to endure the least touch of the hand. But as far as the water is, the said vessel will be cold and wet, where any water has fallen on it; which cold and moisture vanishes as fast as the steam, in its descent, takes place of the water.

He was at pains to say how powerful his engine was, and he actually invented the term 'horse-power' – deliberately making it rather more than most horses could manage so that his customers would not be disappointed.

A few Savery engines were probably used in mines. One was installed to control the water supply at Hampton Court. Another at Campden House in Kensington was still running eighteen years later. But they were not robust. The water was pushed out by positive steam pressure, and that needed high-pressure steam. The solder and the joints could not take the pressure, and as a result the machines kept going wrong. However, the Savery engine was the first practical use of steam power, and under Captain Savery's patent the steam engine came of age.

Shilston Barton is a private house. There appear to be no remaining Savery engines. However, modern copies of *The Miner's Friend* appear from time to time.

81 The Scoresbys, Whaling Scientists of Whitby

The *Dictionary of National Biography* entry for William Scoresby Jnr lists under 'Education' the *Resolution* whaler and Queen's College, Cambridge. His father, William Snr, was educated at the village school, Cropton, and on a ship called the *Jane*, trading between Whitby and the Baltic. These entries hint at the amazing lives of these father-and-son scientists, who spanned all levels of society, as well as the most dangerous parts of the globe.

William Scoresby Snr (1760–1829), son of a farmer, was born in the village of Cropton, 20 miles from Whitby. He first worked on the farm at the age of nine, and did not go to sea until he was twenty, when he became an apprentice on the *Jane*. William was a superb navigator, and in his second year at sea he detected a navigational error which might have resulted in the loss of the ship. Far from being grateful, the mate (whose fault it was) became so unpleasant that Scoresby left the ship in 1781 and joined the *Speedwell*, carrying stores to Gibraltar. It was not a happy voyage: in the Straits of Gibraltar they were captured by the Spanish, and thrown into jail. Scoresby and a friend managed to escape, and made their way home, where Scoresby embarked on his career with the Greenland whaling fleet.

It must have been an extraordinary life. Scoresby never saw a summer in Whitby, always preferring to make the profitable voyage north. He became the most successful whaler ever, taking record catches and making the most profit, totalling £90,000 in thirty years at sea. He also held the record for the highest latitude ever attained by a ship. He was a bit of an inventor, his most famous creation being the 'crow's nest', a barrel hoisted into the rigging to provide some protection for the look-out against the Arctic winds.

Against this background, it is not surprising that William Scoresby Jnr (1789–1857) worshipped his father, and wanted to follow in his footsteps. When he was just ten, William went aboard his father's ship to say goodbye before that summer's voyage to Greenland. When it was time to return ashore, William hid his hat, hoping the delay would result in his being left on board. His father gave in, and the pilots went ashore, leaving young William to begin his great career at sea. He became a captain in his own right when he was twenty-one years old.

Scoresby's journal records a particularly dramatic incident. Chasing after one whale, the other boats couldn't keep up. But Scoresby had noticed that the whale kept to a circular path, and positioned his boat where he expected it to surface. But he was almost too clever for his own good: '. . . having marked the proceedings of the fish, I selected a situation where I conceived it was likely to make its appearance. It arose in the very spot, and though unperceived by us struck the boat such a blow the bottom was driven in, a hole fifteen square feet in area, and the boat sank in a moment. Assistance was not very distant and after a few minutes in hazard of perishing we were happily rescued without having sustained any particular injury.'

William not only tolerated the hard life, he positively cultivated it. Having entered Edinburgh University in 1806, the same year he accompanied his father on the latitude record-breaking voyage, he volunteered for the navy, wanting to experience the life of an ordinary seaman. When he left the navy, he had a bit of luck. Returning home from Portsmouth he met Sir Joseph Banks, the famous botanist on Cook's first voyage. Banks was by then President of the Royal Society – top man in British science – a post he held for forty years until his death in 1820. Banks took Scoresby to a few social gatherings in London, and introduced him to the scientific elite. Perhaps Banks exhibited the brave and muscular whaler as a bit of exotica from the north, but whatever the reason, they became friends and corresponded until Banks's death. Banks suggested to Scoresby that he should start recording the natural phenomena he observed on his voyages, since really good scientific records of the Arctic were rare.

Scoresby turned out to be an excellent natural scientist, not least because of his skill as an artist. His drawings and paintings were superb, often recording dramatic whaling incidents, as well as animals and plants never seen by Europeans. Scoresby was much more than a keen observer, and he began to build up an impressive list of scientific theories and discoveries. He was the first person to suggest that the peculiar colours of the Arctic seas were due to what he called 'minute animalcules', what we would call plankton. Using a microscope, he was the first to record the beautiful shapes of snowflakes – a task made easier, it is true, by working in sub-zero temperatures where the snowflakes do not melt!

He found a surprising result from his 'Marine Diver'. The Diver was a box containing a thermometer that was lowered into the ocean, and could record the temperature at various depths. He discovered that in the Arctic ocean, the deeper you go, the warmer it gets, which confounded previous ideas.

Perhaps his most spectacular work was on magnetism. He discovered that if you hammer a piece of soft iron, it becomes a weak magnet – if you line it up with the earth's magnetic field. Stuck in the ice in Greenland one summer, he found that if he hammered a second piece of iron with the first, the magnet got stronger, and so he built up what is known as the Greenland Magnet. This is now in the museum at Whitby, together with his drawings and specimens, and still lifts a 10 lb weight with ease. Scoresby reckoned that a man lost at sea could quickly construct a compass to navigate home, should he happen to have soft iron nail and a hammer about his person.

Scoresby clearly had the respect of his men. One of his favourite tricks was to mould a lens from ice using the warmth of his hands, and use it to light the sailors' pipes – fire from ice. He became a very moral person, and in particular believed the Sabbath should be respected. Once he entertained a couple of rough whaling captains to Sunday breakfast, and although he prayed fervently following the stream of blasphemy he had witnessed, he caught hardly any whales the following week, and resolved always to be pious on Sundays. He eventually left the sea to become a vicar, and preached in 1826 at St Mary's Church to a congregation mourning the loss in storms of the *Lively* and the *Esk* – the last two whaling ships to sail from Whitby.

The Whitby Museum in Pannett Park, open most days (01947 602908), has a replica of William Snr's crow's nest, and many beautiful original drawings and paintings by William Jnr, as well as the huge magnet he made while stuck in the ice off Greenland.

82 Joe Sheridan, Shannon and Irish Coffee

Shannon airport in the west of Ireland is a surprisingly pioneering place. It is where transatlantic flying really began, where duty-free shopping was invented, and where Joe Sheridan made that crucial aviation innovation – Irish coffee.

Sheridan was born in County Tyrone in 1909. In about 1942 he got a job as a chef at the seaport of Foynes, on the Shannon estuary, a few miles from the present site of Shannon airport. At that time, transatlantic passenger flights were all by flying boat, the idea being that you could land in the water if the weather or fuel consumption got the better of you. Flights left from Botwood, Newfoundland, on the far side, to Foynes, from where passengers got a land transfer or conventional flight to their final destinations.

Being a pioneering transatlantic passenger may have been exciting, but it wasn't as glamorous as everyone hoped. The planes carried twenty-five to thirty people in an unpressurised cabin, on a flight lasting up to eighteen hours. Sometimes planes had to turn back because of bad weather after perhaps four hours of flight. Whether they had made it or not, the passengers would certainly be cold and uncomfortable. Joe Sheridan was working as a chef at

Foynes when the catering manager Brendan O'Regan spotted a gap in the market. Surely they could think of a novel way of warming up and improving the mood of the frozen transatlantic passengers while they waited for their onward flights. Could Joe invent something hot, alcoholic and with an Irish flavour?

Joe Sheridan came up with a brand new drink, known as Irish coffee. It consisted of coffee mixed with whiskey, and topped off with half an inch of cream. The idea was to drink the hot coffee through the cold cream – and it is absolutely delicious. But it wasn't quite as simple as it seemed.

After the war conventional planes took over from the flying boats, but they still used Shannon airport to refuel, and Irish coffee continued to be a great hit. In the 1950s a travel writer called Stanford Delaplane from the *San Francisco Chronicle* came through, and liked the Irish coffee so much that he decided to import it to America. He described it to bartender Jack Koeppler at the Buena Vista bar in San Francisco. Here they attempted to recreate the magnificent drink – but without success. He utterly failed to make the cream float, so he had to return to Shannon for a scientific lesson from the master.

There is a bit of a paradox here. In Irish coffee the cream clearly floats on the coffee. But anyone who drinks conventional coffee with cream will know that it is perfectly possible to mix the cream smoothly with the coffee and it doesn't separate out – which is what happened to the unfortunate

Mr Delaplane. Joe had a trick and a bit of science to help.

This is how to make proper Irish coffee. Put a measure of whiskey – Irish, of course – into a glass that has been warmed so that it doesn't crack. Then add three lumps or a tablespoon of sugar – they use brown sugar at Shannon airport, but it doesn't really matter. Pour in the coffee to within an inch of the top of the glass. The sugar makes the drink taste yummy – but cunningly also makes the coffee more dense, so the cream floats more easily. The other trick known to Irish coffee drinkers is that you pour on the cream – which should be double, and lightly whipped – over the back of a spoon to discourage mixing, but in the Joe Sheridan Bar at Shannon the cream is thick enough to make this unnecessary.

Joe later went to California, where each year more Irish coffee is consumed in San Francisco alone than in the whole of Ireland. He died in 1962 and is buried within sight of the Golden Gate Bridge.

To reach Shannon airport by road, you have to pass through Limerick, so it seems appropriate to recap the recipe in verse:

> Joe Sheridan's cunning hot drink
> Is easy to make – if you think
> That sugar's propensity
> To increase the density
> Ensures that the cream doesn't sink!

They serve a wonderful Irish coffee in Joe Sheridan's Bar at Shannon airport.

83 John Smeaton's Water-wheels

John Smeaton was born in 1724 at Austhorpe Lodge, of which the gatehouse still stands near the fish-and-chip shop on the ring road in Middleton, east of Leeds. As a lad Smeaton was always dreaming and building things, and at school he was called 'Fooley' Smeaton because of his obsession with mechanics.

When he was ten or twelve he went to the coal-pit at Garforth and watched men building a Newcomen steam engine – they called it a fire engine – to pump the water out of the mine. He was fascinated, asked lots of questions, and then went home and built his own little fire engine. He tried it out on his dad's goldfish pond, and rapidly pumped all the water out, which was not at all popular with either his dad or the goldfish! Later in his life he built another steam engine to pump water up the hill to Temple Newsam House.

Smeaton became involved in the building of the canals which snaked across the country in the eighteenth century; in particular, he was appointed engineer of the Calder & Hebble Navigation, which was to run through Dewsbury, Mirfield and Huddersfield. The terrain was difficult and there was great risk of flooding, but he carried out the job with triumph until it was almost done. Then there was a change of directors, and the new board decided they did not need Smeaton, and fired him. The canal was approaching completion when a terrible flood brought near-disaster, and they quickly called him back. He completed the job, and it's still in excellent condition.

The most dramatic thing Smeaton built was the Eddystone Lighthouse. The Eddystone reef is a vicious rocky outcrop that rises just above the waves in the open sea 14 miles south of Plymouth. The first lighthouse there was built by Henry Winstanley in 1698, but was washed away, along with Winstanley (*see* page 379), in the great storm of November 1703. The second lighthouse, built by John Rudyerd, was burned to the water in 1755, and Smeaton was asked to build the third, even though he had no experience of lighthouses.

We know a good deal about what he did, for he wrote a clear and detailed account of it, and his huge book is still available. Ignoring the gloomy advice of the sceptics, he decided to build the whole thing with stone. He did a series of experiments with various cements, looking for one that would work under water, and most ingenious of all he designed the entire tower like a vast three-dimensional jigsaw puzzle, with interlocking pieces. Every piece of stone was cut into a clever shape that would lock it to the next one, even without cement.

He completed his lighthouse in 1759, and it stood there for more than 120 years, until the keepers began to worry that the rock on which it stood was being undermined and washed away by the waves. So a new lighthouse was built on another rock 30 yards away – the one that still stands there today – and the top half of Smeaton's tower was taken down and re-erected as a memorial to him on Plymouth Hoe, the green headland overlooking the Sound. In fact the rock has not collapsed yet, and the bottom half – Smeaton's Stump – is still standing on the Eddystone. Despite another hundred years of buffeting, the stone and the pointing at the bottom look as if they are only a few decades old; only at the top, where it has no protection, is the tower showing signs of decay.

One extraordinary feature of John Smeaton was his versatility. Not only did he build steam engines, canals and lighthouses, he also carried out fundamental scientific research on windmills and water-wheels. His paper to the Royal Society about windmills discussed such things as the optimum shapes and angles for the sails, while his work on water-wheels sorted out a vigorous controversy.

There are two types of water-wheel: the undershot wheel, where the water simply flows underneath and pushes the wheel round, and the overshot wheel, where the water spills into buckets on the top of the wheel and the weight of water in the buckets pushes it round. The French scientist Antoine Parent claimed that the undershot wheel was six times more efficient than the overshot, while

John Theophilus Desaguliers asserted that the overshot was ten times as efficient as the undershot.

Smeaton had had several commissions to build water-wheels, and wanted to know the truth. He reckoned the only way to settle this 'monstrous disagreement' was to run some experiments. He built himself a beautiful model about 4 feet long and 5 feet high, with a water-wheel that he could arrange to drive either undershot or overshot, using water from a cistern. He designed it with various movable parts, so that he could vary the flow of water and alter the drag on the wheel.

He realised that friction was a serious problem, and most of the power available might be used in overcoming it. So he cunningly measured the frictional drag on the wheel by measuring the smallest force that would just keep it turning. Then he knew he had to add this force to any extra force doing useful work.

The paper he read to the Royal Society on 3 May 1759 is hard work to read – much more difficult than his account of building the lighthouse! – and contains sentences such as:

> The area of the head being 105.8 inches, this multiplied by the weight of water of the inch cubic, equal to the decimal .579 of the ounce avoirdupoise, gives 61.26 ounces for the weight of as much water, as is contained in the head, upon 1 inch in depth, 1/16 of which is 3.83 pounds; this

multiplied by the depth 21 inches, gives 80.43 lb for the value of 12 strokes; and by proportion, 39½ (the number made in a minute) will give 264.7 lb the weight of water expended in a minute.

However, his logic appears to be impeccable, and his conclusion is clear: 'The effect therefore of overshot wheels, under the same circumstances of quantity and fall, is at a medium double to that of the undershot. . .'. In other words, he found the overshot wheel twice as efficient as the undershot.

For his work on windmills and water-wheels the Royal Society awarded him a gold medal, and he was one of the earliest engineers to take such a scientific view of the world.

Smeaton's memorial in the church at Whitkirk, Leeds, carries a carved stone relief model of the Eddystone Lighthouse. The real thing still stands, half on the reef where it was built, the top half as a tourist attraction on Plymouth Hoe. The Calder & Hebble Navigation still carries boats between Dewsbury and Huddersfield, and wherever possible millwrights have made overshot water-wheels, following Smeaton's pioneering experiments.

84 William Smith's Geological Map of Britain

Two hundred years ago, most people believed the earth was only six thousand years old, and had been created exactly in the way the Bible says. But a man who lived and worked in Scarborough, who had hardly any education, changed all that. Just by looking at the rocks, he worked out the structure not just of Scarborough but of the whole of England and Wales. This amazing one-man feat almost bankrupted him, but William Smith became known as the Father of English Geology.

William Smith was born in Oxfordshire in 1769, the eldest of three children. His family had been yeoman farmers and William was educated at the village school, which was all the education a boy of that background could expect. Even as a boy he collected fossils. His uncle apparently lent him some books, and he taught himself basic geometry: this was enough to get him a job helping Edward Webb, a land surveyor. Webb was an inspiring teacher, and Smith was soon expert in recognising the underlying soils and rocks of Oxfordshire. However, the picture of the layers of rock that emerged was confusing, and most people thought that each area had its own arrangement. In 1793 Smith was given his first surveying job, on a canal through the Somerset coalfield. This was a wonderful opportunity for him to examine the exposed layers of rock in a different part of the country, work he continued when he was sent on a sort of national canal tour by his employers.

Fossil-collecting had up to this time been a rather haphazard hobby. The strange rocky creatures were fascinating, but made little sense, as this was well before evolution became accepted. Smith's sharp mind and great observational skill were to change all that. Casual observers working in different locations might notice that in one place a layer of sandstone was on top of a layer of, say, shale, whereas in another place the reverse was true. Smith wanted to know if the shale was part of the same layer in each place, or a different one. But how could he do that without digging from one place to the other? By recording where he had found fossils on his travels, he began to work out a system. It made sense if he identified layers of rock *according to the fossils found in them.* By this method he could for instance say whether clay exposed in canal workings in Somerset was part of the same layer he knew in his native Oxfordshire. He amazed two amateur fossil-collectors, the Revd Townsend and the Revd Richardson, when he was able to pick up their fossils and tell them exactly what sort of rocks they had come from.

Because he had travelled so extensively, he began to build up a picture of the layers of rock across the whole country, realising that they were stacked up in a regular order. He also came to an obvious but controversial conclusion – that the oldest rocks must be at the bottom, and the youngest at the top. He earned the nickname 'Strata Smith' and in 1815 he was finally able to publish the first ever geological map of England and Wales, showing the structure of the land. But the project almost bankrupted him, and he had to sell his London home in 1819.

According to his nephew, he had 'scarcely any home but the rocks'. He stayed wherever he was professionally engaged, eventually moving to Yorkshire and, finally, to Scarborough. Although he seemed happy in the town, and fell in with the local worthies, he never recovered financially from making his great map, for which he had been paid just £50.

Scarborough was rather late in having a Philosophical Society: the annual report for 1830 says that the previous 'formation of societies in York, Hull, Leeds and Whitby . . . were enough to raise a blush in the cheek of every inhabitant who was a true lover of nature and a friend of the propagation of science'. Once the society was formed, it needed a museum, and Smith had a brilliant idea. He suggested that the museum should be made entirely circular. Rock and fossil specimens could be set out on sloping shelves round the circular interior, arranged correctly in order of the strata in which they were found. In this way, Smith hoped, the public would come to look on the display not merely as a collection of individual pieces, but as a representation of the way the rocks of the country are organised. Although Smith's collection of rocks was sold long ago, the elegant Rotunda still stands, beneath the Grand Hotel, on the sea front at Scarborough, a wonderful expression of the ideas of William Smith. Around the inside of the dome is a cross-section of the Yorkshire coast, painted by William Smith's nephew, John Phillips, who became one of the most important geologists of his day and a founder of the British Association.

Far from retiring in comfort and glory, Smith fell on hard times. Unlike the vicars and doctors of the Philosophical Society, Smith was a working man with nowhere to live. Luckily the president of the Philosophical Society, Sir John Johnstone, took pity on him and offered him the job of land steward on his estate at Hackness, a few miles west of Scarborough. Smith felt secure but trapped at Hackness, and the only geological work he did there was a map of the estate. Eventually, he won some recognition. In February 1831 the council of the Geological Society voted him the Wollaston medal. This was the first time it was awarded, and was so new that the medal had not actually been struck yet, and had to be presented the following year. He resigned from Hackness, and his supporters were able to get him a pension of £100. But it was scarcely enough, and at the end of his life Smith, whose mind was as active as ever, was unable to take part in the great science he had helped to establish.

The layers are clearly visible in Castle Cliff, Scarborough. At the Rotunda Museum in Museum Terrace, Vernon Road, there is a bust of Smith and a wonderful geological cross-section of the Yorkshire coast, painted by his nephew.

85 Robert Stirling's Engine

This story is a bit of a mystery. Robert Stirling was the minister at Galston parish church, near Kilmarnock, for fifty-eight years. He was a Doctor of Divinity, and he devoted his life to his parishioners – there's a memorial in the church that says so. Yet in 1816, more than ten years before Stephenson's *Rocket* was made and sixty-two years before the internal combustion engine was invented, he patented an entirely new type of engine, an engine that could run on any fuel, required little maintenance, and was safe and efficient. The mystery – indeed the double mystery – is why it didn't catch on, and how a full-time minister of the Church came to make such a staggering advance in engineering science.

Robert Stirling was born at Methven near Perth, and at the age of fifteen went to Edinburgh University, where he studied Latin, Greek, logic and mathematics, before moving to Glasgow to study Divinity; he eventually became a minister in 1816. He filed his first patent just eight days after being ordained, so the engine must have been important to him.

In that first patent he mentions a device that became known as 'the economiser', and the introduction describes vaguely 'improvements for diminishing the consumption of fuel'. He says the economiser is a device for moving heat between one part of a body of gas and another; this does not sound thrilling, and you wouldn't know he was talking about a heat engine unless you had read the whole thing.

But what he proposed was very simple – and revolutionary. He realised that when you heat air, it expands. Could you, he wondered, use that expansion to do work? Well, to make it into an engine, you'd have to make it cycle somehow, which presumably meant heating up a whole cylinder, and then cooling it down again (like the Newcomen engine). Then he had a brilliant idea. Rather than heating and cooling the whole cylinder, wasting energy each time, suppose you had one end of the cylinder hot, and the other end cold; you could simply move the air from one end to the other, so it would very quickly heat and cool, expand and contract.

Stirling used two cylinders: one was the working cylinder, just like the cylinder of any engine, where the piston goes in and out and drives a flywheel through a crank. The interesting part is the displacer. This is another cylinder, connected to the first by a tube, with a lightweight piston in it. The bottom of the displacer cylinder is kept hot (by boiling water, for example), while the top stays cold. As the displacer piston moves up, the air inside is moved from the cold end to the hot end, where it expands.

Because the displacer is connected to the working piston, the expanding air goes up the tube, and pushes the piston. But the displacer is also connected to the flywheel; as the flywheel turns it moves the displacer down, the air is pushed back to the cold end, contracts, and pulls the piston back again. Then the cycle repeats itself.

Why is the Stirling engine so good? For one thing, it's very convenient: you can use any type of fuel, as long as it gets the hot part of the engine up to temperature. So a little model Stirling engine can run on a cup of tea, or even on a plate of haggis. And apart from being convenient, because you burn fuel on the outside of the engine you can arrange to burn it in the most efficient way. This you can't do in an internal combustion engine – which is why they spew out carbon monoxide and other pollutants.

In the second and third patents, Robert is named jointly with his brother James, an engineer. It looks as if Robert had the original vision, but James certainly helped to get the engines made in the foundries in which he worked.

One Stirling engine was lost for many years, and then dug out of a barn by the man who later became Lord Kelvin, Professor of Natural Philosophy at the University of Glasgow. He used it as the subject of his first talk to the Glasgow Philosophical Society. So trying to explain how the Stirling engine worked was the beginning of Kelvin's work on heat, which culminated in his absolute scale of temperature and the laws of thermodynamics.

However, the Stirling engine didn't catch on. It was used for a while to power church organs, because it was so quiet and easy to use. Today it is used in rather specialist applications, including cryogenics, because if you drive a Stirling engine with another engine, it actually pumps heat out of its surroundings.

Why did it never become popular? Clearly, it was way ahead of its time. People didn't really understand how it worked – some people suggested that it was true perpetual motion, which scientists scoffed at. Fuel economy is a popular idea now, but then coal was cheap. The materials available weren't really up to the job either. If they had been invented in the age of steel, Stirling engines would have been much more impressive. Finally, Robert and James Stirling didn't really exploit the ideas, either, and certainly didn't contest patents which infringed their own.

But what is amazing is that a minister, without any connection to the world of industry, should have the vision to see that a new sort of engine was possible, and the skill to make it work, and that he should have done it before most people had even seen a steam train. And it wasn't until 1878, the year Stirling *died*, that Karl Benz patented the first internal combustion engine.

There aren't many traces of Robert Stirling, but his engines flourish; try The Stirling Society, 7 Flint Hill, Dorking, Surrey RH4 2LL (01372 360363); engines are sold by Sterling Stirling, 15 The Pill, Newport, Gwent NP6 4JH; or try this excellent website: http://www.mech.saitama-u.-ac.jp/kiriki/links/.

86 John Stringfellow: The First Powered Flight

People have always wanted to fly. The ancients imagined gods and angels soaring through the heavens, and created such legends as that of Daedalus and Icarus, who made wings from feathers stuck on with wax. In the eighteenth century hot-air balloonists took to the skies, but not until the middle of the nineteenth century were successful flights made by machines that were heavier than air.

Most people think the aeroplane was invented by Orville and Wilbur Wright. In fact, the world's first powered flight took place not in America in 1903, but at Chard in Somerset fifty-five years earlier, and the man who made it happen was John Stringfellow.

John Stringfellow was born in Attercliffe, on the outskirts of Sheffield, on 6 December 1799. When he was a teenager his family moved to Nottingham, and he went into the lace industry, becoming a bobbin and carriage maker – which meant essentially a precision engineer. The lace trade suffered badly from the Luddite riots, and some lace-makers decided to move to the calmer county of Somerset.

John Stringfellow became the leading bobbin and carriage maker in Chard.

In 1827 he married American Hannah Keetch; they settled in Combe Street and had ten children, number four being John – always known as Fred – who wrote the only eyewitness account of his father's work.

John Stringfellow lectured on electricity to the Chard Institution, and in 1831 he launched a hot-air balloon to celebrate the coronation of William IV. He developed amazing skill at making steam engines. In about 1842 he teamed up with William Samuel Henson, an aeronautics enthusiast, and they began to discuss how to fly. They worried about what shape the wings of a plane should be, and how light it would have to be. They reckoned it would be sensible to use birds as models, so they took a muzzle-loading duck gun and shot all kinds of birds, which they weighed and measured, trying to find some mathematical connection between weight and wing dimensions. Eventually they settled on the rook: 'Henson and me generally took the rook as our standard as carrying half a pound to a foot. This bird can be seen any day leisurely flying at a speed not more than 20 miles an hour, and we considered that if we kept our machine within these limits we had a fair chance of success.'

Their basic idea was this. Take any wing – a bit like a bird's – keep it at an angle and push it through the air, and it will generate lift. Stringfellow once shot a square of cardboard across the room, saying, 'Any surface will hold the air with applied power.' This is interesting; most people didn't believe you could apply power to a surface and make it fly. They thought the wings of an aircraft would have to flap, like a bird's.

Stringfellow used to go up to London to visit Henson, and used the train journey to do experiments with the lift generated by various surfaces; he leant out of the window and gauged the lift of wings held in the airstream.

Henson was tremendously ambitious. In 1842 he not only applied for a patent for a 'Locomotive Apparatus for Air, Land, and Water' but also tried to set up an airline! The patent drawings show a monoplane with a 150 foot span, fabric-covered wings, an enclosed cabin, and tricycle undercarriage. Much of the detail – such as the bracing system – is quite original, but the details suggest that the drawing is in fact for a much smaller craft. The craft as specified would not have been strong enough, would not have met the weight criteria, and would have been under-powered. He was granted his patent, for 'certain improvements in locomotive apparatus and machinery for conveying letters, goods and passengers from place to place through the air,' but the proposal for the Aerial Transit Company had to go to Parliament, where it was greeted with derision.

Henson made a model of the plane in his patent; it weighed 14 pounds and had 40 sq. feet of wings. He tried to fly it in the Adelaide Gallery in London, but it was a complete flop – literally. The press had a field day; the papers were full of mocking cartoons. There was, however, a more positive article in *The Times* of 30 March 1843, which concludes that '. . . possession of the long-coveted power of flight may now be safely anticipated'.

Henson and Stringfellow worked together on a new 20 foot model, but by 1845 Henson was losing his enthusiasm. Eventually he got married, emigrated to America, and patented a new safety razor. Stringfellow was left to carry on alone, and when the new model was finished he got workmen to carry it up to Bala Down for testing. He was so upset by people making fun of his work that he did this secretly, at night, and tried the first flight under cover of darkness. It was a disaster – the silk covering of the wings got wet with dew, and became so heavy that the machine could not fly. He tried again in the daytime, day after day, every day for seven weeks, but finally had to admit defeat.

And then, for the first time, he designed his own aircraft from scratch. Accounts are few, but we know that it had a 10 foot wingspan, with swallow-shaped wings, rather than Henson's rectangular design. The wing area was about 18 sq. feet, and its overall weight perhaps 9 lb including the super-lightweight steam engine.

Stringfellow flew his plane for the first time in the summer of 1848, inside the top floor of a lace mill, some 20 metres long. Outside he had had trouble with damp and with cross-winds. His aircraft had no fin, nor anything else to prevent it from veering left or right. So flying it inside, in still air, seemed a good plan. He launched it along a fixed wire, which ran down a slight slope for nearly half the length of the mill; when the aircraft reached the end of the wire it released itself by a cunning catch. The wire launch enabled him to get a good smooth downhill run, so that by the time the machine started flying it was already moving at a reasonable speed, and was also flying exactly level, with no tendency to veer left or right. This last point was important, because the mill has a row of iron pillars down the middle, which means that the flight path was only about 20 feet wide; there was only 5 feet of clearance on either side.

In the first experiment, according to his son Fred, writing fifty years later, the tail was set at too high an angle, and the machine rose too rapidly on leaving the wire. After going a few yards it stalled and slid back as if down an inclined plane; the point of the tail struck the ground and was broken. Once the tail was repaired it was set at a lower angle. The steam was again got up, the machine started down the wire and upon reaching the point of self-detachment, gradually rose until it reached the farther end of the room, punching a hole in the canvas placed to stop it before it hit the wall.

This sketchy account is all we have, but several

local worthies were there to witness this first powered flight, achieved by John Stringfellow in 1848.

Each town sign on the roads into Chard in Somerset shows a picture of Stringfellow's plane; there is a bronze replica in the High Street, and there are various important bits and pieces in Chard Museum.

87 Joseph Wilson Swan and the Perfection of the Electric Light Bulb

Thomas Alva Edison probably deserves the title 'World's Greatest Inventor'. But despite his own claims and those of many American books, he did not invent the electric light bulb. That distinction belongs to Joseph Swan, a chemist from the north-east of England, working alone in his spare time. Swan and Edison both knew there were immense rewards for the man who succeeded in applying the new great power source, electricity, to the universal desire to light every home. The struggle to do so took place in the courts as well as the laboratory, but eventually saw the two men come together.

By 1850 gas lighting had been around for forty years, and was common in shops and posh homes, but gas was smelly, poisonous and expensive. It was not all that bright, either: the gas mantle you may have seen on camping-gas lights, which glows in the flame with an intense greenish-white light, was still a long way off. The gas lighting Swan and Edison would have known in their youth was a smoky yellow flame, so no wonder the new-fangled electricity seemed to offer the promise of a safer, cleaner light. In fact there was an electric light, the arc lamp – first used in Dungeness lighthouse in 1862. The arc lamp was an electric spark between two conducting rods connected to a battery. The trick lay in getting a constant arc, rather than spluttering sparks. This required the rods – usually of carbon – to be kept a constant distance apart, a problem since the rods are constantly burning away in the intense heat of the arc. In commercial applications, clever clockwork mechanisms were devised to first 'strike' the arc, by bringing the rods together, and then separating them to the right distance and maintaining the spark gap as the rods burned away.

These complications might have been overcome, but everyone knew the arc lamp would never become the universal electric light. Apart from the complexity, noise from the spark and the danger, arc lights were just too bright. If you had a lighthouse an arc lamp was fine, but as a bedside light it was seriously over-powered. However, the arc lamp defined the problem: it was rather quaintly called 'the subdivision of the electric light'.

Joseph Wilson Swan was born on 31 October 1828 at Pallion Hall in Sunderland. He left school when he was twelve, and was apprenticed to a firm of chemists, before taking up a position with John Mawson, a chemist in Newcastle. He invented several new processes for the developing photography business. In the 1840s Swan, a keen member of the Newcastle Literary and Philosophical Society, had seen a lecture at which electrical incandescence was demonstrated. A piece of wire was connected across a battery, and glowed orange. It was enough to make Swan think that incandescent lamps were the way to go. There is a problem: generally you either get no glow (wire too thick, battery too weak) or the wire burns out immediately. But if the wire survives, it is nowhere near bright enough to be a useful light. When the coil is glowing dull red, it's at about 700 or 800°C. At about 1000° it would glow yellow, but then the copper would melt. Swan tried a mixture of platinum and iridium, and managed to get the temperature up to about 2000° before it melted, but he still wanted more.

So in his spare time from chemistry he experimented with all sorts of different materials. What we use now is the metal tungsten, but 130 years ago tungsten was both hard to obtain and impossible to work. So Swan chose carbon, which doesn't melt below 3500°. What he wanted was tiny thin pieces, which he made by taking little strips of paper and carbonising them by toasting them gently in an oven without air. He tried all sorts of paper, and he tried spreading them with treacle and syrup and other stuff that goes black when you overcook it. Some of these worked a bit, and glowed brightly, but they were still awfully weak: he could not get consistent success. Although carbon doesn't melt, it burns easily if there is any oxygen about.

The solution seemed obvious: get rid of the oxygen. He tried pumping all the air out of his bulbs with the mercury pump that had just been invented, but this still did not work. There was enough oxygen adsorbed on the carbon – stuck to the outside – to burn it when it heated up. The stroke of genius which was to solve that problem took a while to come to Swan. Meanwhile, he tackled the unsatisfactory filaments themselves. He concluded that the fibrous nature of the paper he used was to blame, and decided to make his own material. The first artificial filaments were made by treating cotton with sulphuric acid, and later ones by dissolving blotting paper in zinc chloride and squirting it into alcohol to make long strings. These were in fact the first artificial fibres, precursors of rayon. He saw their potential, and asked his wife to crochet them into collars and doilies! They can be seen in the Newcastle Discovery museum.

By the late 1870s, when Swan had been working on the problem for a quarter of a century, everything was in place. He had his artificial filaments, carbonised in a furnace without air; the vacuum pump had been improved beyond recognition; and in 1878 he perfected a technique for getting rid of the adsorbed oxygen. When he had pumped all the air he could out of the glass bulb containing the filament, he carefully heated up the filament while still pumping. More oxygen came off the surface of the warm filament and was pumped away. For the first time, he could make his filament glow white, but not burn. He first demonstrated his successful lamp to a few people in January 1879, and then on 3 February 1879 to an audience of seven hundred people at the Literary and Philosophical Society of Newcastle-upon-Tyne. Swan's house, Underhill at Gateshead, was lit with his own light bulbs later the same year.

He patented the pumping process, but he thought the idea of making a filament lamp so obvious it wasn't worth patenting. He reckoned without Thomas Alva Edison. Swan's lamp first worked in February 1879. Four months earlier Edison had made a dramatic, sweeping claim that he had solved the problem of the electric light by using carbonised paper. His cable sent the price of gas shares tumbling on the stock exchange – and in October 1879 Edison patented the carbon-filament lamp. Swan sent a little note to the journal *Nature* saying that he had been making carbonised paper filaments for fifteen years – and it did not work. Edison went on to try fibres of carbonised bamboo, and imported it specially from Japan – but bamboo didn't work either.

In 1881 Swan started producing his carbon-filament light bulbs in a factory at Benwell, and Edison threatened to sue him for infringing his patent. Swan pointed out that he had been making these lamps before Edison applied for his patent. In the end they stopped arguing, joined forces, and formed the Edison & Swan United Electric Light Co.

Swan's most crucial work was done in the greenhouse at Underhill, his home in Gateshead, now a residential home for the elderly.

88 Thomas Telford, the 'Colossus of Roads'

Thomas Telford was born in Dumfriesshire on 9 August 1757. He was apprenticed to a stonemason, and went to work with architects in London; by the 1790s he was heavily into canals, and then he moved on to roads. He became the greatest road-builder of his time. Telford surveyed and built many hundreds of miles of roads – about 900 miles in the Highlands of Scotland, where there had been almost none before he came, and 200 miles in the Lowlands – and the important road from London to Holyhead, which was the principal route to Ireland.

Telford said the road to Holyhead took him fifteen years of incessant labour, but what a wonderful job he made of it! Built in the early 1800s for horse-drawn coaches weighing perhaps a ton, it's still the main road 180 years later – the A5, carrying 30 ton juggernauts to the Irish ferries. To appreciate his wonderful skill, go to Snowdonia, to the lovely little town of Betws-y-Coed, where vigorous streams tumble down the hillside beside the road, and look at the Waterloo Bridge over the river. Built in 1815, it commemorates the great victory of the battle of Waterloo in cast-iron text under the arch.

Telford's road then heads north-west from Betws-y-Coed past Lake Ogwen and over the Nant Ffrancon pass to Bangor. The country is dramatic, and the hills are high, but Thomas Telford surveyed and planned this road so skilfully that the gradient is never as steep as 1 in 20 – which is really easy on a mountain bike – although I'd be a bit happier without the howling wind that usually seems to blow. Mind you, the day we went there to film, the wind was so strong it blew me up the hill at about 15 mph without my having to pedal!

This road through Snowdonia is evidence of Telford's skill as a surveyor, and he also developed strict rules about how to do the actual construction. He suggested in later years that the way to become an engineer was to start by working as a labourer, and get your hands dirty. 'This', he said, 'is the true way of acquiring practical skill, a thorough knowledge of the materials employed in construction, and at last but not least, a perfect knowledge of the habits and disposition of the workmen who carry out our designs.'

On some of his inspection trips he took along his friend, the poet Robert Southey, who described his methods:

> First, level and drain, then, like the Romans, lay a solid pavement of large stones, the round or broad end downwards, as close as they can be set; the points are then broken off, and a layer of stones about the size of walnuts laid over them; . . . over all a little gravel if it be at hand . . .

Telford himself specified that the road should always be 20 feet wide, including a strip of turf at each side. The roadway should be 14 inches deep in the middle, and 9 inches at the sides – so there was a good camber to encourage the rain to run off. The material should be 'gravel of a proper quality, out of which all stones above the size of a hen's egg shall have been previously taken' – although it was all right to use bigger stones at the bottom. The iron tyres of stage coaches crushed the grit into the gaps between the stones and made a smooth surface that rain could not easily penetrate.

Telford also built more than a thousand bridges, and one of the most impressive was to get across the Menai Straits to Anglesey, 200 yards across vicious tides and deep water. The Admiralty insisted that the bridge must be high enough to let the largest ships sail below with masts erect, and he couldn't make a timber frame to build an arch over the top, because they would not allow even a temporary obstruction. Telford designed an amazing suspension bridge, easily the longest in the world at the time. At each end he planned a massive tower,

153 feet above the high water mark. Between them he would hang sixteen chains, and then the roadway would be built hanging from the chains, 579 feet long and 30 feet wide.

The chains were made of 9-foot links, each of thirty-six iron bars half an inch square. Would it be possible to lift these massive chains up the towers? For several nights, as tension mounted, the normally imperturbable Telford was unable to sleep. Finally, on 26 April 1825, hundreds of people on the banks and on boats watched as the chain was floated underneath on a massive raft, and then winched up on cables by 150 men heaving on capstans. When it reached the top of the tower there was a colossal cheer, and three men walked high above the sea to the other tower across the 9-inch wide chain!

On 30 January 1826 the Menai Bridge was opened for traffic, and at 1.35 a.m. the Down Royal London and Holyhead mail coach rumbled over the bridge through blackest night and howling wind. In the morning everyone wanted to cross: flags flew, bands played, and cannons crashed as coach after coach struggled through the heavy rain; so many, in fact, that there was actually a traffic jam on the bridge. Before the bridge was built, 13,000 travellers a year used to cross the Straits by ferry. The crossing took 45 minutes in good weather. The ferry yielded an income of over £800 a year to Miss Williams of Plas Isa, who, when the bridge was built, was granted compensation of £26,557!

A few miles to the east, Telford also built the Conwy Bridge, 327 feet long and designed to match the castle; here, he used a rope sling. The bridge was opened on 1 July 1826 just after noon and first across was the Chester Mail with as many passengers as could possibly find a place on board. The route was solid with spectators, singing 'God Save the King' as loud as they could. There was much revelry; windows were broken in the pubs. Thomas Telford was sixty-nine.

Telford did almost all his greatest work before the coming of trains, but he built many miles of canals. He built the Caledonian Canal, linking the Atlantic with the North Sea via Loch Ness and the Great Glen, with twenty-nine locks. He built the even longer Gotha Canal across Sweden: 53 miles of new canal in a total navigation stretching 238 miles from sea to sea. When he first went to Sweden with two assistants in July 1808 it was his first trip abroad, and he was clearly a bit worried about vital rations, because for the six-day voyage he took extensive supplies, including three 40-lb hams, 90 lb of biscuits and 33 lb of lump sugar, not to mention forty-eight bottles of wine, six bottles of gin and six bottles of brandy. It must have been a jolly trip!

But one of the most beautiful and elegant of all his canal works was also one of the earliest: Pont Cysyllte, which was completed in 1805. This carries the Ellesmere Canal 127 feet above the River Dee in north-east Wales. All previous aqueducts had been massive chunky affairs just a few feet above the river, but Telford introduced a brand new idea – his 'stream in the sky' runs in a cast-iron trough 11 feet 10 inches wide and 1007 feet long; the trough sits on a bridge of eighteen tapering stone piers, 20 × 12 feet at river level and 13 × 7 feet 6 inches at the top. The Pont Cysyllte aqueduct was opened on 26 November 1805; six boats sailed majestically across, and there was much rejoicing. This amazing construction was probably what made Thomas Telford famous, and it stands firm and unchanged, 191 years later, as a monument to his genius. Sir Walter Scott called it the greatest work of art he had ever seen.

Telford's life was full of extraordinary events. In 1788, early in his career, the churchwardens asked him to look at St Chad's Church in Shrewsbury, because the roof was leaking. At the next meeting he told them they needn't worry about the roof until they had taken urgent action to secure the walls. They laughed at him, and said the cracks had been there for hundreds of years – was he looking for work or something? So he walked out, suggesting they should continue their meeting outside in the churchyard. Three days later the church clock struck, and the entire tower collapsed through the roof of the nave. . . .

Hero memorials come in many shapes and sizes, from shopping centres to British Telecom offices, but there aren't many heroes who have had entire towns named after them. In Telford Civic Square in Telford

New Town stands a fine bronze statue of the man whom the poet Robert Southey called 'the colossus of roads'.

Thomas Telford's monuments are many. His statue in Telford is perhaps the most obvious, but my favourites are the bridges at Menai, Conwy, and Betws-y-Coed, and the fabulous 'stream in the sky' at Pont Cysyllte, near Llangollen.

89 Richard Towneley, Recorder of Rainfall

Occasionally the weather forecasters on radio and television say things like 'last month was the wettest since records began'. One day I wrote to Bill Giles and asked him when records did begin, and the helpful reply told me that the first systematic recording of rainfall in Britain began in 1677, and the man who did it was Richard Towneley.

Richard Towneley was born in 1629. His father Charles was killed at the Battle of Marston Moor in 1644. As Catholics, the family suffered a good deal of persecution during the turbulent seventeenth century. Towneley Hall, south-east of Burnley in Lancashire, had been home to the Towneley family since the early thirteenth century. Oliver Cromwell took the house away, but by 1653 Richard had got it back again, and began practising science. He was interested in all sorts of things, but especially meteorology – the air, the wind and the rain.

In 1676 he made a rain gauge, which he described in detail to the Royal Society. He took a 'round tunnel' – presumably he means a cylinder – of 12 inches in diameter, and soldered it to a lead pipe. He wanted to make sure that no nearby building could interrupt the falling rain, so he fixed the cylinder on the roof, and took the pipe down and in through his bedroom window. Nowadays the Meteorological Office advise you not to put a rain gauge on the roof, because wind eddies can sweep rain over the top and give false readings. But Towneley didn't know about that.

In his bedroom he let the water collect in a bottle, to show how much rain had fallen. He measured it three times a day for more than twenty-five years, and faithfully recorded his results. In 1689 he reported the first ten years' observations to the Royal Society, and his first conclusion was that twice as much rain fell on Towneley as on Paris. He said he thought this was because of the high ground in Yorkshire and east Lancashire; the prevailing south-west winds bring in the rain clouds which 'are oftener stopt and broken and fall upon us'. So if you are thinking of going on holiday to look for the sun, then on Towneley's evidence Paris might possibly be a better bet!

Towneley also used to record the behaviour of the wind, and measured the air pressure with a barometer. He recorded his lowest ever reading of 28.47 inches of mercury in the evening of 26 November 1703. That night England was battered by the worst storm in recorded history – the storm that carried away the first Eddystone lighthouse, along with its builder, Henry Winstanley.

Being a politically non-correct Catholic Towneley never went to London to join the Royal Society. Instead he stayed in Lancashire and enjoyed inviting other philosophers to visit him. The brilliant John Flamsteed dropped in just before he became the King's Astronomer, and they became friends. When Flamsteed went to Greenwich, he wanted a super-accurate clock that would run for a whole year so that he could find out whether the earth's rotation was regular. Richard Towneley made the escapement mechanism for this clock.

Pendle Hill, 1,830 feet high and only 10 miles from Towneley Hall, stands in the middle of Pendle Forest, famous for the 'witches of Pendle', who came from two rival families there. They were accused of witchcraft on the unsupported testimonies of a nine-year-old girl from one of the families, a senile woman, and a half-witted labourer; one died in prison but ten were found guilty at the Assizes, and were hanged on 20 August 1612.

Richard Towneley climbed up Pendle Hill with his friend Henry Power on 27 April 1661. They carried a long tube and a bottle of mercury to test what became known as Towneley's hypothesis. He was interested in the 'spring of the air', and believed that if you had a fixed amount of air – as in a balloon – then the pressure and the volume were related; the higher the pressure, the smaller the volume, and vice versa.

So he collected some 'Valley Ayr', and took it a thousand feet up Pendle Hill, and showed that its volume increased – because the pressure at the top of the hill is less than the pressure at the bottom. Likewise he showed that if he collected 'Mountain Ayr' and took it down, then its volume decreased. And he discovered that multiplying together the volume and the pressure always gave the same answer. In other words, the pressure and volume of a fixed mass of air are inversely proportional to one another.

Other people had taken barometers up mountains before, but this relationship was a new idea. Robert Boyle picked it up, investigated it further, and wrote about it in 1663, and ever since then most people have called the relationship Boyle's Law, but at the time Isaac Newton, Robert Hooke and Robert Boyle himself called it Mr Towneley's Hypothesis.

Towneley Hall, a few miles south-east of Burnley, is open to the public and stands in a lovely park, which includes a golf course. Pendle Hill, north-west of Burnley, offers a good stiff climb with a commanding view from the summit; on a clear day you can see Blackpool Tower and North Wales.

90 Richard Trevithick and the First Steam Locomotive

The history of steam engines and trains is frequently confused. Most people think that James Watt invented the steam engine and George Stephenson the railway, but they are wrong on both counts. The first working steam engine was patented in the year that James Watt's father was born, and the first steam locomotive ran in 1804, ten years before Stephenson built one. The world's first steam locomotive was actually built by a Cornishman, Richard Trevithick.

Richard Trevithick was born on 13 April 1771 in Illogan, near Camborne in Cornwall. After doing hopelessly badly at school, he got a job as an engineer at a mine, and his life gradually unfolded as a catalogue of disasters: he was a giant in the field of engineering, yet not one of his inventions brought him wealth. He was swindled, and declared bankrupt; he almost drowned in South America, and he died penniless. Fierce yet tender-hearted, buoyant yet easily depressed, brilliantly ingenious and recklessly imprudent, Trevithick was the most Promethean of inventors.

He had the most amazing strength. One of his tricks as a young man was to carry about a blacksmith's half-ton mandrel. Another favourite was to write his name on a beam with his arm fully extended – and a 56 lb weight suspended from his thumb. He once joined in a sledgehammer-throwing contest in which the aim was to hit the wall on the engine-house opposite. No one else could get it near; Trevithick hurled the hammer clean over the engine-house roof. And in one wrestling match, he turned his burly six-foot challenger upside-down and stamped the imprint of his boots in the ceiling!

Cornwall was an ideal place for a young engineer. The Cornish mines had been worked since Roman times, so to get to the remaining ore, miners had to tunnel deeper – but the deeper they tunnelled, the more water they struck. This water had to be pumped out, using either Newcomen steam engines or the improved machines built by Boulton & Watt of Birmingham. The Cornish didn't take kindly to this 'foreign' invasion, and they repeatedly tried to improve Newcomen's engine, so as to rival Watt's; but the terms of Watt's patent were so wide that the Cornishmen were constantly accused of infringing it. However, James Watt's patent expired in 1800, when Trevithick was twenty-nine.

He had realised that not only could the engine be made more powerful by using high-pressure steam to move the piston, but that he could do away with the condenser, and by replacing the cumbersome beam with a simple rod, he could make it portable. Soon his engines were replacing Boulton & Watt engines in the Cornish mines. But that was only the start. Now that Trevithick had built a portable engine, he could in principle use mechanical traction in place of horses. He built a model that he demonstrated on his kitchen table in 1799, and he had a full-scale steam carriage – the 'Puffing Devil' – ready on Christmas Eve 1801. On 28 December he set off on a 3-mile test run. Unfortunately, after about a mile, he hit a water gully. The overturned carriage was soon righted, but across the road

Trevithick spied a pub. He went in for a drink to celebrate the first mile, then he had another . . . and another. They were still celebrating when the engine boiled dry and the road carriage exploded.

Not a man to be easily discouraged, Trevithick took out a patent for the high-pressure steam-engine, and in 1803 went to Merthyr Tydfil to sell some of his engines to Samuel Homfray, master of Penydaren Ironworks, where pig iron was made and transported down the valley to Cardiff. While he was in the Taff valley, Trevithick watched the horses pulling the wagons laden with pig iron along the iron railway to the canal, and he reckoned that his engines could do the job instead. Homfray backed the idea. In fact, he was so convinced it would work that he wagered another of the mine captains, Anthony Hill, 500 guineas that Trevithick's locomotive would haul 10 tons of iron from the Penydaren works to Abercynon Wharf and pull the empties back, by steam power.

Now Trevithick had to make his dream work, and the day of the great trial was set for 21 February 1804. Trevithick's locomotive was hitched to five wagons, carrying 10 tons of pig iron and 70 passengers, including Anthony Hill. They had some problems: one was that the chimney was too tall to pass under overhanging branches; so they had to cut down a few trees on the way. But they made it; the locomotive hauled its load the full 9¾ miles of track – in a speedy four hours and five minutes, making an average of a little over 2 mph. It was the first train journey in the world! You can still see the remains of the track where the journey took place, along the old tramway that is now the Taff Trail cycle track. The grooves in the stones where the rails used to lie are clearly visible.

The reason that Hill was so confident in waging 500 guineas and declaring the journey impossible was that, like everyone else, he believed you could not get enough friction between the wheels and the rails to pull the load of a train. Trevithick's solution to this was weight; he built his engine up to 5 tons, which meant he had plenty of traction on the rails, especially as he had to haul the load downhill to Abercynon.

However, the track had been built for horses rather than 5-ton engines, and many of the cast-iron tramplates were broken by the massive beast, and Trevithick had to drive it back on the road. As a result the wager was declared void and, more importantly, Trevithick's locomotive didn't catch on. Homfray and other mine owners were not prepared to replace their tram tracks with stronger – and more expensive – ones capable of carrying steam locomotives. This did not become economically acceptable until the cost of horse fodder mounted during the Napoleonic wars a few years later. By then, Trevithick was in South America seeking his fortune, but some young engineers in the north were happy to make locomotives for the new tracks – Matthew Murray and George Stephenson.

Trevithick made another engine to run on a circular track in London; he called it 'Catch me who can', and charged an admission fee of 1*s*. He issued a challenge to run his engine for twenty-four hours against a racehorse. But no one took up the challenge, and he closed the show, having not even covered the cost of laying out the railway.

He went off to Peru, and spent eleven years making and losing fortunes in mining. By the end, he was surviving by eating monkeys and wild fruits. He just avoided being eaten by an alligator in Colombia, he almost drowned, and he ran out of money. By an amazing chance, he met in a hotel a young man who paid for his passage home – George's son Robert Stephenson. Trevithick got home in 1827, and died penniless six years later.

The Penydaren locomotive ran down to Abercynon on what is now the Taff Trail, south of Merthyr Tydfil; a replica locomotive at the Welsh Industrial and Maritime Museum in Cardiff runs on the first Saturday of each summer month. Open 10–5; 01222 481919.

91 William Ashbee Tritton and his Tank 'Little Willie'

At the beginning of this century, military experts were convinced that the next war would be won by the cavalry, who galloped so fast they could run rings round anyone on the ground. But the experts reckoned without the invention of the machine-gun. Machine-guns simply mowed down the cavalry.

Infantry were able to escape machine-gun fire by digging themselves deep trenches, but then they were stuck, and in the first two years of trench warfare in the First World War no unit moved more than 3 miles. There was complete stalemate, brought about by machine-guns, trenches, barbed wire and mud. What they needed was a whole new method of warfare.

The Duke of Wellington claimed the battle of Waterloo was won on the playing fields of Eton. Perhaps a tank historian may suggest the First World War was won at the White Hart Hotel in Lincoln, because every week for many months Lieutenant Walter Wilson and William Ashbee Tritton met there to discuss the tank.

William Ashbee Tritton was born in Islington on 19 June 1875, the son of William Birch Tritton and his wife Ellen Ashbee. He became an engineer, and after working for various companies moved as general manager to Fosters in Lincoln, who made agricultural machinery. In 1911 he became Managing Director.

The First Lord of the Admiralty was a young chap called Winston Churchill – this was twenty-five years before he became prime minister – and he floated the absurd idea of a sort of 'land-ship' in which troops and guns would somehow remain safe from machine-guns, float across no-man's-land to the enemy lines and over their trenches, and thus be able to destroy them.

Churchill must have thought to himself, 'Who knows about mud? I know: Tritton, king of agricultural machinery.' Churchill had seen a Foster's tractor crossing a large ditch, and asked Tritton whether a machine could be constructed that could cross trenches. He appointed a land-ships committee on 20 February 1915, and at the end of July sent Wilson up to meet Tritton in the White Hart, and explain what sort of vehicle he wanted. First, the sides of the vehicle must be able to stop machine-gun bullets. Second, it should have no wheels to get bogged down in mud or ensnared by barbed wire. Third, it had to be able to get out of trenches.

On this basis Tritton got to work, and on 19 September – within thirty-seven days of the first meeting – had produced a prototype, which he called Little Willie, after himself. It had funny steering wheels at the back, which persisted into the Mark II, called Big Willie. Within a few months they had an armoured vehicle ready to tackle the machine-guns, the mud, and the trenches – a vehicle with no wheels at all.

The walls were made of half-inch steel plate, enough to stop machine-gun bullets. There were no wheels; drive was provided by caterpillar tracks. (These were invented in 1906 by another agricultural engineer, David Roberts, for the Hornby chain tractor, but no one wanted them, so he sold the idea to the Americans, and Tritton had to buy it back again!) Perhaps Tritton's most crucial idea was the tank's extraordinary shape, with a high rising front, about 6 feet off the ground. The point was that if it did get into a trench the tank effectively had its own ramp: the front end was almost at the top of the trench already, and the tank could simply drive up, out of the trench, and away.

In the Fosters factory a secret name was needed for these new vehicles, because the enemy had to be kept in the dark. So they were officially labelled 'Water carriers for Mesopotamia'. That was a bit of a mouthful for everyday use in the factory, so the workers called them 'water tanks', and eventually just 'tanks'.

The first real Tritton tanks went into action in France on 15 September 1916 with a standard crew of seven or eight men. After a few teething troubles, they were a resounding success, and the stalemate of trench warfare was finished. Tritton was knighted in 1917, and became Sir William Tritton, but poor David Roberts received no credit at all; he died in 1928 without getting even a letter of thanks.

There is a Mk IV Tritton tank in the Museum of Lincolnshire Life in Lincoln, and various tanks at the Bovington Tank Museum, east of Dorchester, and at the Imperial War Museum in London. Close beside Lincoln's beautiful cathedral, at the top of Steep Hill, the White Hart is a pleasant and comfortable hotel, but not cheap.

92 John Tyndall's Blue Sky

Although Tyndall's story is fairly extraordinary, he might have remained a competent but obscure physicist but for his charm and amazing ability to communicate scientific ideas to any audience. The impact he made on the public resulted in him getting to the very top of his profession, succeeding Michael Faraday at the Royal Institution – and working out why the sky is blue.

John Tyndall was born in Leighlinbridge, County Carlow, on 2 August 1820. Although the family owned a little land, they were quite poor and only the 'superior intellect' of John's father (also John) made sure that young John received a decent education at the nearby National School. He took an immediate interest in mathematics and obtained a job with the Ordnance Survey of Ireland, followed by a similar post in England. He ended up as a maths teacher at Queenswood College in Hampshire. It is here that Tyndall's character and scientific ambition really began to show themselves.

Having hauled himself up by his bootstraps to a fairly comfortable position, Tyndall realised that Queenswood College wasn't going to satisfy him intellectually. Together with a colleague, Edward Frankland, Tyndall travelled to Germany and enrolled himself at the great age of twenty-eight in the University of Marburg, where his tutor was Herr Bunsen, after whom the laboratory burner is named.

Although his first scientific paper was on the 'Phenomena of a Water Jet', Tyndall settled into some pretty obscure physics. He was particularly interested in the effects of pressure on crystals, which sounds rather dull but led him to work in Wales on how slate cleaves, and then to the Alps where the way glaciers move and crack puzzled physicists: how can apparently solid ice flow like a river? Perhaps the most dramatic outcome of this work was Tyndall's transformation into an accomplished Alpinist. He loved the mountains, and became one of the first men to scale the Matterhorn, and was the first to climb the Weisshorn in Switzerland. Yet none of this merited any public acclaim. All that was to change thanks to a brilliant lecture he gave in 1853.

Tyndall was invited to deliver one of the prestigious Friday lectures at the Royal Institution in London, where the great Michael Faraday was in charge. The lecture, whose title 'On the Influence of Material Aggregation upon the Manifestations of Force' is meaningless to most of us, was delivered on 11 February. It produced an extraordinary impression, and in May of the same year he was unanimously chosen as Professor of Natural Philosophy in the Royal Institution, working alongside Faraday.

This dramatic transformation seems to have

resulted from Tyndall's brilliant performance in public. He was a great experimental scientist – but an outstanding demonstrator. He devised working experimental demonstrations of scientific ideas and techniques that immediately impressed and thrilled both scientists and the public. If he'd been alive today, he would no doubt have had his own television series!

Some of his demonstrations have become classics. To show the idea of resonance, he had a piano installed in the basement of the Royal Institution below the main lecture theatre. Upstairs he had a cello on a long pole, which passed through a hole in the floor and connected to the sounding board of the piano. When someone played the piano downstairs, the cello seemed magically to play itself, the strings resonating to the notes played on the piano. The hole in the floor is still there.

Another idea that interested him was 'total internal reflection', an optical phenomenon where light travelling through a piece of glass does not emerge into the air, but is instead reflected back into the glass. To show this, Tyndall invented the light pipe. All you need is a torch and a bucket with two holes. Seal one hole with a clear window, and fill the bucket with water, which will pour out of the remaining hole. Now shine your torch through the window and into the stream of water emerging on the opposite side of the bucket. It is well known that light travels in straight lines – yet it disappears!

Instead, if you put your hand into the water, it is lit up by the light trapped in the stream by total internal reflection. Tyndall predicted that this phenomenon could be useful in telecommunication, and indeed that is exactly how fibre-optic cables use light to carry information round corners.

In 1867, when Faraday died, Tyndall took over as the Superintendent of the Royal Institution. Much of his work was to do with the way gases absorb radiation – it was Tyndall who showed that ozone absorbs ultraviolet light. As part of his investigation, he shone beams of light through filtered, very clean air. And he saw nothing. Normally you can see the beam, but no one had really stopped to wonder why. He now knew that the light beam you see from a spotlight or slide projector is in fact light scattered from tiny particles normally present in the air. And then came the bolt from the blue (almost literally). Since sunlight has to pass through air laden with these tiny particles, then surely a great deal of it must be scattered? So why can't we see the beam? Then he realised that we can see the light scattered from the sun. Different sized particles tend to scatter light from different parts of the spectrum – larger particles scatter more red, small ones more blue. If the dust in the atmosphere was mainly small, then it would scatter blue light *and that is why the sky is blue!*

Tyndall made his own blue sky to demonstrate this, of course, and you can do the same. By shining a beam of light from a slide projector through a tank of water, you can scatter more and more light by adding a little powdered milk. The tank takes on a distinctly blue appearance from the side, but when you look directly at the projector through the water and particles, it looks first yellow, then orange, then red, as you add milk powder. As the blue light is scattered from the sunlight, what is left looks yellow, which is why the sun is yellow. Adding more milk produces a lovely red glow, just as at sunset you look at the sun through more atmosphere, with more particles in the way.

John Tyndall died after accidentally taking an overdose of chloral hydrate, but left a legacy of great science, and the idea that scientists have a responsibility to make their work interesting to the public.

Tyndall was a brilliant lecturer, and the Irish branch of the Institute of Physics organises a set of Tyndall lectures in schools every year.

93 John Walker – Strike a Light!

It is a cliché to say that we take many modern inventions for granted, but in the case of the friction match it is particularly justifiable. Life without electricity would be pretty hard, but you can manage with fire: candles for light, and gas, coal or wood for heating and cooking. But things would get very uncomfortable if you couldn't actually light your fire. Yet before John Walker's invention of 1826, there wasn't a reliable, instantaneous method of lighting a fire.

Fire-making technology had been around for thousands of years. The earliest methods relied on friction, typically between two bits of wood. Although it is possible to do this by simply spinning one piece of wood against another using your hands, if you try you will find it difficult to get enough speed. So the first real fire making machine was the Fire Drill. It looked like the bow part of a bow-and-arrow, and you used it by wrapping its string round a pencil-shaped piece of hard wood, which you pressed into a hole or depression in a plank of soft wood. Moving the bow back and forth causes the hard wood pencil to spin, and as you press down the friction between the pieces of wood makes the plank smoulder. Next you need tinder – dried rags, wood shavings, or grass – that will easily catch fire. The tinder is placed where the pieces of wood touch, and hopefully – with a bit of blowing and encouragement – the tinder will catch fire. Once you had fire, the aim was to keep it alight. Not surprisingly, the search was on for something more convenient.

In John Walker's time the tinder box was probably the most common fire-lighting device. Using the friction of a piece of iron or steel struck with a piece of flint, its great advantage over a fire drill is that it will instantly produce white-hot sparks. These are allowed to fall onto the tinder stored in the box, which with a bit of skill can be encouraged to smoulder and catch fire. The tinder box was fairly portable, but certainly wasn't quick enough to allow you to light a candle if you wanted to get up in the middle of the night. Actually getting the tinder to catch fire was tricky, but you also had to transfer the fire to a candle, and then to whatever you wanted to light. It is actually rather difficult to transfer the flame directly to wood. To circumvent the process, sulphur-tipped matches were sometimes used. These didn't themselves make fire, but the sulphur would catch from the tinder, and would in turn light the wooden match.

Chemistry was applied to making fire from the seventeenth century. In Germany in 1669, an alchemist called Brand (rather a good name for a chap who made fire) discovered phosphorus by boiling urine. When exposed to air at anything like room temperature, it spontaneously catches fire. The difficulty lies in controlling it, and phosphorus burns are particularly nasty. Robert Boyle marketed a match based on sulphur-coated wooden matches being drawn through phosphorus-coated paper. It was very expensive, and didn't catch on. The Promethean match was an equally frightening invention, but at least the ingredients didn't spontaneously catch fire. It consisted of a glass vial of concentrated sulphuric acid (not something you'd want to carry around in your pocket) wrapped in paper, which also contained something to provide oxygen, and something like sugar to catch fire. Breaking the glass vial (said to have been done with the teeth) caused the whole lot to catch fire. The dawning of the steam age and the start of the industrial revolution happened without a safe, portable and convenient way of making fire.

So that was the state of play when John Walker of Stockton-on-Tees came along. He was born on 29 May 1781, the third son of John and Mary, at 104 High Street, Stockton, where his father ran a grocery, wine and spirit shop. John went to grammar school, where he learnt Latin and got a taste for science. He left school at fifteen to become apprentice to Stockton's principal surgeon, Watson Alcock. By the time he obtained his surgical qualifications in London and returned to become Alcock's assistant, he had become too squeamish to be a surgeon. So instead he went to Durham and then York to train as a chemist. Finally, in 1819, at the age of thirty-eight, he opened a chemist and druggist shop at 59 High Street, Stockton. (It is now Boots the Chemist, which seems fitting.) He was nicknamed 'Stockton's Encyclopaedia' because of his great knowledge of botany, geology, astronomy and, most importantly, chemistry.

We know a little about John Walker's chemist business from his day-book, in which he recorded his sales. These included medicines, though the frequent use of mercury compounds must have polished off a few customers. He also sold cosmetics, and ingredients for cooking – the sort of things you can find in a chemist's today. From about 1825 he recorded several sales of combustible mixtures to farmers and young men, possibly for making percussion caps for guns. He sold a variety of mixtures, and we don't know if this is because he was merely filling orders, or because he was experimenting. On one occasion he had been preparing such a mixture when he accidentally scraped the mixing stick on the hearth – and it caught fire.

The crucial thing was not that the powder caught fire – he knew it would do that, and others made similar mixtures. The point, which he seems to have seen immediately, was that it was capable of setting the stick on fire. His mixture consisted of potassium chlorate and black antimony sulphide, which ignites at a very low temperature. Friction of the stick on the hearth raised the surface temperature just enough for the mixture to catch. Walker used the mixture to tip matches, and called them 'Sulphurata Hyperoxygenata Frict.', a deliberately misleading name to protect the formula. The first sale, to a solicitor called Mr Hixon, is recorded in the day-book on 7 April 1827. He also wrote that this was 'box No. 30', which suggests he might have given the first twenty-nine away. Later that year, he renamed his invention: on 7 September 1827 he sold 'Friction

Lights' to a Mr. Fenwick. Eighty-four Lights cost 10*d*, the tin 2*d*.

Walker seems to have decided not to let his good fortune change his life. Although urged to patent his matches by, among others, Michael Faraday, Walker declined. 'I doubt not it will be a benefit to the public,' he said. 'Let them have it. I shall always be able to obtain sufficient for myself.'

Stockton-on-Tees is heavy with memorials, from John Walker Square off the High Street (with a bust of the wrong John Walker!) and the Matchmaker Brasserie, and the John Walker pub round the corner, to original matches in the Green Dragon Museum, open Mon–Fri 9–5; 01642 674308. There are plaques at the location of his chemist's shop in the High Street (now Boots!) and opposite at his birthplace.

94 Barnes Wallis and the 'Impossible' Bouncing Bombs

I am not generally in favour of war, nor of weapons, but while I was at school in the 1950s my friends and I read avidly about the heroes of the Second World War, which had been going on when we were born, and was still a recent memory for our parents and teachers. Of the books I read then, the one that left the greatest impression on me was Paul Brickhill's *The Dam Busters*, and I was captivated by the ingenuity and the dogged perseverance of its hero, Barnes Wallis.

Barnes Wallis was born in Ripley in Derbyshire on 26 September 1887. His father was a not-very-successful doctor who had suffered from polio, and the family was never well off. However, Barnes was a smart boy, and managed to get a place at Christ's School in the centre of London. It was rather a Dickensian school with wooden beds and a concrete rugby pitch, but the science teacher was way ahead of his time; he believed that science was best taught by experience, rather than by rote learning.

The day before war was declared, according to Brickhill, Wallis abandoned his family on holiday in Dorset and went back to his office at Vickers, where he worked as an aircraft designer. The works stood in the middle of Brooklands – the birthplace of track motor racing, with the first ever banked track – near Weybridge in Surrey.

Wallis wanted to end the war quickly, and reckoned the best way would be to disrupt the industrial heartland of Germany. Coal mines and oil fields were difficult to attack, but he wondered whether it might be possible to blow up some dams. The point of attacking dams was that the Germans needed water to provide hydroelectric power for many factories, and cooling for others. Water was involved in many crucial industrial processes, and water was needed to top up the canals that provided vital transport links. But the particular fact that Wallis latched on to was that the German steel factories needed 8 tons of water to make a ton of steel. Deny them the water, and steel production would grind to a halt; then there would be no tanks, no guns and no ammunition – and no more war.

Wallis dived into the literature, and looked up the specifications of the major dams in the Ruhr Valley – the Möhne, the Eder and the Sorpe. He did some sums and figured out that an ordinary bomb dropped on top of one of these dams would have no chance of demolishing it unless it weighed 30 tons – but this was much more than any existing plane could carry. So he had to find a way of doing the same job with a smaller bomb.

Eventually, after much head-scratching and experimentation, he decided the best chance of success would be to explode a bomb under water against the base of the dam wall. He did some experiments on small-scale models and came to the conclusion that one of these dams could be breached by a correctly placed explosion using only 3 tons of the new explosive RDX. This would mean a bomb weighing only 5 tons, which could just be carried by the new Lancaster bombers.

The question was how to place the bomb against the base of the dam wall. No bomb-aimer could drop a bomb within a couple of feet of the wall from any sensible height; in practice, most bombs fell hundreds of yards from their targets, and Wallis's bomb had to be spot on. The bombs could not be dropped as torpedoes to slice through the water and stick into the walls because the dams were well protected by submarine nets and floating booms.

Then Wallis remembered reading that Nelson claimed to have 'bounced' cannon balls off the water to cause more damage to enemy ships, and he wondered whether bouncing might solve his problem. If the bomb were dropped over the lake, and bounced over the boom and the submarine net to hit the parapet of the dam, it would sink down the wall and would be sure to end up in the right place. But could a 5-ton bomb really bounce on water?

You can skip flat stones across the water by throwing them hard and low with enough spin to keep them level – but bouncing a bomb was a very different matter. Wallis started testing his idea in the garden at his home in Effingham, near Leatherhead in Surrey, by catapulting marbles at a tin bath full of water. The children, back from Dorset, helped note the results and retrieved the marbles from the flower beds.

He moved on to lead balls, which he fired across Silvermere Lake, now in the middle of a golf course; no doubt the mud on the lake-bed is still loaded with lead. His experiments seemed to show that you could bounce anything on water as long as it was travelling fast enough to hit the surface at an angle of less than 8°. He calculated that even 5-ton bombs would bounce if they were dropped from an aircraft flying at 240 mph exactly 60 feet above the water.

The authorities were sceptical; they said he was mad, and laughed at the idea of bouncing bombs –

'quite impossible!' they said. But Wallis was stubborn and persuasive, and eventually convinced them that he could bounce bombs up to the dam walls.

However, a bomb travelling at such a speed might bounce away from the dam wall when it struck. Wallis carried out a long series of tests firing golf balls along the water in one of the huge ship-testing tanks at Teddington, where film shot under water by a brave camerawoman in a glass box showed that the balls behaved better when given backspin.

Backspin may not have been Wallis's own idea; his colleague Farrimond Ogden was an expert on mines, and may have suggested both the use of a cylindrical casing and the principle of backspin for directional stability. In practice, backspin seemed to have three effects. First, because the underside of the missile was spinning forwards, in the direction of travel, the effective speed of impact was increased, which ensured that the missile would bounce even if there were slight waves or other interference – just as with backspin a tennis ball will 'sit up' and bounce higher. Second, if one end of the cylinder hit the water before the other, the bomb would dig in and veer off in that direction; so if the left-hand end hit first, the bomb would turn left, and therefore miss the centre of the dam. With backspin the bomb was stabilised and fell level, so that it set off straight down the lake. Third, when the missile hit the dam and began to sink, the backspin made it hug the dam wall as it fell through the water, so it was bound to be lying against the wall when it reached the bottom.

The bombs were eventually built as steel cylinders, about 5 feet in diameter and 6 feet long. They were held horizontally across the belly of the aircraft, and spun at up to 500 rpm with an electric motor before being dropped. Fitted with hydrostatic fuses, they exploded not when they hit the dam wall, but when they had sunk 30 feet below the surface of the water.

The bombs had to be dropped from exactly 60 feet and, as the pilots found, judging this height over water at night was difficult and dangerous. Luckily some bright person came up with the idea of fitting two spotlights below the aircraft, one at each end, so that the spots converged when the aircraft was at the right height. The navigator peered down, watched the spots, and called out 'Down, down, up a bit, steady . . .' and the pilot could keep exactly to 60 feet.

The bombs also had to be dropped at the right distance in front of the dam so they would bounce against the wall and not over it. A bomb-sight expert produced a clever gadget – just a triangle of plywood with a peephole at one corner and a nail standing up on each of the other two corners. The bomb-aimer looked through the peephole at the dam, and released the bomb when the nails lined up with the towers on the dam wall.

The best time to breach the dams was in mid-May, when the water level was at its greatest. Barnes

Wallis was given the go-ahead for the bouncing bombs on 26 February 1943; so he had only eight weeks to prepare for the raid. Meanwhile the RAF brought together some of their finest bomber crews to create a new squadron, 617 Squadron, and they started secret training.

On 16 May 1943 nineteen Lancaster bombers took off in the early evening from Scampton in Lincolnshire, and by the light of the full moon headed for the Ruhr Valley. They succeeded in blowing huge holes in two of the target dams, the Möhne and the Eder. Millions of gallons of water poured out. Objectively, the raid was not the strategic triumph that Wallis had hoped for. The dams were repaired fairly quickly, and there was enough water in other reservoirs to sustain most of the German war effort. Meanwhile many civilians and prisoners of war were killed by the floods of escaping water, and eight Lancasters – with fifty-three courageous airmen – failed to return from the raid.

However, the propaganda value of the dams raid was colossal. It did wonders for the morale of the nation at a low point in the war, and the whole country was amazed and delighted at the ingenuity and daring of this extraordinary venture.

A stubborn man, and difficult to work with, Barnes Wallis designed many wonderful things, including the legendarily strong spiral fuselage for the R100 airship, later used in the Wellington bomber, and a huge climatic test chamber, used to test equipment at temperatures as low as −65°C, in winds of up to 50 mph, at atmospheric pressures equivalent to an altitude of 70,000 feet. However, he will always be remembered for the dam-busting bouncing bombs.

Silvermere Lake, where Wallis tested his bouncing bomb ideas, is now part of a golf course. Many of Barnes Wallis's inventions, including a bouncing bomb, a 'Grand Slam' bomb, and a Wellington bomber, are on display at the Brooklands Museum, Weybridge (01932 857381).

95 James Watt's Improvements and Doubts

James Watt is incredibly famous – but for all the wrong things. He had a brilliant mind and came up with some stunning ideas, but he would never have completed anything useful if he had not been controlled and driven by tycoon Matthew Boulton. Most people think James Watt invented the steam engine, but that is completely wrong; Newcomen engines were pumping water from mines all over the country by the time James was born on 19 January 1736.

James Watt was born in Greenock on the Clyde, the son of a prosperous carpenter. He was a sickly lad, and constantly ill. Four elder brothers and one sister all died in infancy, and his younger brother and sister also died young. James grew up expecting poor health, suffered recurring migraines, and was a lifelong hypochondriac, and yet he lived to be eighty-three!

In 1763, while working as an assistant instrument-maker in Glasgow University, Watt was brought a model Newcomen engine, which had just been repaired, and was asked to get it working. He managed to get it running, but only just; the engine was highly inefficient. In May 1765, while he was walking on a Sunday afternoon in the Green of Glasgow, he had a vision of how to make the Newcomen engine more efficient by using a separate condenser. Within a few hundred yards he had the whole thing worked out: as he put it, 'I had not walked further than the golf-house when the whole thing was arranged in my mind.'

The drawback of the Newcomen engine was that when the cylinder was full of steam, the whole cylinder had to be cooled with cold water in order to get the steam to recondense for the power stroke. Then the whole cylinder had to be heated up again before it would fill with steam. An enormous amount of heat was being wasted. Watt talked this over with his friend Joseph Black at the university, and Black explained his new ideas about latent heat, which he had worked out for the whisky distillers. Even when you have water at 100°, you need a lot of extra heat – latent heat – to turn it into steam. That latent heat is half the cost of making whisky, and was the heat being wasted in the Newcomen engine.

Watt's idea was to keep the working cylinder hot, but to connect it to a cold container – the condenser. When the cylinder was full of steam, the tap was opened to this second container, and all the steam condensed in there. Then the tap was closed, and the cylinder was ready to fill with steam. Because it was still hot, little steam was wasted. This made a huge difference. In 1768 Watt applied for his first patent, which basically specified three things: that the working cylinder was to be kept hot, that the steam was to be condensed in a separate container; and that he intended 'in many cases to employ the expansive force of steam to press on the pistons' (although in practice he never did this; it was left to Trevithick to make high-pressure steam engines).

Almost as important to his career as that patent was his meeting with Matthew Boulton for the first time. They took an instant liking to one another. Boulton was a forceful Birmingham businessman, a tycoon with energy and vision, exactly the opposite of Watt. It was Boulton who turned Watt from a dreamer into a Hero. But it took some years. First, Watt went off and dug the Monkland Canal. He was consulted and praised by John Smeaton, John Rennie and Thomas Telford, and yet he thought he was useless, and hated dealing with people and arguing about money.

Watt was always short of financial backing, and to feed his family he kept having to go off and survey canals and design bridges, which unfortunately was rottenly paid. In 1770 the magistrates of Hamilton wanted a new bridge over the Clyde, and asked John Smeaton if he would design it. He said he would charge a fee of £10. 'Far too much,' they said and hired Watt, who did it for 7 guineas!

Then in 1773 his Scottish backer Dr Roebuck went bankrupt, and his wife died, and James Watt finally took the plunge and moved to Birmingham, where he went into partnership with Matthew Boulton at the Soho Works. Boulton provided him with the most skilled craftsmen he could find, and enough money and time to work on the engine, and tried to keep Watt's mind fixed firmly on it. Watt had made a small engine that nearly worked in a workshop by the stream behind Dr Roebuck's house, Kinneil, at Bo'ness on the Firth of Forth, but it took him ten years to get a full-size engine running – and that was with the drive and avuncular assistance of Matthew Boulton. Watt kept going off after other hare-brained schemes, but Boulton eventually persuaded him that, once his engines worked, they could make money by selling them to the owners of mines in Cornwall.

The major technical difficulty was to make a steam-tight piston-and-cylinder combination. Newcomen engines were run with perhaps an inch clearance all the way round the piston, with rope or leather wound round the outside and a couple of inches of water on top. But Watt's engine needed an airtight fit, and no one could make cylinders that were truly cylindrical. Before 1775 all cylinders had been cast, the small ones from brass and the big ones from iron, but they were far from perfectly shaped.

Making the piston airtight in an imperfect cylinder was a dreadful problem. Watt tried everything he could think of, including pasteboard baked with linseed oil, papier maché, and even horse and cow dung. Nothing worked. Oil seals were hopeless, because the oil emulsified in the steam and turned into a white cream.

In the end he realised he had to get an accurately bored cylinder. He went to John 'Iron-mad' Wilkinson, who had just invented a new boring machine designed to make cannons. This machine made it possible, for the first time ever, to produce a cylinder that was both circular in cross-section and parallel throughout its length. Wilkinson delivered the first cylinder to Soho in April 1775, and within weeks Watt got his engine going, just ten years after he had had the idea. Immediately Boulton persuaded him to design two much bigger engines, of which the first was a 38-inch blowing engine for John Wilkinson's blast furnace, and the second a 50-inch pumping engine for Bloomfield Colliery near Tipton. When this was started, in March 1776, it produced a dazzling report in the local press, which said it used only a quarter of the fuel of a common (i.e. Newcomen) engine.

For twenty years John Wilkinson made all the cylinders for the Boulton and Watt engines, until they began to make their own in the Soho Foundry. Boulton and Watt supplied each customer with plans, and nominated the suppliers, but the customer ordered all the parts and paid the engine builders, including the chief erector, who was usually a Soho employee. Then, for twenty-five years, the customer paid Boulton and Watt a royalty of one-third of the coal they saved relative to a Newcomen engine of the same power. This was not too popular with the colliery owners of the Midlands, but was wonderful for Cornwall, where coal was expensive. Within a dozen years, fifty-five Boulton and Watt engines were up and running in Cornish mines.

Then Boulton persuaded Watt to make a double-acting engine, with working strokes in both directions, because he foresaw the need for rotational motion. To convert reciprocal motion of the pistons into rotational motion of a wheel or axle, the most obvious connection was the crank, which was well known, and yet when James Watt first used a steam engine to generate rotational motion he perversely refused to use a crank! Unfortunately, in 1780 James Pickard, button-maker of Birmingham, took out a patent for an engine that included a crank. Watt was furious, and claimed that his ideas had been stolen. He threatened to sue. He also said the crank was an old idea, and could not be patented! However, he then applied for patents for five different mechanisms in order to convert reciprocal to rotary motion, including the sun-and-planet system. The sun-and-planet is all right, but it's much more complicated than just a simple crank. Nevertheless, Watt would not use another crank until Pickard's patent had expired.

Watt's double-acting engine was his most successful development, and it led him to his finest idea – parallel motion. As he told his son, many years later, 'I am more proud of the parallel motion than of any other mechanical invention I have ever made.' The problem is that the piston goes vertically up and down, and it has to push and pull an overhead beam, because to begin with that is what the engines were – beam engines. The beam pivots about its centre; so its end doesn't go vertically up and down, and if you try to connect the end of the piston directly to the beam you either get a lot of leaks, or you break the piston rod.

But make another half-beam of the same length, connect the ends with a rod, and connect your piston rod to the middle of this rod, and the problem is solved. Wherever the beam moves, this mid-point will always move in a straight line up and down. And this Watt parallel linkage was used in every sort of engine for at least 100 years. Indeed it's still occasionally used today.

James Watt was a genius: often miserable, stubborn, and resistant to change, but absolutely brilliant. He refused to use high-pressure steam, and delayed the further development of the steam engine by at least twenty years. He and Boulton would not allow their colleague William Murdock to develop either the steam carriage or gas lighting. Yet Watt invented a copying machine, sun-and-planet gears, and this wonderful parallel motion, and Boulton and Watt steam engines were the best in the world until Trevithick arrived on the scene in 1800, when Watt's patent ran out.

There's a Boulton and Watt steam engine in the Science Museum in London and a working one at the Kew Bridge Steam Museum, Green Dragon Lane, Brentford, Middlesex TW8 0EN (0181 568-4747). Watt's name is remembered in the units of power – watts and kilowatts.

96 Henry Winstanley and the First Eddystone Lighthouse

Some 14 miles off Plymouth lies one of the most vicious reefs around the coast of Britain. The Eddystone Reef has been a sailors' nightmare for hundreds of years. Right in the middle of the approach to Plymouth, its hard red rocks just show above water at high tide, so they are difficult for a lookout to see, and present the most dangerous obstacle possible. Hundreds and hundreds of ships have been wrecked on Eddystone.

In 1688 William of Orange became William III. He brought his fleet of 400 ships into Plymouth for his first winter as king, and established his main naval arsenal there, in what is now Devonport. In 1694 he declared there should be a lighthouse on the reef. The only problem was, who could build it? This story is about the first Eddystone lighthouse, which was built at the very end of the seventeenth century by an eccentric joker and fabulous showman called Henry Winstanley.

Henry Winstanley was born at Saffron Walden in 1644, and became an engraver and builder of weird gadgets. He became rich, and bought five ships. Unfortunately, in 1695 two of them were lost on the Eddystone Reef. Winstanley rushed to Plymouth to investigate, demanded to know why there was no lighthouse on Eddystone, and when he heard they were looking for an architect he said, 'I'll build it!'

He had never built anything before – but then no one had ever built a lighthouse on a wave-swept rock in the open sea. There was only one possible site – the only rock big enough to put a lighthouse on. It was 30 feet across, it barely rose out of the waves at high tide, at a slope of 30°, it was harder than concrete, and it was 14 miles out to sea.

To get out there he had to set off from Plymouth with his workmen and their tools at high tide, so that the ebb helped them out of the Sound. Then by sailing and more often rowing for six hours they could with luck reach the reef just before low tide, and have two or three hours there before having to row back. Often the trip out took eight or ten hours, and more often than not the sea was so rough they could not even land, and simply had to go back again. To get there at all was possible only in the summer, between July and October, and even then the weather often prevented any trip for ten days at a time. The critics said it couldn't be done. . . .

The first thing to do was bore twelve holes in the rock into which he could fix heavy iron stanchions. Making those twelve holes took the whole of the first summer. In late October 1696 the twelve great irons were put in the holes and molten lead poured in round them to fix them firmly into the rock.

In 1697 they cemented stones to the rock around the irons, but unfortunately there was a war going on, and in June work was delayed when a French privateer turned up and captured Winstanley. The Admiralty sent a stiff complaint to the French, whereupon Louis XIV, realising that the French needed the lighthouse as much as the English, declared, 'We are at war with England, not with humanity!' He released Winstanley, tried to persuade him to stay and work in Paris, and sent him back with loads of expensive presents. By the end of the second summer they had built a stone pillar 12 feet high.

On 14 November 1698 Henry Winstanley climbed up to the lantern and lit a dozen tallow candles. In Plymouth there was pandemonium. Fishermen came in with the astonishing news that Eddystone was showing a light; people flocked out on the Hoe with telescopes, trying to get a better view. Winstanley had done it! He had lit the Eddystone! The pubs were packed with sailors rejoicing and sometimes weeping – for the first time ever they would know where the reef was in the dark. The only people who could not join in the celebrations were Winstanley and his crew. The weather was so bad it was five weeks before they got back to land.

Winstanley's Tower was 24 feet in diameter and 120 feet high. His own engraving of the lighthouse was captioned to explain how it all worked: 'An engine crane that parts at joints to be taken off when not in use, the rest being fastened to the side of the house to save it in time of storms, and it is to be made use of to help landing on the rock, which without is very difficult.'

And up below the lantern: 'The State Room, being 10 square, 19 foot wide, and 12 foot high, very well carved and painted, with a chimney and two closets, and 2 sash windows with strong shutters to bar and bolt.

'The lanthorn that holds the lights is 8 foot square, 11 foot diameter, 15 foot high in the upright wall: having 8 great glass windows . . . and conveniency to burn 60 candles at a time besides a great hanging lamp.'

Above the entrance was a tablet that said (in Latin) 'H Winstanly of Littlebury in the County of Essex, Gent, designed and built this lighthouse, AD 1699.' (There isn't a Latin word for Gent, but he put it in anyway!)

For five years no ship was wrecked on Eddystone whereas before the lighthouse had been built one wreck a month was not uncommon. However, the weather was fierce and in the worst storms some waves broke right over the building. The keepers said the impact of the waves often knocked crockery off the table, and made them seasick. The critics said the lighthouse would never last – it couldn't survive the winter. Henry, fed up with the carping, boasted publicly that he had one crowning wish in life – to be in his lighthouse during the greatest storm that ever was.

His chance came in November 1703. There had been two weeks of severe gales, and all the ships coming in from the Atlantic arrived days early; meanwhile outgoing ships could not leave; so all the harbours and estuaries were crammed with ships. On Thursday 25 November came the lull everyone had been waiting for, and on Friday morning Henry went out to the lighthouse with his maintenance crew, to carry out repairs before the winter.

Just before midnight there blew up what may well have been the worst storm this country has ever seen. We know about it because the journalist and author Daniel Defoe toured round the country afterwards assessing the damage. Men and animals were lifted off their feet and carried for yards through the air. Lead roofs were ripped like tissue paper off a hundred churches. Fifteen thousand sheep were drowned in floods near Bristol. Four hundred windmills were blown over. A thousand country mansions had their chimney stacks blown down. Eight hundred houses were completely destroyed. And all those ships, crowded into anchorages, were blown into one another and on to the rocks; some eight thousand sailors were drowned that night, within yards of land.

Henry Winstanley's wish was mercilessly granted; he died in his lighthouse during the greatest storm that ever was. In the evening of Friday 26 November the Eddystone lighthouse showed a light as usual. By daybreak on Saturday there was no sign that the lighthouse had ever existed, except for a few bent pieces of rusty iron sprouting from the rock. . . .

Nothing remains of Winstanley's lighthouse, although the stump of Smeaton's 1759 lighthouse still stands on the same lump of rock.

Benjamin Wiseman's Windmill

Windmills have been used for thousands of years to grind corn and to pump water in order to irrigate crops. Rumour has it that the idea was invented in Persia, but anyone who has felt the power of the wind must realise that in principle there must be ways of harnessing that power, so windmills were probably built long before history was recorded.

Over the centuries there have been many designs of windmill, but one of the major problems they all have to tackle is how to take power from wind coming from any direction. The simplest idea is to use a vertical axis; the standard cup anemometer for measuring wind speed is like this. Whichever way the wind blows, there is always a force pushing the arms round.

A simple device much used for irrigation in Africa is made by sawing an oil-drum in half, and bolting the two halves off-set to a vertical shaft. This makes a cheap and reliable wind-pump, but is not very efficient. Technically this device is called a Slavonius rotor, and is often seen on the forecourts of garages, spinning in the wind and advertising tyres or oil.

The latest wind-farms use what look like three-bladed propellers mounted on horizontal shafts on top of high towers. These are much more efficient than the oil-drum machines, but require much higher technology. The top of the tower has to be free to turn; there has to be a mechanism for turning it to face the wind; the generator has to be at the top of the tower, and is therefore awkward to maintain; and so on. There is quite a price to pay for efficiency.

In 1783 Benjamin Wiseman Junior, a merchant of Diss in Norfolk, took out a patent on a revolutionary kind of windmill, which was like four boats sailing round in a circle. They sailed around a vertical shaft, which solved the problem of variable wind direction. Boats can easily sail downwind and across the wind; only when sailing directly into the wind is there a real problem. Therefore whatever the direction of the wind, three of the four sails will provide some turning power, and they will easily overcome the resistance of the fourth. As each mast goes round its circle, the sail fills on one side, then 'goes about, as it faces straight into the wind, then fills on the other side, grows fuller and fuller until suddenly it gybes, and the boom smacks over to the other side'. This is lovely to watch, although a sudden burst of high wind might cause major damage rather quickly.

Wiseman was concerned about winds that were too light and winds that were too strong; he covered both possibilities in his patent. Inside the mill he designed a beam to be pushed round by a horse when the wind dropped, so that the windmill would not stop, but be driven through a ratchet arrangement, so that if there were a sudden squall the horse would not be driven round at 30 mph. And if the wind got really strong, a cunning governor system would throw a lever and lower all the sails, so the mill would stop.

We have found no record to show whether Benjamin Wiseman Junior ever built one of his windmills, nor whether he made any money from his patent. Perhaps it was too complicated to catch on – there were a great many moving parts to go wrong – but don't you wish all those modern wind-farms had mainsheets filling with wind, as suggested in 1783 by Benjamin Wiseman Junior?

 All we know of Wiseman is in his 1783 patent.

98 William Withering's 'Flower of Physic': Heart Disease and *Digitalis*

The human heart is a tough little bundle of muscles, about the size of your fist, with astonishing powers of endurance and consistency. Its job is to pump blood around the body, and on every beat it squeezes the blood out with considerable force – enough to squirt perhaps 16 feet up in the air if you cut a major artery. The heart beats about once a second, 3,600 times every hour, thirty million times a year, for perhaps seventy years. That's more than two thousand million times, and the heart rarely misses a beat; it never has time off. So it's hardly surprising that in later life it sometimes goes a bit awry.

Two hundred years ago people died from cholera, typhoid and all sorts of other preventable diseases, and half of them died young, so that the average life expectancy was thirty or forty years. Today we have controlled those diseases, at least in the affluent parts of the world, and so people live much longer. This means that the heart is much more likely to run out of steam, which is why today heart disease is a major cause of death – not because our hearts are less healthy, but rather because we have removed many of the obstacles that used to shorten human lives.

One of the common forms of heart trouble is fast atrial fibrillation; the natural rhythm of the heartbeat breaks down and the heart races, feebly fluttering. The best-known treatment for this condition is Digoxin or Digitoxin pills, made from extract of the foxglove, *Digitalis purpurea*.

The meticulous country doctor who discovered *digitalis* was not a brilliant thrusting medical pioneer, but a tedious plodder called William Withering. Born at Wellington in Shropshire on 17 March 1741, he studied medicine at Edinburgh, and became a physician in Staffordshire, where his girlfriend persuaded him to take an interest in botany.

In 1775 two things happened that were to make his name. He found the foxglove, and he was invited to join the Lunar Society of Birmingham. This was a gathering of extraordinary scientific brilliance, founded in 1766 by tycoon Matthew Boulton, the vast and entertaining Erasmus Darwin (Charles's grandfather), and their doctor, William Small. The society met once a month, usually for dinner in Boulton's house, on the night of the full moon, so that they would have light to ride home again after dinner; that was why they called themselves the Lunaticks. When Small died, Darwin thought they should have another doctor, and introduced Withering, hoping that his 'philosophical taste' would appeal to Boulton, who promptly invited Withering to join the Society.

So Withering left his practice at Stafford, took over Small's practice, and moved to Birmingham. Meanwhile his girlfriend had interested him so much in plants that for years he had studied them, gathered and catalogued information, and in 1776 he published a huge botanical treatise with a ridiculously long title that started *A botanical Arrangement of all the Vegetables naturally growing in Great Britain. With descriptions of the Genera and Species According to the celebrated Linnaeus.* Erasmus Darwin tried to persuade him to change the title to something simple like 'British Plants', but he insisted on keeping the full twenty-four lines! They had quite a bitter argument over it, especially when Darwin discovered Withering was such a prude he had throughout the book avoided blatantly sexual words such as stamen and pistil!

Withering may have been irascible and a bit of a bore, but he was extremely successful. By the time he was forty-six he was the richest doctor in England outside London. He moved into Edgbaston Hall – an imposing building which is now Edgbaston Golf Club – and he had the distinction of having the first water-closet in Birmingham.

However, what made him really famous was his interest in plants, and in particular in one gypsy remedy. One of his patients was dying of heart disease and Withering thought the case was hopeless. But the patient, unwilling to give up, took a gypsy remedy, and got better. So Withering spent months tracking down the gypsy in the savage outback of Shropshire to ask what this magic potion contained. The vital ingredient was foxglove.

Withering was intrigued. He decided to do some experiments of his own, to find out whether foxgloves really were good heart medicine, and if so which was the best part of the plant. He tried every bit, in all sorts of different ways, and after experimenting on 163 patients found that the best formulation was dried powdered leaf, administered to the patients by mouth. This was in 1775 – and to this day there is no better treatment for fast atrial fibrillation than extract of the foxglove.

When he became very ill in 1799, his friends said, 'The flower of physic is indeed Withering.' And when he died a foxglove was carved on his memorial stone in the little church at Edgbaston.

William Withering lived in Edgbaston Hall, now Edgbaston Golf Club; his memorial in Edgbaston Old Church on Church Road has a foxglove carved in stone.

99 William Hyde Wollaston Allows Duffers to Draw

Some heroes come up with a single idea or invention; others are incredibly versatile. Here is a man who in the early 1800s produced fifty-six scientific papers, on subjects ranging from fairy rings in the garden to dark lines in the spectrum of the sun, and why the eyes of a portrait on the wall seem to follow you around the room. He made a fortune from platinum. He invented the reflecting goniometer and a telescopic blowpipe. He very nearly got the top job in British science. But the most appealing of all his achievements was the invention of a machine to help in sketching.

William Hyde Wollaston (1766–1828) was born in East Dereham in Norfolk, and intended to be a doctor. Indeed he practised at Huntingdon and Bury St Edmunds before trying London, and setting up practice in the Strand. By then he was thirty-one and not doing as well as he would have liked; he failed to be appointed physician at St George's Hospital. In 1800 he retired from medicine. Some sources suggest that his reason for quitting was not annoyance over the St George's job, but that he had decided he was emotionally unsuited to being a doctor. On one occasion, as he told his friend Henry Hasted, he was so upset about a patient that he burst into tears. On 29 December 1800 he wrote: 'Allow me to decline the mental flagellation called anxiety, compared with which the loss of thousands of pounds is as a fleabite.' Keen to avoid all sources of stress, he vowed never to marry. Wollaston may have been happy, but he clearly realised that with his practice gone, he had to make some money.

He was already a Fellow of the Royal Society, and his desire to spend more time as a scientist must have helped him decide to quit medicine. He also worked out how to make money from what had been a hobby. He set up a laboratory in his house at 14 Buckingham Street, which he kept absolutely secret. He worked on platinum, which had caused real problems. It has a high melting-point, and is very resistant to chemical attack, so it ought to have been useful – but no one had found a way of making it into practical objects. Wollaston discovered a method, but did not reveal it until near the end of his life – by which time he had made £30,000.

Walking in the Lake District with Henry Hasted, a vicar and Fellow of the Royal Society, Wollaston decided to sketch the beautiful landscape. According to Hasted, Wollaston had extraordinary eyesight, being easily able to identify distant plants while on horseback. But he turned out to be a hopeless artist. So in 1807 he invented and patented the Camera Lucida. He seems to have invented the name also; the Camera Obscura was a well known artists' aid and amusement, consisting of a darkened room (the literal translation of 'Camera Obscura') or box with either a pinhole or lens in one wall, which projects an image of the outside world on to the opposite inside wall. Wollaston's device did not operate in the dark, which explains the use of 'Lucida', meaning light, but it isn't a box either. Perhaps he just recognised the need for a marketable name.

Apparently his inspiration came from seeing a glass-topped table. He realised that it is possible to see simultaneously something reflected in the glass, and the floor beneath the table, and his patent details several devices which make use of this principle. The simplest version is just a piece of glass at an angle of 45°. You place the glass over your sketching pad and look down through the glass at the paper. You will see the pad as usual, and you will also be able to see the scene directly ahead of you, reflected into your eye by the surface of the glass. You then simply trace around the reflection with your pencil. This sounds brilliant, but in practice there are several problems, all of which Wollaston addressed. First, you will be drawing a mirror image of the real scene. Second, it appears upside down, which makes it almost impossible to glance from the sketch to the real subject to see how you are doing. Third it is impossible to focus on the pencil tip and the distant scene at the same time. Finally, if the scene is very bright or very dark, it may be difficult to see the pencil or the sketch 'through' it.

Wollaston's first improvement was to use two reflections. In front of the piece of glass, he attached a mirror. The angle between the two was to be 135°, and it was used in the same way as before – only now the reflection was the right way up, and correct from left to right. He tackled the focus difficulty with a magnifying lens under the piece of glass. The brightness problem was more tricky, but he came up with two solutions. The 'split mirror' Camera Lucida had a special mirror instead of the piece of glass. The silvering did not cover the whole surface: instead he applied it as a triangle. If you used the device near to your eye, the shape of the silvering was impossibly blurred, but the effect was to give a more or less reflective mirror depending upon whether you looked through the base or the pinnacle of the triangle. In this way you can alter the relative brightness of the sketch and subject. The commercial version used a dangerous-sounding 'split pupil' design, which used the same principle, except that you adjusted brightness by moving your eye over the edge of the mirror, so that some of your pupil looked at the mirror, some directly at the sketch.

Although the Camera Lucida and papers about fairy rings do not sound very serious, Wollaston was regarded as one of the leading scientific figures of his day. When the great Sir Joseph Banks died, he had been president of the Royal Society for forty-two years. He had wanted Wollaston to succeed him but

Wollaston declined, knowing that Sir Humphry Davy wanted the job.

Charles Babbage, the great computer pioneer, occupied Wollaston's house after his death. He said of his friend that 'the most singular characteristic of Wollaston's mind was the plain and distinct line which separated what he knew from what he did not know . . . his predominant principle was to avoid error'. Among his contemporaries, he was known as 'the Pope'.

Wollaston's house stood in woodland behind what is now a private home in Dereham, Norfolk.

100 Ted Wright and the Ferriby Boats

The black muddy banks of the Humber at North Ferriby, just upstream from the Humber Bridge, are bleak and featureless – hardly a promising place for a great discovery. Yet thanks to the persistence and skill of a local teenager, Ferriby turned out to be the site of one of the greatest archaeological discoveries of modern times, which in turn revealed the quite unexpected engineering skills of Bronze Age Yorkshiremen.

In the 1930s young Ted Wright and his younger brother Willie were already keen on geology and fossil-hunting. They made regular trips to the

Ferriby deposits, just a mile from their home, to look for molluscs, insects and animal bones. Naturally they hoped to find tools and other human artefacts, but without much success. However, they kept returning to the site, with its layers of flint, peat and clay, because the repeated washing by the waters of the Humber scoured away layers of mud, leaving more solid things sticking above the surface.

The tides in the Humber reveal some parts of the bank only every few years. In early September 1937 conditions were good, and the boys were busy probing with walking sticks and scraping with their trowels at anything that looked promising. Suddenly Ted came across three massive objects projecting from the mud at a shallow angle. Although only nineteen, Ted was expert enough to realise that these were the ends of huge planks of wood, and he thought he knew what they were part of. He called to his brother that he had 'found a Viking ship'. Willie was naturally sceptical, but wandered over to take a look. 'By God,' he said, 'I think you have.'

A little more scraping revealed what an extraordinary find this was. Beneath the mud they found that the planks were still connected, stitched together with what turned out to be twisted yew. The joints were packed with moss and the edges of the planks seemed to have a sort of tongue-and-groove arrangement. The boys had never seen anything like it. Just as astounding was the size of the boat. Prodding with their walking sticks, they found as they walked that for about 20 feet the remains went deeper below the surface, and then for a further 20 feet became less deep. They unearthed the other end of the planks nearly 43 feet away. They were soon forced by the rising tide to abandon the boat.

Ted went up to Oxford, but managed to return to excavate the boat further in 1938 and 1939, helped by members of Hull Geological Society. A trench dug across the boat revealed that it had five bottom planks, together with the remains of one side plank. The stitching fascinated them: the yew 'withies' were tied through holes in the planks, and then over long pieces of wood which ran the length of the seam. These sealed the seams and held in the moss packing. They still had no idea how old the boat was, and they tried to find parallel discoveries. There were none.

The investigation was now cut short by the outbreak of war, which took Ted away from the Humber, apart from infrequent military leave. On one visit home, when the bank was particularly 'clean', Ted went down to see if more of the boat had been revealed. There was a bit more detail, but the really amazing discovery came 160 feet away from the original site. Clearly visible was the end of the centre plank of a second boat – Ferriby 2.

It now became clear that the scouring action of the tide which had revealed the boats in the first place, now threatened to destroy the remains, which were soft and couldn't stand unsupported. They backfilled the digs as much as possible, but had to cut off a couple of yards length of Ferriby 1, which would otherwise have been destroyed. Ted removed more in 1943. Some timbers were stored at the Wrights' home in North Ferriby, the rest were deposited with Hull Museum for safe keeping. Sadly they were destroyed when the museum was bombed.

Nothing more could be done until 1946, when a full-scale rescue of the now dangerously exposed boats was organised; it was almost a disaster. The director of the National Maritime Museum at Greenwich was keen to salvage the boats intact. This was going to be difficult because the site was exposed for only four hours between tides. The plan was to dig trenches down both sides of the first boat (F1), leaving it stranded on a clay plinth. A steel plate would then be dragged underneath it, slicing off the boat in a block of mud, which could then be dragged up the beach using the steel plate as a sledge. But as the plate slid under the boat, the mud began to move, breaking the fragile timbers. They were forced to slow down – but the tide was rising. Having exposed so much of the boat, the rescuers faced seeing it destroyed in the strong Humber currents. Ted then took what he described as one of the hardest decisions of his life: taking a saw, he cut his beloved boat in two. When it was done, he put his head down and wept while the exposed half was dragged up the beach to safety.

Ted wasn't to see the boats again for twenty-five years. The timbers were taken to Greenwich for conservation, and he embarked on a career in industry. He never stopped thinking about the boats, trying to work out how they had been made – and when. He thought they must be very old, but most authorities would not put them before 'early medieval', because they were so sophisticated. In 1951 radiocarbon dating was invented, but the one British laboratory equipped to carry out this process had a massive waiting list. The eventual result was staggering: the boats were 3,300 years old: Bronze Age!

So how were these boats used? There were no signs of rowlocks, and Ted concluded the boats had been paddled, a view confirmed by the discovery of a paddle of the right age. Taking the Humber's fierce currents into account, he calculated that eighteen paddlers would be needed to power a boat during the mile-and-a-half crossing – which neatly coincides with the likely number of seats. Before the Humber Bridge was built, Ferriby was an important crossing place, and the Ferriby Boats were probably used to transport passengers and goods, including cattle – some of the stitches show signs of having been kicked by hooves.

The boat timbers met with a sorry end. The primitive conservation process did not work, and the tanks containing the boats became smelly. Although the order to destroy the boats was not carried out, they were allowed to dry out, so these spectacular treasures from the Bronze Age are not suitable for public display.

This would have been the end of the story, except that in 1963 Ted was once again on the mud at Ferriby, this time with his son, when he spotted something. 'Stand still, Rod,' he ordered, 'and don't move until I tell you. You are standing on the third boat.'

There's a reconstruction of a Ferriby boat in the Greenwich Maritime Museum, and the mud near the north end of the Humber Bridge is still thick and dark and pregnant with secrets. Plaques in the riverside car park at North Ferriby tell the story.

Further Reading

The best single source of information about our heroes is *The Dictionary of National Biography* published by Oxford University Press. We always look in *DNB*, and find many of our heroes there. What is more, most of the entries are reasonably short and accurate.

The series of books by Samuel Smiles and L.T.C. Rolt are also excellent sources, and easy to read: Smiles, *Lives of the Engineers* (including Smeaton, Metcalfe, Telford, Boulton and Watt); *Self Help*; Rolt, *Thomas Telford; James Watt*; *Great Engineers*, Bell, 1962; Allen & Rolt, *The Steam Engine of Thomas Newcomen.*

For a gazetteer of scientific hero sites, try Trevor I. Williams, *Our Scientific Heritage*, Sutton, 1996, or Charles Tanford & Jacqueline Reynolds, *A Travel Guide to Scientific Sites of the British Isles*, Wiley, 1995.

For an analysis of innovations, G.I. Brown, *The Guinness History of Inventions*, Guinness, 1996, Donald Clarke, *The Encyclopedia of Inventions*, Marshall Cavendish, 1977, or Patrick Robertson, *The Shell Book of Firsts*, Ebury Press, 1974.

INDIVIDUAL HEROES

Baird, John Logie, *Sermons, Soap and Television*, Royal Television Society, 1988

Beaver, Patrick, *The Match Makers*, Henry Melland, 1985

Bessemer, Sir Henry, *An Autobiography*, Engineering, 1905

Clarke, E.F., *George Parker Bidder, the Calculating Boy,* KSL Publications, 1983

Dixon, *Literary Life of W. Brownrigg*, 1801

Fisher, Richard B., *Edward Jenner*, Andre Deutsch, 1991

Gould, M.P., *Frank Hornby*, 1915

Hammond, John H. and Austin, Jill, *The Camera Lucida in Art and Science*, Adam Hilger, 1987

Irving, G., *The Devil on Wheels* (Kirkpatrick MacMillan), Alloway, 1986

Kelly, Alison, *Mrs Coade's Stone*, Self Publishing Association (Lloyds Bank Chambers, Upton-on-Severn, Worcs), 1990

McArthur, Tom & Waddell, Peter, *Vision Warrior, The Hidden Achievement of John Logie Baird*, Scottish Falcon, 1990

McClintock, Jean, *History of the Pneumatic Tyre*, 1923

McHale, Des, *George Boole, his Life and Work*, Boole Press, 1985

Mackay, James, *Sounds out of Silence, a Life of Alexander Graham Bell*, Edinburgh, Mainstream, 1997

Majdalaney, Fred, *The Red Rocks of Eddystone* [Winstanley], Longman, 1959; White Lion, 1974

Mansbridge, A., *Margaret McMillan, Prophet and Pioneer,* 1932

Peltonen, Markku (ed.), *The Cambridge Companion to Bacon*, Cambridge, 1996

Penderill-Church, John, *William Cookworthy*, Bradford Barton, 1972

Penrose, Harald, *An Ancient Air* [Stringfellow], Airlife, 1988

Rolt, L.T.C., *Isambard Kingdom Brunel*, Longman, 1957; Penguin, 1980

——, *The Cornish Giant* [Trevithick], Lutterworth, 1960

Sharpe, Evelyn, *Hertha Ayrton, A Memoir*, Edward Arnold & Co., 1926

Sier, Robert, *Rev. Robert Stirling DD, Inventor of the Heat Economiser and Stirling Cycle Engine*, L.A. Mair, 1995

Sobel, Dava, *Longitude* (John Harrison), Fourth Estate, 1996

Tickell, Sir Crispin, *Mary Anning of Lyme Regis*, Lyme Regis Philpot Museum, 1996

Tiltman, Ronald Frank, *Baird of Television. The Life Story of John Logie Baird*, Seeley, Service & Co., 1933

Whittle, Sir Frank, *Jet*, Pan, 1957

Wright, Edward, *The Ferriby Boats, Seacraft of the Bronze Age*, Routledge, 1990

Index of Places, Inventions and Discoveries